THE YOUTH DOCTORS

Patrick M. McGrady, Jr.

THE YOUTH
DOCTORS

Coward-McCann, Inc. New York

Copyright © 1968 by Patrick M. McGrady, Jr.

Library of Congress Catalog Card Number: 68-14311
PRINTED IN THE UNITED STATES OF AMERICA

TO ILYA AND COLLEEN

Acknowledgments

The Youth Doctors could not have been written without the sympathy and cooperation of many people, some of whom must remain anonymous.

For having graciously opened the doors to the Rejuvenation Scene's inner sancta, Dr. Alex Comfort, Dr. Wolfgang Goetze-Claren, Dr. Nathan W. Shock, and Dr. Max Wolf merit my special gratitude.

Gunther Stuhlmann's continually sound advice and translations of German-language source material have been invaluable to me.

Two editors made my labor more efficient and enjoyable than it otherwise might have been. I thank Ellis Amburn for having encouraged me to write this book and Mrs. Patricia Brehaut Soliman for her superb editing of the manuscript. For their criticisms of several sections of the manuscript, I am grateful to Dr. Alex Comfort, Dr. Charles H. Barrows, Jr., Karl Ransberger, Dr. Louis Joel Feit, and my wife, Colleen. I alone, of course, am responsible for the contents of *The Youth Doctors*.

For their patient assistance in unearthing some of the long-buried material on rejuvenation and gerontology, I thank the librarians of the Yale Club, the New York Public Library, the American Medical Association, the New York Academy of Medicine, the Institut Pasteur, the Copenhagen Medical School, the Goethehaus Library in Frankfurt, the Shelton Public Library in Washington, Jacqueline Duhau of the Paris office of *Newsweek,* and the administrators of the Seventh International Congress of Gerontology in Vienna.

And a special thank-you to my father, who charitably postponed a similar study to help me unstintingly and expertly.

I am also grateful to the following people who have been generous in sharing their knowledge and ideas with me, often at considerable personal inconvenience:

Dr. Ana Aslan, Dr. Charles H. Barrows, Jr., Dr. Lucien Bavetta,

Norman Bedford, Dr. Harry Benjamin, Dr. Albert Best, Dr. Johan Bjork-sten, the Rt. Rev. Herbert Herschel Blackschleger, Geoffrey Bocca, Dr. François Bourlière, Dr. Bernard Bovet, Mrs. Brenda Brody, Dr. Marthe Brown, Dr. D. B. Chandra, Dr. D. F. Chebotarev, Dr. Alex Comfort, Mrs. Lillian DePartee, Ruthe Deskin, Dr. Anastasius Dontas, Dr. Leroy E. Duncan, Jr., Dr. Gunther Eichhorn, Dr. W. King Engel, Dr. Louis Joel Feit, Dr. Albert Fields, Cora Galenti, Dr. Hans Giese, Dr. Wolf-gang Goetze-Claren, Dr. Hyman Goldstein, Dr. Gerald J. Gruman, Dr. D. A. Hall, Dr. Denham Harman, Dr. Hellmut Haubold, Dr. René Basile Henry, Judith Heidler, Marcel Herminjard, Dr. Zdenek Hruza, Dr. Stanley W. Jacob, Raymond Jaussi, Dr. Adam Jores, Mrs. Tatiana Kirschner, Dr. Alfred Kment, Dr. Lev Vladimirovich Komarov, Dr. Robert R. Kohn, Dr. Herbert Kupperman, Dr. A. Landsberger, Dr. Else K. LaRoe, Grant Leake, Dr. Irwin S. Lubowe, Johnnie Lee Macfadden, Michael Robinson McGrady, Patrick McGrady Sr., Bronwen Meredith, Dr. Walter Michel, Ann Miller, Charles A. Miller, Mrs. Doris Minton, Rolf S. Müller, Dr. Paul Niehans, Claude Nobs, Dr. Heinrich Nowakow-ski, Dr. Simon Oeriu, Chris O'Hara, Dr. Norman Orentreich, Anthony Palma, Dr. W. John Pangman II, Dr. John Parente, Hal Parets, Jürgen Petermann, Dr. A. Picouret, Dr. G. Z. Pitskelauri, Dr. Ivan Popov, Dr. Robert W. Prehoda, Karl Ransberger, Dr. Tiberius Reiter, Dr. Louis Scarrone, Dr. Fritz Schmid, Dr. Siegmund Schmidt, Alan Searle, Dr. Hans Selye, Dr. Nathan W. Shock, Dr. Albert Simard, Dr. Joachim Stein, Peter M. Stephen, Dr. Bernard Strehler, Gloria Swanson, George W. Van Tassel, Dr. Frederick Verzar, the Henry Agard Wallace family, Dr. Paul Weiss, Dr. Max Wolf, and Dr. Heinrich Wrba.

Contents

Illustrations follow pages 96 and 256

THE YOUTH DOCTORS

CHAPTER ONE

The Youth Doctors

*Whatever aging people say to the contrary, we all re-
gret our youth once we have lost it. The famous wisdom that is supposed to be ours in age doesn't help
a bit.*

MARLENE DIETRICH

To find out what is being attempted in the name of helping
people to live longer, more vigorous lives, I have just completed a
two-year investigation into rejuvenation which took me some
twenty thousand miles across America and Europe. I visited
twelve countries and tracked down every promising clue to the
whereabouts and identities of the great youth doctors and their
celebrated patients. I have ransacked medical libraries, attended
scientific gatherings, read thousands of papers and books, recon-
noitered dozens of cocktail parties in Hollywood, New York, Paris,
London, Hamburg, Copenhagen, Barcelona, the Riviera, Vienna,
and Geneva for leads, and interviewed on tape hundreds of rejuvenators, academicians, gerontologists, physicians, biochemists,
famous rejuvenates, and doleful rejuvenates *manqués*.

While I am fully aware of the limitations of the various rejuvenation therapies now being practiced around the world, I find myself
quite enthusiastic about much that I have seen. The rejuvenation
art, now nearly the exclusive province of the great *Fingerspitzen-*

gefühl* youth doctors, is slowly becoming a science that will revolutionize clinical medicine.

That the work of the youth doctors is largely a secret—even to
specialists in the aging science field—is revealed in a recent statement by Leroy E. Duncan, Jr., MD, Chief of the Adult Development and Aging Branch of the National Institute of Child Health
and Human Development:

"This is an area of intrinsic fascination, a poorly understood
area, an area that has no effect on medical practice, but one that
may one day have a great impact on that practice."

Clinical rejuvenation is an old medical specialty, preceding by
several millennia Ponce de Leon's quest for the Fountain of Youth.
Until recently, though, only those who had heard about the youth
doctors and could afford to pay their considerable fees were able
to avail themselves of treatment. Quite suddenly, or so it has
seemed, the whole vast realm of rejuvenation has begun to mush-
room in prominence and promise.

The moment we perceive the need to drive ourselves harder to
cover even less ground in our highly competitive society, we tend
to panic, to overcompensate. Some give up. Others, in desperation,
try anything that promises to put them back on a competitive par
with their juniors.

In her beautiful little classic *Gift from the Sea*, Anne Morrow
Lindbergh described the reaction of middle-aged people to the
handicap of their years:

"We Americans, with our terrific emphasis on youth, action, and
material success, certainly tend to belittle the afternoon of life
and even to pretend it never comes. We push the clock back and
try to prolong the morning, overreaching and overstraining ourselves in the unnatural effort. We do not succeed, of course. We
cannot compete with our sons and daughters. And what a struggle
it is to race with these overactive and under-wise adults."

The youth doctors tempt the middle-aged with the hope of staying in the running—not forever—but for a few more years. Not
everyone has access to this extraordinary, quasi-clandestine branch
of medicine. But the political, financial, cultural, intellectual,
and, oddly enough, the *medical* elites of our society are already

---

* A German word denoting a highly intuitive diagnostician or practitioner; literally, fingertip touch.

enjoying their services. These are precisely the people one would expect to feel most threatened by and appalled at the sudden energy decline that begins in one's forties. They also possess the will and the means to do something about it.

Thanks to steady progress in theoretical and experimental gerontology, however, the day is probably not far off when every American family will have its own rejuvenator or youth doctor—just as it has its own dentist and pediatrician. By rejuvenator I do not mean geriatrician. A geriatrician is a clinician who uses orthodox medical techniques to soften the trauma of advanced old age, usually on behalf of rest-home inmates. The rejuvenator, on the other hand, is concerned with the aging process itself, signs of which are evident in youth and need to be dealt with as early as possible.

What the Consciousness-expanding Scene has been to the late 1960's, the Life-extending Scene will be to the 1970's, '80's, '90's and 2000's. Society is ripe for rejuvenation. Even more to the point, rejuvenation may soon be ripe for society.

The tantalizing, but elusive, idea of youthfulness at any age is the number one obsession of our people in our time. The old are ashamed of having squandered it. The middle-aged attempt to revive it by gamely plastering and painting over the insults of time. And the young—even they—are conscientiously passing for younger still. Only small children, relatively immune to the neuroses of society, still have fun playing grown-up.

It is impossible to reckon how much money is spent annually on the spectrum of goods and services that promise to endow us with a more youthful image. You name it—in music, fashion, design, transportation, diets, leisure activity, in our whole style of living—whatever bespeaks youthfulness has an edge on a competitive product that doesn't.

In appealing to older women to use commercial artifices that will make them look younger, advertisers use eggshell caution. One never calls an American woman "old"—any more than one would insist on knowing her true age, or telling her to act her age. (Although I called my grandmother "Grandma," my children are under orders from on high to call theirs only by a first name diminutive.)

A common advertising technique is to present a product

designed specifically for "young people," and then to add "and
for the young in heart, too," relegating no one to the Arctic of age.
Thus, one manufacturer ballyhoos an electric razor "for legs that
wear miniskirts. And legs that would like to." Another poses an
attractive model of indeterminate age in a blush-pink layout selling a colored shampoo with the accompanying copy: "Pink is for
girls . . . It's the one shampoo made just for girls. Because pink
is just for girls. You're a girl, aren't you?"

Sometimes, the superpersuader, anxiety, is rolled out of Madi-
son Avenue's arsenal. Juxtaposing a black-and-white "before"
shapshot of three dowdy women in masculine suits to a colorful
"after" of the same women in graceful, feminine attire, a recent
cosmetics ad warns: "Your makeup's changed radically over the
years. Now, it's the face beneath the makeup that concerns you.
That's why it's probably time for Eterna 27."

Though equally desperate, men and women tend to ask totally
different things of their youth doctors. Most men are fairly
straightforward about their intentions. They want to be saved from
the humiliation of impotence; they seek the restoration of primary sexual function. Women, on the other hand, want a visible
rejuvenation of secondary sexual characteristics—smoother skin,
firmer breasts, a generally more youthful appearance. It is the
rare and somewhat peculiar male who would adopt "boyishness"
as a part of his rejuvenation program, but a reversion to "girlish-
ness" is a temptation that many middle-aged women cannot resist.

In general then, women are more susceptible to a "look
younger" pitch. The hip, fiftyish female can make an admirable
stab at trying to look thirty, and even get away with it. Unfortunately, too often she attempts seventeen, with grotesque results.
We have come a long way from the days of the first talkies, when a
Greer Garson would intentionally get herself up to look fifteen
years older in order to project that quaint era's ideal of glamour
and sophistication. In the Swinging Sixties such an act would be
unthinkable.

A kind of borderline rejuvenation is available to the rich woman
who requires a delicate combination of coddling and coercion to
reduce, relax, and escape ennui. This is provided by the posh,
usually expensive "beauty farm" or "health farm" (less kindly

called a "fat farm"). The principal beauty farms are Elizabeth Arden's two Maine Chance estates in Arizona and Maine, the Golden Door, Rancho la Puerta, the Texas Greenhouse, the Swiss Bircher-Benner Sanatorium, the French Clinique Diététique in Champigny, and Ann Robinson's Sunshine Terrace in Croton-on-Hudson, New York.

These costly country institutions are mainly rest and recreation havens for the lonely, the distraught, the reclusive, and the undisciplined who need armies of mothers to get them to reduce and take care of themselves. Mainly, the farms clear up cluttered skins, give the girls a tan, thin them down, and pamper them with a nonstop round of beauty treatments and flattery. I asked one Elizabeth Arden saleswoman whether the beauty-farmer experienced a rebirth of adolescent sentiments as well as looks. "I think all that should be kept out of it," she answered in a honey-sweet British accent, "all this psychological nonsense. Mostly it's just that they feel good, they look good, their skins are clear and their eyes are bright. They go every year, same dates, same rooms—most of them."

Maine Chance notwithstanding, the psychology of the middle years is every bit as important as its physiology and cosmetology. In the fifties and sixties there is an almost instinctive yearning to recover one's long-lost youthful enthusiasm.

More and more, says Dr. Alex Comfort, Medical Director of the Medical Research Council Group on Ageing in Britain, these years "take on the guise of a second adolescence. Reactions to the 'second puberty' are diverse. Sexual reassessment, ranging from the appearance of repressed elements like homosexuality to the pursuit of reassurance with new partners, is common. Social opportunity for change is high, and the middle-aged have the means and experience to do things they feared or could not afford to do in youth."

Who thinks so little of life or is so superstitious that he would turn down a chance to have his body's clocks turned back—even if only for a few years? What creaky Wall Street mogul would not surrender a fortune to savor his next spring with the taste buds of his teens?

Orthodox medicine, however, states flatly that there is no such thing as rejuvenation. There is a widespread—and unfair—assumption that only a charlatan would try to do anything about senescence. As a result, the field of rejuvenation has been peopled largely by fools and heroes, including some heroic fools and foolish heroes. The middling, garden variety of researcher or doctor has shunned it.

Indeed, the history of rejuvenation is so heavily tainted that most rejuvenators themselves do not use the word. Instead, one hears "revitalization," or "regeneration," or "aging retardation," or (careful now) "reversing senescence." The new generation of rejuvenation quacks has found, however, that these euphemisms are easily deciphered by the youth-hungry, and business suffers not one iota from their conservative poses.

I use the word rejuvenation. Not that I believe that anybody can be made twenty years, or even one day, younger chronologically. But we most definitely can be made to feel and look and act and think younger than we usually do. And it is probable that our lives can be measurably extended. Rejuvenation means to me what biochemist Denham Harman calls "living longer better." No more than this.

This is still quite a bit. Several of gerontology's most brilliant researchers are convinced that there are secrets to be learned that will give us productive life-spans of up to eight hundred years. Curiously, charlatans rarely hint of longevity possibilities extending beyond one hundred and twenty-five or one hundred and fifty years.

The appeal of rejuvenation is hard to overestimate. The youth doctors tell me that *any* mention by the press of their techniques inevitably provokes a torrent of mail. According to one rejuvenator-clinician, "bookings" resulting from even casual newspaper publicity average 10 percent of the total letters received; from articles in the posh women's beauty magazines, up to 50 percent.

Unfortunately, there is no consumer guide to rejuvenation. It is difficult to distinguish the quack from the competent doctor in a single meeting. The medical societies exist principally to protect the interests, especially financial, of their members. Many of the least scrupulous youth doctors I came across in my investigation had MDs. A medical education is no guarantee of aptitude, integrity, sincerity, or intelligence. Often the youth doctor "outsider" seems far more solicitous of his patients' welfare than his more reputable brethren.

Out-and-out quackery is, however, given short shrift in *The Youth Doctors*. The sex-stimulating gimmicks almost always may be labeled as either useless or dangerous. They include the water-suction breast developers, the electrode anal shock thrill devices, the vaginal masturbation gadgets, and a flock of sexual potency-restoring tonics. Usually, only grossly exaggerated claims will prompt the government to embargo these devices. Mail-order vendors, however, can rely on their clients' imaginations to provide selling points.

Nor have I spent much time on purely sexual rejuvenation programs. I was amused last summer, though, by a brochure advertising a "Nude Marathon," presented as "the first scientific attempt to explore the removal of clothing as a facilitator of emotional transparency and interpersonal honesty," held during the summer of 1967 at Deer Park, Escondido, California (admission $75 per head, by the way). The ad explained:

"Embarrassment and other problems associated with a negative self-image will be the primary concern of sensitive therapists in a carefully structured setting . . . Although some nudists will be admitted to the marathon, it is felt that the emotional impact and its beneficial results will be greater for persons who have not experienced social nudity and they will be given priority . . . An attempt will be made to maintain an even balance of the sexes . . . This will be a continuous participation experience from Friday evening until Sunday afternoon, with provision made for sleeping periods. Opportunities for follow-up and consolidation of emotional gains will be provided."

Checks, the invitation added, were to be sent to a named "pioneer in the development of peak-oriented therapy."

Several other areas of borderline rejuvenation have been bypassed by this book since they are adequately treated elsewhere. I have tried to confine myself to the unmapped territory of hard-core rejuvenation—that which promises to reinvigorate or revitalize higher life systems and/or prolong life-spans in a substantial manner. I have, however, included a section on cosmetic rejuvenation because of its popular appeal and because its most celebrated clients are also clients of hard-core internal rejuvenation therapists.

The Youth Doctors presents as accurate, as fair, as specific (including the citing of fees, which are intended as no more than approximations of what might be charged a would-be rejuvenate) and as comprehensive a report on the Rejuvenation Scene as I have been able to write. I have tried hard not to allow personal reactions to color unduly my treatment of ideas and individuals, but I realize that, inevitably, they must have some influence.

I am utterly fascinated by the prospects for rejuvenation and by what I have seen with my own eyes.

I have observed animal life-spans quadrupled by the simple breeding device of using young parents, generation after generation. I have talked with a biochemist who tells of nutrients that have increased the half-survival time of his laboratory rats—a remarkable achievement. I have seen a mangy old mongrel dog near death brought to bushy-tailed adolescence by means of a long-forgotten technique of extracting assumed aging factors from its blood. I have corresponded with another biochemist who believes he knows (and is credited by a growing coterie of scientists as knowing) the secret of aging and who has been given a $250,000 grant by a major drug firm to develop an enzyme that conceivably could extend our lives by several hundred years. I have spent weeks unearthing the inside story of how the world's most famous youth doctors helped one of our major fiction writers to overcome the physical and intellectual challenge of senility—only to have their efforts later sabotaged by a surrender to vice that eventually destroyed him.

I have seen fantastic physical transformations. Pouchy, wrinkled movie stars have had the debris of years wiped from their faces, enabling them to resuscitate their screen careers and, sometimes, to ensnare young men as lovers or husbands.

I have followed closely the evolution from the "Erector Set" monkey-gland surgeons of the twenties and thirties to the highly competent youth doctors of today who achieve excellent results in treating hormone-caused male impotency. Harley Street physician Tiberius Reiter may have revolutionized sex rejuvenation for older men by buttock implantation of testosterone (male hormone) crystals that last up to six months. Another experimenter has found that a dab of currently proscribed DMSO on the penis can often produce a quick erection for impotents.

During my travels in search of the Fountain of Youth, I found that an ostensibly preposterous idea could be every bit as intriguing as the most starchly scientific therapy. I had heard about a "rejuvenation machine" located in the middle of a California desert. Skeptical as I was, I had to see it. After driving three thousand miles from New York, I stared with disbelief at the glistening white dome looming up against the clear desert sky a few miles off the 29 Palms Highway. As advertised, it *was* the largest rejuvenating apparatus (if unfinished) in the whole world.

Its inventor, George W. Van Tassel, a fifty-eight-year-old wind- and sunburned former safety inspector for Howard Hughes, calls it the Integratron. The Integratron (whose intricate coil-winding formulae were allegedly given to Van Tassel by a UFO rider) is supposed to be the opposite of a cyclotron. As the latter accelerates matter and bombards it to release energy, the former is designed to charge matter with energy. Resembling an old-fashioned observatory, it is 38 feet high, 53 feet in diameter, and built of sixteen laminated Douglas fir arches, fitted together like the blocks of a Chinese puzzle—without a single nail, screw, bolt, or metal part of any kind. Van Tassel's brainstorm is financed mainly by contributions to the Ministry of Universal Wisdom, Inc., a nonprofit religious-scientific enterprise controlled by his family.

Within the dome, huge armatures, powered by diesel-fueled air compressors propelling turbine blades, are equipped to produce electric potentials ranging from 47 to 100,000,000 volts. According to Van Tassel, prospective rejuvenates will simply walk in a 270-degree arc under the armatures, "recharge their batteries, so to speak," and emerge healthier, handsomer, and younger. It will be free. For all.

The idea is not as bizarre as it may sound. For years scientists have toyed with the notion of using electricity to recharge the body's cells. In 1958, a Hungarian scientist, Dr. J. M. Barnothy, made a group of mice look younger merely by housing them within magnetic fields for periods of from one to four weeks. This group proved 30 percent more active on the average than normal, untreated mice, acquired total immunity from cancer

metastases, and in many cases experienced regression of transplanted breast cancers.

"We're primarily working on a principle to create a high-inten-
sity magnetic field big enough for people, the same as was used for
mice," says Van Tassel.

Under the Integratron, cells would be brought into resonance
with their own frequency and recharged. Few of gerontology's hot-
shots have given much thought to exploring bioelectricity as a
possible key to aging. Most would admit, however, that it plays
some sort of role.

While the Integratron treatments will be gratis, an interesting
fact revealed in the course of my investigation is the huge differen-
tial between the actual cost of the most famous rejuvenation treatments and the ransom demanded of the patient. Take the deep
face peel, for instance. It has been taken over by greedy lay practitioners through default of the plastic surgeons and dermatologists. What the operator charges from $2,500 to $3,500 to apply
costs her (women predominate in this field) less than 5 cents per
patient.

Although procaine is included in state medical benefits behind
the Iron Curtain, this Rumanian rejuvenation therapy has become
a gold mine for Western doctors. Since patients are supposed to get
shots three times a week for life (with brief hiatuses), a handful
of patients can provide their therapist with a very decent income
at $10 or $15 per injection. The procaine mixture itself costs less
than 10 cents per ampule to make.

Actually, quite impressive rejuvenation results can be gotten
free, although many people do not appreciate or believe in anything that is not expensive. The first thing is to want—but *really
want*—to be more youthful and to *believe* you can do it. Attitude
alone, as any experienced youth doctor knows, can work miracles.
Frequently, the only functional aspects of so-called rejuvenation
regimes are do-it-yourself high-protein, low-carbohydrate, and
low-fat diets, regular exercise, steady physical and intellectual
work, and avoidance of toxins such as tobacco.

We of the twentieth century have our rejuvenation work cut out
for us. The conquest of aging in one sense becomes tougher every
day. The distinguished aging authority François Bourlière, professor of gerontology at the Paris Faculté de Médecine, points out

that today a person of eighty has fewer years to live than his ancestor of 1805—despite antibiotics and cardiotonics, anticoagulants and antihypertensives, reeducation, and home care.

Our weird, bustling, unnatural metropolises ("termitariums," Bourlière calls them) have given birth to a whole new degenerative pathology. Bourlière points out that our human nature never quite adjusts to our termitariums. We kill ourselves trying, though. We have richer diets and more sedentary work habits. We choose professional specializations that rule out hobbies ("those tokens of balance and countless joys"), succumb to "collective and contagious drug addictions" (Bourlière includes coffee and tea in this category), and we are plagued by air, water, and food pollutants. Such factors work unceasingly and insidiously against our chances for a vigorous old age.

As weighty as the technical obstacles seem, the quest for effective rejuvenation has always been further complicated by a widely held superstition that nothing can or should be done to slow down or reverse the aging process. This book explodes that superstition by showing precisely what already has been achieved. It is an optimistic report on those who want to stay young and the doctors who try to keep them that way.

CHAPTER TWO

The Tradition

What is the longest anyone has ever lived?

It's one of those simple questions a child asks his father. If the father is honest with him, he has to give a simple answer: I don't know.

Actually, no one knows.

It's a very good question, though. It's a question gerontologists have been trying to answer ever since they've been in business. They have harbored the suspicion that if they could just lay their hands on someone who had crashed the life-span barrier, they might determine how he did the trick. Moreover, they might come closer to answering a question they have cared to ask themselves only in comparatively recent years: What is aging?

There is a bewildering plethora of claimants to the title of The Oldest Old Man—and few supporting documents. Unlike redwoods and giant mollusks, people have no annual rings to assure honest count. The birth certificate, however, gives us reasonable proof of age. Of the authenticated records, that of a *Québecois* named Pierre Joubert, who died in 1814 after one hundred and thirteen years and one hundred days of life, takes first prize.

Others have probably lived close to one hundred and twenty years and possibly even more, but beyond the highlands of authenticated testimony lies a quagmire of extravagant, believe-it-or-not folklore. If you are a dyed-in-the-wool Fundamentalist, you know that Methuselah lived for nine hundred and sixty-nine years (his father Enoch having expired at three hundred and sixty-five, in the cradle, so to speak). Flavius Josephus, the Jewish historian-soldier, attributed the antediluvians' longevity* to having been "beloved of God." It is embarrassingly evident that few have since enjoyed such divine affection.

Scientists are sticky about accepting longevity claims. That wily Shropshireman the famous "Old Parr" was pointed out for centuries as an example of a clean-living old gentleman from the country who might have lived forever had it not been for an unfortunate sojourn to corrupting, high-living London. Even the esteemed surgeon William Harvey, who performed Parr's autopsy, attested to his boasted age of one hundred and fifty-two.

The customary reward for reaching the century mark in England is a Royal birthday card. Parr got that, plus a headstone in Westminster Abbey. But did he deserve it? Recent investigation has revealed that the Thomas Parr born in 1483 was probably at least two generations removed from the Thomas Parr who died in 1635. Since legends are dear to Englishmen, it seems unlikely that, at this late date, he will be asked to relocate.

Before the exposé, however, rejuvenators played games guessing how Old Parr had managed to attain his century and a half. To the cell therapist Paul Niehans, the answer was obvious. What Harvey referred to as Parr's "well-developed and heavy" testicles obviously impelled him beyond the normal life-span. Moreover, said Niehans, they were incontestable proof that "there exists a relationship between longevity and the internal secretion of endocrine glands, in particular the sex glands." Other youth doctors, most notably members of the "Erector Set," made similar inferences from Harvey's provocative observation.

Interviewing old people does little to enlighten us about the means used to achieve great longevity. Newspapers ritualistically pry old age "recipes" out of locals on their post-ninetieth birthdays. But the message is tediously familiar: avoidance of alcohol, cigarettes, and wild, wild women. Refreshingly, Dr. André Larivière suggests we not take these virtuous exhortations too seriously. If the oldsters are clean-living now, says the author of *Les Fontaines de Jouvence,* their decrepitude is probably responsible. There is nothing like age to make one forgetful of one's go-to-hell youth:

* Adam died at nine hundred and thirty; Seth at nine hundred and twelve; Enos at nine hundred and five; Kenan at nine hundred and ten; Mahalalel at eight hundred and ninety-five; Jared at nine hundred and sixty-two; Lamech at seven hundred and seventy-seven; Noah at nine hundred and fifty.

"They mistake cause and effect. They believe that their virtues —often acquired at the eleventh hour—have provided them with long life. But their moderate eating is explained by their lack of teeth; their impotence by glandular degeneration; their sobriety by an eroded digestive tube."

Centenarians with the DTs, coffee nerves, and nicotine-stained teeth are not unknown. One Irishman, supposed to have died at one hundred and twenty, confessed on his tombstone that his secret for long life was a whisky habit that rendered him so formidable-looking that death itself was afraid of him. Voltaire and Kant, each reputed to have drunk ten to twelve cups of coffee a day, lived past eighty. Elizabeth Durieux, a Savoyarde, was said by rejuvenationist Serge Voronoff to have drunk forty cups of coffee a day until her death at one hundred and four. History records platoons of pipe-smoking little old ladies who reached the century mark.

At one hundred and three, Philippe d'Herbelot was asked by the Sun King, Louis XIV, how he managed to keep so fit. His answer: "Sire, after fifty I made a point of keeping my heart closed and my wine cellar open." Long-lived, cherry-cheeked rummies are plentiful. A venerable English statesman once opened a press conference after a brief illness with the aside: "Gentlemen, you have the good fortune to be witnessing an extraordinary occurrence. I am about to drink a glass of water."

The individual oldster, then, is of little help in telling us how to repeat his feat. What's more, his physician is usually just as much at sea in trying to explain his longevity. A case in point is the fanny-pinching, irascible old Colombian Indian named Javier Pereira, who was examined in 1956 by doctors at The New York Hospital. His claim to one hundred and sixty-seven years was implicitly accepted by his marveling examiners, Frank Glenn and Arthur Okinaka, both MDs. Their guess was that clean mountain living had been conducive to his extraordinary life-span. When Pereira died at "one hundred and sixty-nine," however, the Glenn-Okinaka report was attacked by gerontologists as naïve and inconclusive.

One old man who held very specific notions on how to keep young and live long was the Venetian-born nobleman-architect Alvise (Luigi) Cornaro. His rejuvenation formula was elementary: eat and drink little. Even today, four centuries later, this simple theory is viewed as a good guess at the "how to" of long life. Overeating has been implicated by gerontology's top biochemists as a prime aging accelerator.

Somewhere between the age of thirty-five and forty, a dissipated, deathly-ill Cornaro was admonished by his physician to slow down his hectic pace—or face the music. Slow down he did, but it was the last advice he ever took from a physician. "No man," he wrote, "can be a perfect physician to anyone but himself."

Cornaro stopped eating ices, fruits, salad, fish, pork, tarts, pastry, and garden stuffs. He gave up vintage spirits and drank the more digestible "new" wines. He shunned heat, cold, fatigue, interruption of his naps, "excessive venery," bad air, and overexposure to sun and wind. His daily diet never exceeded twelve ounces of foodstuffs (broths, bread, and eggs) and fourteen ounces of liquids (mostly wine). Except once. When friends "teased" him into a piddling, two-ounce daily increase in victuals and drink, it put him out of commission for a full month.

It took Cornaro one year to rid himself of the "cold and moist stomach, stitches and spices of the gout . . . the continual slow fever and perpetual thirst" that had eroded and tormented him. At eighty-three the feisty bigamist wrote his *Treatise,* in which he boasts of still enjoying horseback riding, gardening, tranquil socializing, reading, comedy writing, and playing with his grandchildren. He died in 1565 in his ninety-ninth year.

Cornaro has been criticized for having sermonized the poor from a golden pulpit. The Marquis Francesco Eugenio Guasco branded his "principles" so much hot air "without . . . an exemption from care and mental solicitude [which] can never be assured to us, unless we possess the same means which enabled our author to secure them unto himself."

As we explore the roots of rejuvenation and life-extension theories, we find recurring themes. Javier Pereira's story illustrates the hard-dying quality of the hyperborean (*hyper*—beyond, *Boreas* —north wind) or Shangri-la legend of a faraway land where people live for hundreds of years. For centuries, dreamers have sought the Abode of the Blest, the Persians' Land of Yima, the Celts' paradise Tir na nog (the Land of Youth), St. Brendan's Island, Avalon, Atlantis, Antilia. Columbus thought he had found terrestrial paradise along the coast of Venezuela near Trinidad. But as access to the remotest corners of the world has been gained, this rejuvenation theme has faded in popularity.

There is also a phoenix theme, which has to do with long-lived and immortal animals. The phoenix, in its most common legendary form, is described as an Indian bird which lives on air for five hundred years, whereupon it flies to Heliopolis and is burned to ashes on the temple altar. The next day, the young phoenix, rising from the ashes, already has its feathers. By the third day, he is full-grown and, after a wave to the priest, flies off toward the horizon. Some scientists believe that turtles and fishes do live very long lives, longer certainly than human beings. But snakes, which were thought to rejuvenate themselves by simply slipping out of their old skins, are not such long-livers as once was believed.

The Endymion or Sleeping Beauty theme is, however, still very much alive. Endymion was placed in an eternal sleep by Zeus. The benefits from his enforced nap were an uneventful immortality and preservation of his good looks. Today, this idea is the *raison d'être* for the Life Extension Society, whose motto is "Freeze—Wait—Re-animate." While waiting for the Godot of perfected, bottled, cut-rate rejuvenation, one would be deep-frozen for years—even centuries, if necessary.

The freezing would begin promptly after clinical death (heartbeat cessation) has occurred, and before biological death (deterioration of nonrenewable cells) has set in. Initially, the body is iced to about 40° F, while a heart-lung machine takes over blood circulation. Then the blood is drained from the body, and a mixture of DMSO (dimethyl sulfoxide) and glycerine is perfused into it to eliminate lethal water-crystal formation in the tissues.

Businessmen have already begun to sell "Cryo-capsules" (at $5,400 per, plus an annual $500 storage fee) for the prospective longevous sleeper. To date, only one cryonaut has had a go, a former professor of psychology who died in 1967 of cancer. His son intends to have him revived when a cancer cure is found, and drastic rejuvenation becomes practicable. "I can see no point at all in resuscitating anyone just for a few years," says the son, who has given up a profitable career to devote his life to cryogenic preservation research.

Meanwhile, alone in a Phoenix, Arizona, cryotorium run by a

man ironically named Francis E. Hope, the professor lies in an 11-foot-long hermetically sealed cushion suspended over 150 gallons of liquid nitrogen whose fumes constantly swirl about his body. The nitrogen keeps the temperature at a rather fresh —322° F.

Unfortunately, no one has yet determined how to go about reviving any clinically dead person, cure him of cancer, and perform radical rejuvenation—all in one fell swoop. Even more important, the best scientific opinion holds that DMSO-glycerine cannot preserve complex biological specimens. The foremost DMSO authority, Dr. Stanley W. Jacob of the University of Oregon Medical School, who has pioneered DMSO's clinical applications, is deeply skeptical about such experiments. "We can," notes Jacob, "take isolated red blood cells or spermatozoa or skin and freeze it solid with the use of DMSO and/or glycerine, and after thawing, the tissue is viable. If one tries to do this with an organ the size of a dog kidney or heart, however, it cannot be accomplished. And it cannot be done with a whole animal." Unhappily, the professor's chances of surviving his icy confinement seem about as good as Robert Falcon Scott's were in Antarctica.

Another ancient theme, a rather broad concept Gerald J. Gruman calls the fountain theme, is as popular as the big sleep. It holds the promise that life can be enhanced by use of certain substances. This theme underlies most of the existing rejuvenationist quackery—and some entirely legitimate scientific speculation as well.

The most famous (but not the first) Fountain of Youth was the one sought by Juan Ponce de León on Bimini. He appears to have been seeking a fountain whose source was believed by medieval scribes to begin in Paradise and meander through India. In view of the sixteenth century's predilection for misplacing India by about eleven thousand miles, this is not as absurd an interpretation as it sounds. Deceived by storytelling Indians, the hardy Spaniard instead stumbled onto Florida in 1513, where today one encounters, alas, no rejuvenating waters, but a torrent of wheezing pensioners accelerating the aging of their skin by overexposure to the sun's ionizing radiation.

In the fountain category, one would also place such legends as the philosophers' stone, which, in liquid form, was said to become a rejuvenescent elixir, and the Holy Grail, believed to have been the chalice used at the Last Supper and brought to England by St. Joseph of Arimathea. Here, too, would go the cupboard full of alchemical nostrums, ranging from the "gold liquor" (made from real gold) that Roger Bacon recommended to Pope Nicholas IV, to Raymond Lulle's recipe for the salt of Oriental pearls. The gold liquor was said to be so potent that the Comtesse de Desmont was able to go through three sets of teeth and two growths of coiffure during her, yes, one-hundred-and-forty-year life-span. Pearl salt is simply prepared. One dissolves the pearls in distilled vinegar and mixes this solution with dew collected from wheat stalks during the month of May.

Fortunately for the man in the street, youth-giving panaceas have not always been beyond reach of the slender wallet. In Louis XIV's time, Tabarin set up a rejuvenation stand on the Pont Neuf and sold the exotic, odoriferous Orvietan at popular prices. Orvietan was reputed to be a precise blend of gentian, angelica, scorzonera (viper's grass), juniper, iris of Florence, cloves, antimony, snakes, honey, white wine, and treacle.

Despite the odd democrat-rejuvenator, however, most formulas for youthfulness have emptied the buyer's purse. Gerocomy, a time-honored practice of using adolescents to rejuvenate the old (usually sexually), is traditionally costly, as roués on the Champs Elysées and Miami Beach dowagers can attest. King David tried it with the sweet, pristine beauty of Abishag—but with no success. Gerocomy prescriptions are not necessarily libidinous. David is said not to have had intercourse with Abishag. And the rejuvenation idea of the Italian sixteenth-century alchemist Lama (related by Gilbert Gensac in *Nous Vivrons 150 Ans*) is more quaint than it is degenerate:

> A small bedroom well-shuttered should be prepared, and five small beds, each large enough for just one person, should be installed therein; then have five young virgins, that is, under 13 and in good health, sleep there. In the spring toward early May, a hole should be made in the bedroom wall, through which should be passed the neck of a long-necked vase, whose glass body should be exposed to the fresh air. It is not hard to see that when the little room will be filled with the breath and expired substance of these five young virgins, the vapors will travel continually from the neck

into the body of the vessel where, because of the cool air surrounding it, they will be condensed into a very limpid water, that is, a tincture of the most admirable efficacity and which one quite properly might call an elixir of life, since, by means of several drops of this liquor administered at the first symptoms of a sickness which threatens to become acute, it attacks and breaks up the disease-causing substance until one's animal strength returns and chases it from the sick body by means of an invisible perspiration.

Most rejuvenating substances, from the Reverend Herbert Herschel Blackschleger's phyballooomm-rich Vivicosmic disc* to Ana Aslan's Gerovital, are fountain-type rejuvenators.

The alchemists, who first systematized the theory and practice of rejuvenation, were on the right track. When they failed, it was because of the tremendous complexity of technological problems involved—not for any lack of foresight. While there might be little of their science that we would be tempted to loot today, many of their hunches were astoundingly good. And if patients did not add to their years by drinking the alchemists' *elixir vitae,* many were helped by nothing more than the interest, hope, and sympathy alchemists extended to them. If their cures were a little outlandish, consider, as Larivière notes, the clutter of diagnosis and prescription characterizing today's "organized medicine":

"For the same sickness, one will treat you with powders or chemical potions; a second will inject iodine or a hyposulfite into your veins; another will fill you up with oxygen like a balloon; somebody else will snip off a few nerve endings; others will inject billions of dead or comatose microbes."

The alchemists had two objectives. One was to manufacture cheap gold; the other, to concoct or discover a rejuvenation or prolongevity elixir. The two were closely related. It was believed, for instance, that dining from golden vessels provided one with a gold-base elixir.

It was the Chinese, especially the Taoists, who established the pattern for all alchemy. The Han emperor Wu Ti was counseled by Li Shao Chun in the first century B.C.:

* Phyballooomm is described by Blackschleger, a faith healer, as "a goodly amount of healing rays," which, in addition to the disc's organic cereals, mineral elements, natural organic positive yeast, and psyterra, are alleged to produce "Sanctified Living Water," which will quicken memory, heal wounds, remove pain, calm nerves, and improve vigor and resistance to disease.

"If you make sacrifice to the furnace, you will be able to transmute cinnabar [mercury ore] into gold. When the gold shall have been produced, you may make of it utensils for eating and drinking. Through using them, your life will be prolonged."

It took science many centuries to manage the feat of transmuting one metal into another. Today the cyclotron is used to bombard elements with high-speed particles, altering their atomic weight. The process also occurs naturally, for radioactive elements in time become metamorphosed (*i.e.*, radium to lead).

The most flamboyant Chinese rejuvenationist on record was Ko Hung, who revealed that Lao-tse's (the founder of Taoism) incubation in his mother's womb lasted a minimum of sixty-two years. Small wonder that the white-haired sexagenarian baby was affectionally called "the old boy" by his playmates.

Ko was Mr. Sunshine, a true optimist. He asks, "But why are we reluctant to make a trial [of Taoist rejuvenation methods]? If only a slight success should come out from this trial, gaining thereby only two or three centuries of life, would this not be still better than the early death of the masses?"

The key to Taoist rejuvenation was a list of "hsien" (immortality) substances, which included turtle broth, crane eggs, peaches, and a tough monkey killed by suffocating it with a special mineral. The Taoists considered durable materials the most powerful rejuvenating agents. Spoilables, such as cereals, were mere subsistence foods, regarded with disgust since they impaired one's chances for eternal life. Herbs were at the bottom of the list (although they would rise in later Chinese traditional medicine). Hard minerals, such as mica, "which, if put into a blazing fire . . . will never be destroyed, and if buried under ground will never decay," were the best of all "hsien" prescriptions.

Certain aspects of Taoist theory survive today. The rules for Taoist exercise, which mimed the movements of long-living animals like the tortoise, were written down in a manuscript published in 1779 by the Jesuit Father J. J. M. Amiot and later unearthed by Per Henrik Ling, who made it the basis of Swedish gymnastics. The Taoists thought of physical exercise as a means to improved breathing and sexual activity—without which rejuvenation was deemed impossible.

As for breathing, it was not simply a matter of getting air into and out of the lungs. The would-be immortal was instructed to breathe "embryonically," forcing gulps of air into the farthest corners of his body, eventually reaching his essence, or spermatic fluid. This he did with great precision, using his mind's eye to guide the air into the right places.

The adept was confronted with a bit of a puzzle as far as sex was concerned. For while an active sex life was a must, his *ching* (sperm) had to be conserved at all costs. The solution was an elaborate system of *coitus reservatus* performed with teenagers of the opposite sex, whereby one tried to bring one's partner to orgasm but remain unspent oneself. According to Tao Tsang, "He who is able to have coitus several tens of times in a single day and night without allowing his essence to escape will be cured of all maladies and will have his longevity extended. If he changes his woman several times, the advantage is greater; if in one night he changes his partner ten times, that is supremely excellent." The mind boggles at the chaos that must have marked affairs between two Taoists dead set on eternal youth.

Taoist dieting went way beyond present-day high-protein/low-fat programs. The adept was required to live on nothing but saliva and air. For those lacking total self-mastery, a daily meal of roots, berries, and fruit was the maximum permissible. By keeping the bowel relatively empty of feces, it was felt that one avoided poisoning the system. For a more recent hypothesis on the role of auto-intoxication in senescence, see the discussion of Metchnikoff in Chapter Fifteen. Such a diet, of course, necessitated a full medicine chest to bolster wan apostles.

Eventually the Taoist disciple was rewarded with eternal life, but his apprenticeship was laced with uncomfortably long spells of vulnerable mortality. Wang Chen's case history is instructive. At seventy-nine he began the diet, exercise, breathing, and sex prescribed by Taoism. But it wasn't till he was one hundred and nine that he looked like a youth of thirty—and it took him several hundred more years before he was guaranteed immortality. At that point he had options of going straight up to heaven, vacationing in the Isles of the Eastern Sea, or just hanging around on earth.

Latin alchemy, which we know better than the other varieties, probably came from North Africa through Sicily and Spain to Europe. For many years it was the fashion to deride Roger Bacon (1214-1294) as an outrageous fraud. Despite his erudition (he studied at Oxford and the University of Paris, and spoke a half dozen languages), he had recklessly forecast, in *De Secretibus Operibus,* that:

> Machines for navigation can be made without rowers so that the largest ships on rivers or seas will be moved by a single man in charge with greater velocity than if they were full of men. Also cars can be made so that without animals they will move with unbelievable rapidity; such we opine were the scythe-bearing chariots with which the men of old fought. Also flying machines can be constructed so that a man sits in the midst of the machine revolving some engine by which artificial wings are made to beat the air like a flying bird. . . .

In view of his fantastically good batting average on predictions, it should be remembered that he also believed "a far longer extension of life is possible."

Bacon's interest in rejuvenation may have been influenced by his religion (he was a Franciscan). He reasoned that if Methuselah could live a thousand years *after* the Fall, and if the Fall represented a shortening of longevity, then, "It follows that this shortening is accidental and may be remedied wholly or in part."

Sin and unhygienic habits weaken the species, surmised Bacon: "Fathers are weakened and beget weak sons with a liability to premature death. . . . Thus, a weakened constitution passes from father to sons, until a final shortening of life has been reached, as is the case in these days."

Bacon's analysis of senescence depended heavily on the work of Aristotle, Galen, and Avicenna, who subscribed to the "cold-dry" theory of aging. Briefly, this theory holds that, at a certain point (some believed at conception, others at approximately age thirty, the body undergoes a metamorphosis, turning colder and drier, losing its precious innate heat and moisture, and acquiring the surface wrinkles and functional inertia of advancing degeneration. Today's dermatologists often talk in such terms.

Modern pharmacology can trace its roots back to John of Rupescissa, whose work with alcohol—originally believed to be the fifth element, or quintessence—and other chemicals paved the path from alchemy to iatrochemistry, or medical chemistry. Today's medicine is heavily oriented toward chemical therapy, the use of drugs in treating various diseases.

The opposite tendency, toward biological therapy, derives its philosophy from a Renaissance alchemist, Paracelsus, a Swiss physician born in 1490 as Theophrastus Bombast von Hohenheim. Most of the great rejuvenator-doctors of history are of this natural, or biological, therapy school.

Paracelsus was a pioneer medical disestablishmentarian, a cocksure improviser of unorthodox therapy who junked the lot of prevailing materia medica when it didn't work for him. A persevering healer of a gamut of "incurable" ailments with highly original methods ("if God will not help me, so help me the Devil"), Paracelsus attempted to be parson at the wedding of surgery and medicine.

Bombast was his middle name, and bombast was the man. At one time he was official physician to the town of Basel, where he lectured at the university. A student once described him as glaring, "with wild, intense, hungry, homeless, defiant, and yet complaining eyes; the eyes of a man who struggles to tell a great secret, and cannot find words for it, and yet wonders why men cannot understand, and will not believe what seems to him as clear as day."

Always rebellious, always the iconoclast, the stepper-on-toes, perpetually in trouble, Paracelsus was expelled from town after town by offended local authorities and forced to vagabond around Europe. His travels, however, gave him an education in empirical medicine that probably was, as he supposed, superior in every way to the medical principles provided by the dusty classical treatises.

Once, he ceremoniously displayed his contempt for the old masters of medicine by setting fire in a public place to their venerable texts. He is recorded as having shouted, "I tell you boldly that the hair from the back of my head knows more than all your writers put together; my shoebuckles have more wisdom in them than either Galen or Avicenna; and my beard more experience than your whole Academy."

Paracelsus was quite another man at the patient's bedside, however—gentle, thoughtful, comforting. He witnessed every ugly pathological affliction of his time, from venereal purulence and nonspecific itch to snakebite, violent epilepsy, mysterious poxes, menstrual hemorrhages, gangrene, and impotence.

The basis therapeutic agent, he was convinced, was nature. He once observed:

"In Nature's battle against disease, the physician is but the helper, who furnishes Nature with weapons, the apothecary is but the smith who forges them. The business of the physician is therefore to give to Nature what she needs for her battle. Nature is the physician. . . . Ere the world perishes, many arts now ascribed to the work of the devil will become public, and we shall then see that the most of these effects depend upon natural forces."

Paracelsus, in effect, was telegraphing the big scientific punch of the Enlightenment. The great philosophes (Godwin, Condorcet, Franklin, Descartes, Priestley, Francis Bacon, *et al.*) would develop this idea, honing it to a fine rationale for man's perfectibility. The bright lights of the Renaissance believed that nature was good. The quick, tough minds of the seventeenth and eighteenth centuries confirmed empirically that nature was good, so good that man could physically enrich and lengthen his days on earth. Reason told them so. But they finally realized too, alas, that rejuvenation was not for tomorrow—but for tomorrow's tomorrow.

Ben Franklin, foreshadowing cryogenic preservation of humans pending perfection of rejuvenation techniques, wrote: "I wish it were possible to invent a method of embalming drowned persons, in such a manner that they may be recalled to life at any period, however distant, for having a very ardent desire to see and observe the state of America a hundred years hence, I should prefer to any ordinary death, the being immersed in a cask of Madeira wine, with a few friends, till that time, to be then recalled to life by the solar warmth of my dear country."

The spirit of the Enlightenment was embodied in the methodical, tackle-anything brilliance of René Descartes, who believed that self-discipline and study would reward him with more than a hundred years of happy life. But even Descartes was ultimately forced to acquiesce to the drab, dispiriting reality that the practical science of his day was technically unequal to his sophisticated theories. The savant who told his patroness, Queen Christina of Sweden, that he contemplated living forever, lived only fifty-four years.

Shortly before he died, Descartes wrote, "in place of finding the means to conserve life, I found another, much easier and more certain, that of losing the fear of death."

If the philosophes instructed their era in how to dream of rejuvenation, it remained for the likes of Cagliostro to fleece and disabuse the dreamers. The late 1700's were, Cagliostro's biographer, Thomas Carlyle, reports "the very age of impostors, cutpurses, swindlers, double-goers, enthusiasts, ambiguous persons; quacks simple, quacks compound; crackbrained, or with deceit prepense; quacks and quackeries of all colours and kinds. How many Mesmerists, Magicians, Cabalists, Swedenborgians, Illuminati, Crucified Nuns, and Devils of Loudun! To which the Inquisition-Biographer adds Vampires, Sylphs, Rosicrucians, Freemasons, and an *Etcetera* . . . as if Bedlam had broken loose. . . ."

If his portraitists have painted Cagliostro (né Guiseppe Balsamo in Palermo, in 1743) in his true colors, then he was the prototype for every major charlatan to come in succeeding years. Jack-of-all-rejuvenation-trades, Cagliostro, we are told, was: "Pupil of the Sage Althotas, Foster-child of the Scherif of Mecca, probable Son of the last King of Trebisond; named also Acharat, and Unfortunate Child of Nature; by profession healer of diseases, abolisher of wrinkles, friend of the poor and impotent, grand-master of the Egyptian Mason-lodge of High Science, Spirit-summoner, Gold-cook, Grand Cophta, Prophet, Priest, and thaumaturgic moralist and swindler. . . ." *

Cagliostro's youthefying arsenal ran the gamut from "thaumaturgic [miracle-performing] Hemp-silks; Lottery-numbers, Beauty-waters, Seductions, Phosphorus-boxes . . . Wines of Egypt . . . A forty-days' course of medicine, purgations and sweating-baths," to "Fainting-fits, Root-diet, Phlebotomy [bleeding], Starvation and desperation . . . Liquid gold . . . Cantharides [an aphrodisiac composed of dried beetles] . . . Love philtres and Divining rods." As is true of every bunco artist, he traveled far, wide—and fast. Not surprisingly, his pigeons were Europe's titled nobility. One

* Lest one think that exotic titles are out of fashion among the youth doctors, here are just a few of the references the Rev. Herb H. Blackschleger uses to identify himself: Kalki Avatar; Supreme Council of Terra; Michael, the Messiah; Elijah, the Prophet; Cosmic Rev/Rabbi; Thinking Agent of the Nameless One; Doctor of Sacred Theology; Doctor of Natural Science; Prelate, Neoplatonic Church of Religious Science; Regional Leader Radiant Associates, Inc.; Founder of Lhudeiam; and last, but certainly not least, Bachelor of Science in Electrical Engineering.

after the other would give him introductions to the great houses of Italy, Greece, France, England, Germany, Holland, Russia, Poland. One after the other, his wealthy clients would be deftly fleeced.

Cagliostro's shenanigans gave youth doctoring a bad name it still has not entirely overcome. Admittedly, the years since have seen many others of Cagliostro's breed play cruelly and opportunistically upon human naïveté. But one hundred years had to pass before serious enthusiasm could be mounted for another youth doctor.

The exact date of the next great rejuvenation explosion was June 1, 1889; the forum was the Société de Biologie in Paris. In addition to biologists, several hundred nonmembers squeezed into the auditorium to hear a report by an erudite, cosmopolitan, bearded gentleman with the exquisite name of Charles Edouard Brown-Séquard. The Society's average age was said to be seventy-one. What he had to say would be avidly absorbed by every one of his elderly colleagues. Pushing aside his lecture notes, the 6-foot 4-inch scientist euphemistically summed up what had happened when he gave himself an injection of animal testicular extract:

"Before beginning my formal lecture, I must tell you of my latest experiment. I am 72 years old. My natural vigor has declined in the last 10 years. I have injected myself . . . [and] today I was able to visit (*rendre visite*) young Madame Brown-Séquard . . . [the injections have] taken 30 years off my age."

No account of criminal rape has ever had a more sensational impact than this otherwise humdrum domestic indiscretion. Looking squarely into the eyes of his audience, Brown-Séquard described in detail his curious self-experiment, which he had been contemplating for the past twenty years.

Historians tend to dismiss Brown-Séquard's last revelation as senile eccentricity. This is unfair. As early as 1869, he had theorized to his students at the Paris Faculté de Médecine: "If it is possible to inject the testicular product of a vigorous animal into the veins of an old man, one would probably obtain a notable improvement in this individual's weakened powers." And the idea of creating a testicular-rejuvenating serum had obsessed him ever since. After all, his predecessor in the chair of experimental medicine at the Collège de France, Claude Bernard, had just brought to light the functioning of the endocrines ("glands of internal secretion," as he named them), and the remarkable biomedical properties of hormones were even then prophesied.

Brown-Séquard was no quack. He had pioneered in blood research and brilliantly described the nervous system and animal heat. He had been the first to analyze the spinal cord's physiology and was presently editor of the prestigious *Archives de Physiologie*. The posthumous son of a Philadelphia-Irish seaman and a French mother, born on the volcanic island of Mauritius in the Indian Ocean in 1817, he liked to think of himself as a British subject. His approach was Paracelsian, pragmatic, empirical.

Before the Société de Biologie, Brown-Séquard laid forth the chronology of his rejuvenation experience: "Last May 15 with the assistance of MM d'Arsonval and Henoque, I removed one of the testicles of a very vigorous 2-3-year-old dog. After cutting the entire organ into little pieces, I put them into a mortar, adding a little water . . . then mashed the pieces to obtain as much juice as possible. After adding more water . . . I poured [it all] into an excellent filter paper. The filtering proceeded slowly . . . and four-and-a-half cubic centimeters of a rather transparent, pink liquid was collected."

Then, he explained, a similar extract from a guinea pig was obtained and injected into the leg as he had done with the dog extract. The shots were quite painful, causing a red inflammation of tissues, insomnia, and "violent" dolor.

"Before May 15, the day of my first injection," he said, "I was so weak I always had to sit down after standing for a half-hour's work."

"The following day," he added, "and even more so afterwards, a radical change came over me, and I . . . recovered at least all the strength I had possessed many years ago. A great deal of laboratory work hardly tired me at all."

Then his impotence was no more. He resumed his old habit of running up and down stairs; he was able once again to work for three or four hours after dinner; the dynamometer and ergograph showed that his strength had increased considerably.

Le Matin, a Paris daily, began a Rejuvenation Institute Fund. Old men from everywhere pestered Brown-Séquard's office with pleas for injections. But the more the public got excited about "the elixir," the more bitter and indignant became the scoffers. The *Deutsche Medizinische Wochenschrift's* answer to the frenzy was typical of the professional cynicism: "His fantastic experiments . . . must be regarded as senile aberrations." The *Wiener Medizinische Wochenschrift* jeered: "The lecture must be seen as further proof of the necessity of retiring professors who have attained their threescore and ten years."

Subsequent researchers have attempted to follow the Brown-Séquard recipe precisely, but have been unable to reproduce his results. In the end, it becomes evident that his own rejuvenation probably can be accounted for as a placebo effect—brought about by his faith in himself and the power of autosuggestion.

Yet without doubt, and even if there was not enough hormone in the extract to do the job, as most endocrinologists now suspect, Charles Edouard Brown-Séquard deserves praise for getting the science of endocrinology, which has done so much for making old age a more hospitable place to live, off to a blazing start.

CHAPTER THREE

The Erector Set

A man comes to me, suffering from Cancer, TB or many other dangerous diseases, and, in addition, he is impotent. He says, "Doctor, fix up the Impotency and let the Cancer go hang."
"DOCTOR" JOHN ROMULUS BRINKLEY

"I do hope," said Dr. Alex Comfort darkly, "that you're not going to spend too much time writing on these gland-transplant people. You'll spread the false impression that the attempt to re-tard aging is peopled exclusively with quacks."

"The heroes," I assured him, "will get equal time. But, after all, it was the Voronoffs and Niehanses who made the twentieth century rejuvenation-conscious. For better or worse."

Comfort was concerned about aging study being strapped with the image of the early, renegade youth doctors for fear that official funding sources would confound charlatanism and serious re-search—and consequently withhold grants. His concern has been shared, and quite properly, by his colleagues in gerontology for many years.

Comfort has a point. Establishment gerontologists, by and large, are about as distant from the derring-do Roaring Twenties rejuvenators, with their testicular extracts and ovary implants, as one could imagine. The do-anything-for-a-buck quacks still operate, but their grants are restricted to whatever they can shake from their patron-patients' pocketbooks.

But just as the editors of Soviet encyclopedias correct historical "errors" by simply scissoring out entire chapters of previous editions, so gerontology has tried to consign its early deviationists to oblivion. The controversial pioneers, the rejuvenation "bootleggers," who had the field almost entirely to themselves for the first half century, are only rarely touched upon in the literature, and even then their theories are appallingly distorted.

I am interested in this "Erector Set," a circle of doctors who specialized in restoring the power to command an erection to old men, not because they have been abused or because they deserve rehabilitation. They cannot be said to have gone "unrewarded" in their lifetimes, for they all died rich. I write about them only because their legacy is very much with us—and because its significance has not yet been satisfactorily evaluated. It is from the ashes of the Erector Set that modern gerontology, phoenixlike, has risen. As such, it cannot be ignored.

For most men, impotence, the failure to "honor madame's signature," as the French put it, is the most irksome and embarrassing aspect of senescence. In the overwhelming majority of cases, it is impotence alone that drives a man to consult a youth doctor. Women, on the other hand, are more concerned with surface erosion than with diminishing sexual activity per se.

Often confused with male infertility, which is an entirely different matter, impotence is simply the inability to perform the sexual act. It may be caused by disease or by structural deformity. These are cases for the internist. The youth doctor, however, is usually consulted by aging males who find themselves impotent for nonpathogenic reasons. Insufficient hormone production is popularly, but incorrectly, believed to be a major cause. Herbert Kupperman, MD, a Manhattan endocrinologist, estimates that no more than 10 percent of complaints of impotence are due to hormonal disturbance. "Ninety percent," he says, "are psychogenic, caused usually by inhibiting environmental or subjective factors." Most often it's simply due to boredom with one's spouse.

"I get cases like this with monotonous regularity," one youth doctor told me. "A sixty-year-old businessman with the best will in the world can't do a thing for his sex-starved wife. He doesn't know why. He feels guilty. But then question him a little further and you'll suddenly discover he's a jack-in-the-box as far as some stripteaser or his secretary is concerned."

Unlike women, men do not undergo a "climacteric," resulting in inevitable impotence and sterility, in their late years. Ninety-year-old fathers are not that uncommon. Dr. Wilhelm Stekel, a prominent sexologist, is categoric about man's womb-to-tomb libido: "In man the capacity for erection begins on the day of birth and extinguishes with death."

The male erection is conditioned not only by psychic, but by nutritional and general physiological factors as well. But the psyche dominates all other factors. Even poor old Brown-Séquard was prepared, toward the end of his life, to admit that the "miraculous" revitalization of his sex life at age seventy-two was probably due more to autosuggestion than to any biochemical phenomenon. Yet even while he was obstinately convinced that he had concocted the equivalent of a rejuvenating male hormone ("testicular product"), Brown-Séquard scrupulously declined to exploit it commercially.

It did, however, occur to many other less principled individuals that mankind ought not to be deprived of so eminently attractive, so eminently necessary, so eminently *salable* a commodity as canned youth.

The Erector Set flourished from the beginning of the Great War until the first days of World War II. Some of its members, such as Eugen Steinach, were unquestionably competent, sincere scientists. Others, like John Romulus Brinkley and Clayton E. Wheeler, were opportunists, incompetent doctors, preyers upon the gullible. Still others, such as Serge Voronoff, in their youth showed promise as men of science, but betrayed that promise by giving in to greed in later life.

What is particularly intriguing about the Erector Set is their success stories. One cannot be certain they were nothing but bunkum. Not all of their favorable "revitalization" or "reactivation" results can be laid at the door of placebo, or autosuggestive effects, since some remarkable operations were performed on animals, which are theoretically immune to placebo factors. Some mysterious biochemistry may have been, in part, responsible. In any event, their claims cannot be dismissed out of hand. Forty-five years ago, Dr. H. L. Hunt, in the *American Journal of Clinical Medicine*, felt it necessary to put in a good word for "Those advocating operative gland procedures [who] have been outrageously [calumnied] and have been called short and ugly names —names intolerable and mean. These defamatory invectives and bitter amplifications have usually emanated from men in our profession as destitute of sincerity as they are improvident of knowledge."

Hunt might have had Eugen Steinach in mind when he wrote that. Steinach (1861-1944) was a greatly reviled, hotly debated, Jewish Viennese physiologist-endocrinologist who contrived a unique vasoligature technique (tying off of sperm ducts from the testicle to increase hormone production) that, he alleged, "raised the platform of efficiency" for older men.

Steinach was an outcast, personally and professionally. His closest friends described him as paranoid. Harry Benjamin, MD, a New York aging clinician who knew him well in old Vienna during the years between the world wars, describes him as a lonely, embittered, angry man.

Pitied by some of his colleagues, despised by others, Steinach was the perfect example of a scientist who stumbled onto an exciting rejuvenation novelty, tried to keep it within bounds—and then saw it become sensationalized and distorted, in a popular frenzy that he was powerless to subdue. Despite some impressive results, he was reserved, almost noncommittal, about his technique. "Within modest limits," he said, "the process of aging can be influenced."

Steinach never performed his vasoligature personally. He didn't trust himself with the knife. But patients were hungry for anything that promised to give them a bit more vigor, a better memory, and increased efficiency in their old age. The cream of Vienna's academicians flocked to him, many of them accompanied by their personal surgeons. Steinach's rejuvenates included no less a luminary than Sigmund Freud, the father of psychoanalysis. The noted Viennese orthopedist Adolf Lorenz credited the operation with making possible his own professional comeback at age seventy-two.

The concept of vasoligature first occurred to Steinach at age thirty-one, when he read a paper that attributed the frog's libido to the filling of the seminal vesicles with semen. For years afterwards he experimented with rats, trying to determine the correlation between the sex glands and general vigor.

Testosterone, the male hormone, is produced by different cells from those that produce spermatozoa. This hormone affects the secondary masculine traits, such as depth of voice, growth of beard, muscles, and so forth, brings on puberty; and, as far as youthfulness and aging are concerned, helps to speed tissue-building, stimulate appetite, and conserve the body's protein.

Twenty years later Steinach severed the sperm ducts of an impotent old rat to see what would happen. In the space of fifteen minutes, the male rat assaulted a female nineteen times! Steinach theorized that if he could block off the flow of the sperm-producing cells in the testicles, the spermatozoa would back up and, thus, stimulate a greater flow of hormones into the blood.

His inaugural human trial was performed in 1918 on a seedy, balding 108-pound coachman who looked much older than his forty-three years. Dr. Robert Lichtenstern, a distinguished Viennese surgeon, did the cutting. Eighteen months later, Steinach recorded: "This man with his smooth, unwrinkled face, his smart and upright bearing, gives the impression of a youthful man at the height of his vitality."

Steinach at first used the forbidden word "rejuvenation"—for which the medical profession sharply reproached him. Finally he was obliged to use the euphemism coined by Harry Benjamin: "reactivation."

His early operation was referred to as Steinach I. This simply involved tying off the canal through which sperm flows. Dr. André Larivière, the French authority on rejuvenation, describes the more sophisticated Steinach II: "It suppresses the external testicular function and re-inforces its internal function. The organism is no longer exhausted by the loss of this precious liquid, which is replaced by prostatic secretion and the gland's activity is then directed exclusively toward its hormonal function, pouring all of its product into the blood."

Termed "the poor man's Voronoff," after Europe's celebrated goat-gland rejuvenator, it was used particularly for prostate conditions and gonad insufficiency. While there seemed to be no physiological dangers attached to it, the fact that the patient was rendered sterile sometimes produced unfavorable psychological reactions.

Somewhat timidly, surgeons began to copy the techniques (even Paul Niehans, who had yet to begin cell therapy, began to experiment with it for a while), but most eventually favored the Voronoff-type gland transplant.

Finally, with the analysis and synthesis of testosterone in the mid-1930's by Adolf Butenandt, a German biochemist, vasoligature—whose *raison d'être* was hormone stimulation—became a dead issue. (Recently, however, the technique has again been discussed in scientific circles, this time as a birth-control measure, especially for men in underdeveloped countries.)

Harry Benjamin believes that the controversial nature of Steinach's work (probing into sex-gland function) kept him out of the puritanical United States, where he badly wanted to emigrate from his World War II Swiss exile. Steinach was convinced that he could round out his lifework only in America. When his visa application was turned down, it plunged him into a depression from which he never emerged.

In an unofficial epitaph to the work of a rejuvenation pioneer, Benjamin tried to put Steinach's work into perspective:

"The only 'sexual' factor in 'rejuvenation' was the use of the sex gland. A restoration of sexual potency was incidental to the general re-energization of aging men and was only mentioned as such. But this could never satisfy a sensation-hungry press and public or quiet the vaudeville comedians who were untiring in confusing the methods of Steinach with 'monkey glands.' Consequently more criticism arose, and the serious scientific efforts of Steinach and his co-workers were severely handicapped."

Endocrinologist Herbert Kupperman, on the other hand, doubts that Steinach's vasoligature could have stimulated any extra hormone production at all, and he insists that any "results" obtained by this method have got to be explained otherwise. And that—despite the nagging record of spectacular (albeit brief) improvements in many patients—remains orthodox medicine's verdict on Steinach today.

Clayton E. Wheeler was an astute mail-order rejuvenator whose top-hat manners and extravagant enjoyments made him a Flapper Era legend. Wheeler specialized in goat-gland serums. Feeling that the distaff market was being neglected by rejuvenators specializing in testicular extracts and the like, he addressed himself, with flowers and hand-kissing, to a predominantly female clientele. He learned that women favored injection and suppository rejuvenation, while men were dubious about anything less than full gland transplants with the surgeon's scalpel.

Wheeler turned out to be a thoroughgoing phony. When his "glandular extract suppositories" were examined by government analysts, they were found to be desiccated hamburger. His photographs of "Dr. Wheeler's Experimental Laboratory for Goat Serums" were actually of a cocoa-butter suppository assembly line in San Francisco. The Catalina Island goats he pictured in his brochures, awaiting transportation as the source of his serums, were not really his property nor even used by him for any purpose.

Flagrantly, he included pictures of San Quentin Prison in his literature, hinting that he had done his early research there. This claim too, was false. It was intended to give the impression that Wheeler had been responsible for the bona fide experiments of Dr. Leo Leonidas Stanley, the prison's chief surgeon. Dr. Stanley had transplanted testicles from freshly expired hanging victims into senile lifers. He had also experimented with goat-gland serum injections. Dr. Stanley's results were good, leading him to infer that his transplants stimulated memory, alertness, physical endurance, and strength. Unfortunately, his experiments were not extensive enough to permit conclusive findings.

Wheeler ballyhooed his ampules principally as rejuvenation agents, but he didn't hesitate to imply that they possessed panacea properties good for everything from paralysis agitans to lumbago and angina pectoris. Curiously, Wheeler himself suffered from angina. For treatment, he quite sensibly consulted a regular physician.

Wheeler's case was dramatically closed by the principal actor himself. Soon after the government's prosecution of Wheeler for mail fraud began, the youth doctor blew his brains out on board his yacht. Others, however, were brought to bay by the government. But the most preposterous, the most successful of them all —John Romulus Brinkley—seemed untouchable. "Where Brinkley was concerned," notes his biographer, Gerald Carson, "the machinery of social control seemed to be stalled by some mysterious malfunction."

The "malfunction" is explained by the fact that Brinkley, who contributed heavily to both political parties in Kansas and loaned them his Kansas radio station KFKB ("Kansas First, Kansas Best") for their diatribes, could drag any would-be prosecutor and his party down into disgrace with him.

True, he had to do a bit of fast shuffling toward the end. He eventually had to move his clinic and radio station across the Mexican border, but the trip did not deter his Stateside patients from eagerly handing over their $750 to have their scrotums packed with goat glands.

Which of the famous gland transplant men was first with the idea is still debated. Each insisted he was the pioneer; each claimed that his technique was superior to the others'.

"So far as I know," boasted Brinkley on one occasion, "I was the first man that ever did this operation of taking the goat testicle and putting it in the man's testicle, yes, sir. . . . The glands of a three weeks' old male goat are laid upon the non-functioning glands of a man, within twenty minutes of the time they are removed from the goat. In some cases I open the human gland and lay the tissue of the goat within the human gland. The scrotum of the man is opened by incision on both sides. . . . I find that after being properly connected these goat glands do actually feed, grow into, and become absorbed by the human glands, and the man is renewed in his physical and mental vigor."

While many of Brinkley's patients apparently did enjoy a temporary reinvigoration, there is no record of any extraordinary longevity or burst of youthfulness due to his treatments. After a brief upsurge of startling vigor, his patients customarily fell back into their debilitating senility. When this happened, Brinkley's reply was simply: Come back again for another go. And don't forget your wallet.

It is difficult in retrospect to believe that John Romulus Brinkley ever really happened. His is truly an "only in America" saga, far from flattering to the land of opportunity that he mined so profitably. With no more than a smudgy $100 doctor's diploma from the Eclectic Medical University of Kansas City, Missouri, this peppery, insolent promoter succeeded in selling the testicles of six thousand Toggenburg billy goats to sixteen thousand Bible Belt impotents as part of a rejuvenation operation similar to those pioneered by his European contemporaries Eugen Steinach and Serge Voronoff.

Despite his followers' enthusiasm, Brinkley's only proven rejuvenation was the one he continually performed on his bank account, which eventually totaled $12,000,000. He was the most formidable radio pitchman of all time, using the booming 1,000,000 watts of radio station XENT across the Mexican border to promote his product: "Astonishing sexual vigor," the specifics of which "cannot be more than hinted at." In his glorious heyday, the bespectacled doctor with the golden Van Dyke beard found himself driving a Stutz Bearcat, piloting a Lockheed Electra, cruising in the poshest (150-foot) yacht ever seen in American waters, being feted all over Europe,* and almost—but not quite—sitting in the Governor's mansion in Topeka, Kansas. Looking back at his spectacular career, he chortled: "For a poor boy, up from bare feet in Jackson County, North Carolina, this, dog me, is something!"

Brinkley put his adopted home of Milford, Kansas (population 200 upon his arrival), on the map with his rejuvenation clinic. His first try at goat-glanding was, he tells us, a whimsical venture. Observing the carryings-on of farm animals in a nearby field, he pointedly declared to one of his impotent patients: "You must have seen just what I've seen—those rams and buck goats. You wouldn't have any trouble if you had a pair of those buck glands in you." "Well," was the alleged rejoinder, "why don't you put 'em in?"

After overcoming his natural diffidence, Brinkley transferred the animal's masculinity to his neighbor's scrotum. Within two weeks, so the story goes, the patient's libido returned to normal. Although the patient had been sterile as well, a year later the vanguard rejuvenate had sired a baby boy, named—appropriately enough—"Billy."

Brinkley steadfastly insisted upon the superiority of his method over those of his Continental competitors Steinach and Voronoff.

---

* Incredibly, "Doctor" Brinkley was awarded another doctorate—his most treasured "honor"—by the venerable Royal University of Pavia. It was later rescinded.

According to a Brinkley brochure, after giving the Steinach ligature a whirl, he perfected a new, improved "compound" operation, surpassing Steinach by "transplantation of a *NEW ARTERY* and a *NEW NERVE*," making the operation "absolutely permanent." As for Voronoff's quartering of his testicle inserts (in order to assure greater exposure to a blood supply), Brinkley pooh-poohed this as absurd.

His cordial, hayseed style was irresistible to neglected oldsters looking for sympathy and some answer to their desperation. Rural people tended to mistrust what must have seemed to them hypereducated physicians, especially after Brinkley had exposed their gouging tactics.

"Don't let your doctor two-dollar you to death," he cautioned. "Come to Dr. Brinkley . . . take advantage of our Compound Operation . . . I can cure you the same as I did Ezra Hoskins of Possom Point, Mo."

Not that Brinkley ignored rich folks, who were just as anxious as the poor to preserve their failing faculties. Dr. J. J. Tobias, chancellor of the University of Chicago Law School, gleefully gave the youth doctor one of his most powerful testimonials. "I'm a new man," he declared. "It's one of the great things of the century."

Brinkley separated his operations into classes, like European railway coaches. He advertised a POOR FOLKS' TREATMENT, THE AVERAGE MAN'S TREATMENT, and THE BUSINESSMAN'S TREATMENT. In addition, he let it be known that, for a $5,000 fee, he would obtain a *human testicle* for the highest class of patient, through the offices of "an old-time friend in one of our large cities." This package included a dual warranty: that the transplant would take, and that it had originated from a man no older than thirty-five.

Brinkley possessed a trait common to most youth doctors: enormous gall. People loved him, and he worked his rejuvenation therapy long and strong, from 1915 (the date of his diploma) until a few months before he died in 1942. The beginning of his end as a Kansas practitioner came when he invited the State Board of Medical Registration and Examination to witness his "Four-Phase Compound Operation." Its visit resulted in what is probably the most accurate description we have of Brinkley's technique. President J. F. Hassig described it as:

> An incision about two inches long in the inguinal region under a local anesthetic, exposing the spermatic cord, identifying the vas deferens, slitting it and injecting each way through a blunt needle, about two cubic centimeters of one-half per cent Mercurochrome, after which the vas was tied above and below the slit, and then completely severed.
>
> The epididymis was partially separated from the testicle and into the loose tissue was planted the fresh gland of a young Toggenburg goat, and the epididymis was then sutured back to the testicle, and the wound tightly closed with cat gut sutures.

The outcome of Brinkley's demonstration was revocation of his license to practice medicine in Kansas. Eventually, his house of cards collapsed altogether under a welter of malpractice and bankruptcy suits. No record survives of how many patients he injured or killed with his inadequate antisepsis. The "doctor" always attributed his patients' demise to a mysterious "peritonitis," having nothing to do with his operation. Yet, thanks to his lawyers' acumen, his creditors barely touched his fortune.

The days after World War I witnessed an explosion of Brinkley-style quackery in the United States, most of it swiftly liquidated by the government and organized medicine. If rejuvenation today has a bad name, we can thank, above all, John Romulus Brinkley and his Continental counterpart Serge Voronoff, who turned the noble struggle for aging retardation into a garish freak show.

Serge Voronoff was far more intelligent and more competent than Brinkley. A suave, charming cosmopolite, born of rich Russian vodka manufacturers, the thin, angular surgeon emigrated to France in 1884 and quickly became assimilated (*"plus français que les français,"* as Paul Niehans describes him). During the Great War, Voronoff served as *médecin-chef* of the Swiss Hospital at the French front, performing hundreds of successful bone grafts on maimed infantry *poilus*. In recognition for his service, he was given the chair of experimental surgery at the Collège de France,

where his state-financed liberty quickly led him to toying with
the idea of rejuvenation.

At the war's outbreak, he had delivered a paper to the French
Academy of Medicine on a monkey thyroid graft he had performed on the neck of Jean G., a fourteen-year-old Corsican cretin.
The results, he reported, "surpassed the most optimistic forecasts." Time and again thereafter the crudely retouched before-
and-afters of Jean G. were reprinted to demonstrate that animal
grafts could "take" in humans.

Voronoff was uniquely qualified to discuss that great bane of
aging males: impotence. Before the war he had served as attending physician to the eunuchs of the harem of Khedive Abbas II in
Egypt. A man lost more than his ability to procreate when he lost
his *précieuses,* explained Voronoff: "Examination of male verte-
brate animals, including man, after removal of the genital glands
shows distinctly the nature of the influence of the internal secretion of their glands on the whole organism as affecting not only
the secondary male sexual characters, but also the growth and development of the body as a whole, the brain and skin cells, the
bones and tissues. The physical and intellectual qualities of animals and of men are as intimately conditioned by the hormones
secreted by the testicles as are the secondary sexual characters."

As for the relationship of gonads to aging, Voronoff observed
that his eunuchs rarely lived past sixty, and that when they died
they looked like centenarians.

With cool hindsight, he came to certain conclusions as to why
previous rejuvenators had been so unkindly treated by history.
Why had they missed out on the great rewards that awaited the
man who could wheedle the secret of rejuvenation from nature?
Why had the brilliant Brown-Séquard failed pathetically with his
dog and guinea pig extracts? Why had the bizarre animal tissue
and gland grafts attempted by scores of experiment-minded surgeons along the Rhine and Danube become antique medical curi-
osities?

Where had these brilliant men gone wrong?

Voronoff's answer to that question was that they had all tried
heterogeneous grafts, from one animal group to another—grafts
that would probably never work. He would use only *anthropoid*
glands on his patients. His instinct told him to use human donors.

More easily said than done, however. Optimistically, he advertised for volunteers who could appreciate the obvious (to Voronoff) truth that: "Restoring the vital energy, the productive force of a Pasteur is well worth a slight mutilation of a robust laborer [which] . . . in no way diminishes the donor."

Exactly *two* "robust laborers" presented themselves to supply contemporary "Pasteurs" with their "surplus" pendants. They did not, however, appear to be motivated by the altruistic spirit the aristocrat-surgeon had foreseen. "At the price these persons have calculated their precious gonad," he huffed indignantly, "the graft would be accessible only to millionaires."

Further reckoning led Voronoff to another, less ideal, but infinitely more practical solution. "Fortunately," he wrote, "we have in the animal world a close relative from whom we can make such a loan with a minimum of scruples: orang-utangs, chimpanzees, gibbons."

The greatest monkey hunt of all time was on. From the equatorial forests of central and west Africa, hunters white and black began ensnaring the outraged anthropoids by the hundred and shipping them across the Mediterranean to Voronoff's vast, hillside *singerie* below the majestic Château Grimaldi, on the outskirts of Ventimiglia on the Italian Riviera. The British and Belgians—perhaps fearful that the scalpel-wielder might begin looking north for "volunteers" if he weren't given his simians—gave him carte blanche to their African lands.

As things turned out, Voronoff's clientele *was* restricted, by and large, to the millionaire class. Not (it should be said in defense of the proletariat) because greedy laborers inflated the value of their testicle donation, but because of Voronoff's arbitrary estimate of the worth of his own services and four strips of monkey gland! Starting at a rock-bottom price tag of about $5,000, Voronoff squeezed his rejuvenates for colossal fortunes.

For all the ridicule heaped upon Voronoff by the music hall comics, however, those determined to buy a fresh sexual start never let themselves be laughed out of their grafts. Altogether, it's estimated that he did some two thousand transplants.

Unlike the scrupulous Steinach, Voronoff was never overly modest in his claims of effectiveness. He was precise in calculating that "testicular grafts cut back aging from six to ten years and restore physical and intellectual aptitudes that an old man had fifteen or twenty years previously."

Piously, he confessed that perhaps fifteen out of one hundred of his grafts might not take. Most, though, would last "six, eight, or ten years." The fact that many of his patients returned every couple of years or so for "retreads" does little credit to their intelligence.

At the summit of his prestige Voronoff was lecturing all over the world on his discovery of the Fountain of Youth. The peripatetic Voronoffs were seen at all the famous International Set oases, nightclubs, casinos, fancy restaurants, and grand hotels. Their comings and goings were duly chronicled by an enthusiastic press that never tired of interviewing them. All of Who's Who in society appeared to have had *"une Voronoff."* Even the *Encyclopaedia Britannica,** in one of its less lustrous moments, assigned him to write its text on "Rejuvenation." His article made clear that the writer was no Schweitzer or Pasteur. It read, in part:

"The only remedy [for aging] is to graft a young testicle, whether that of a *young human being*** or of an ape, by which the tone-giving substance is provided, so as to increase the vitality of all the cells which are weakened but are not yet atrophied and therefore still able to renew themselves, and thus effectively to rejuvenate the whole organism."

The medical establishment, it would appear, did not inquire too strenuously into Voronoff's medical manipulations, techniques, or results. But it did object loudly to his popularity. Because of his unorthodox means of presenting his work to the public, the once-esteemed insider rapidly became a pariah. In 1920, when he was going to present his first collection of grafts to a surgical congress in the grand amphitheater of the Paris Faculté de Médecine, the assembly president, a Professor Hartman, brushed him aside and addressed the group: "Gentlemen, our colleague Dr. Voronoff was supposed to deliver a paper. But I think that we have been adequately apprised by the articles published in this morning's newspapers."

* Understandably, because of the commotion that ensued from Voronoff's career of gaffe and scandal in later years, the *Britannica* never again referred to "Rejuvenation" in its tomes. Indeed, one is hard put to find mention of it in *any* standard reference work, except the dictionary.
** Italics mine.

Voronoff, purple, replied by shouting "Coward!" and by proceeding to rent the Marey Institute at Auteuil, near Paris' Bois de Boulogne, in order to show off to the press a rejuvenated billy goat, a rejuvenated ram, and a rejuvenated old man. The pioneer Viennese youth doctor Max Wolf (now of Manhattan), who spent summers with the Voronoffs, states that, on several occasions, professional meetings would erupt into near-riots when delegates would formally protest the glaringly fraudulent photographs of "case histories" presented by Voronoff.

Perhaps Paul Niehans understood Voronoff's lofty pride better than anyone else. The two were close, alike in many ways and perhaps even a bit jealous of each other. Voronoff died before Niehans effected his celebrated cure of Pope Pius XII in 1954 with cell therapy. Had the Russian known how much Niehans would reap from this refined method of tissular transplant, he might well have put forth his own patent claim. In *La Greffe Testiculaire du Singe à l'Homme,* Voronoff speaks of doing therapeutic subcutaneous injections of "minuscule" thyroid fragments ("as large as the head of a needle"). Such a technique comes very close to what Niehans has always claimed as his own baby: cell therapy. Voronoff simply failed to develop the concept because he worried that the body might absorb overly fragmented organs too quickly.

Voronoff's last days, recounted here for the first time thanks to revelations to the author by Paul Niehans in Vevey in 1966, were so nightmarish as to make a dreadful mockery of the surgeon's career. "He was," says Niehans, "proud, brilliant—but careless. Toward the end he was a sad man. He came often to Vevey to see me. His ideas were soundly based, all right, but he began to be troubled by the fact that nobody seemed to be following in his footsteps.

"I was able to watch both Steinach and Voronoff perform, and so profited from their mistakes. I noticed, for example, that Voronoff lined his testicle implants with silk. That was why they never took. I made a small pocket without silk, and my implants always took."

According to Niehans, Voronoff became careless immediately after the departure of his assistant-nephew, Dartigues, from his clinic. Left alone, Voronoff began to neglect elementary—but vital precautions.

"At the end he made a horrible discovery," says Niehans. "It undid him inside. One day he came to me and confessed, 'I have to tell you this. I can no longer be seen in public.'"

Shortly before he died, Voronoff perceived that many of his rejuvenates were having serious trouble with their grafts. The patients, naturally, blamed the doctor. Voronoff, naturally, blamed his patients. In *La Durée de la Greffe des Glandes Endocrines* he defended himself by attacking the complainants' characters: "As for the causes of unsuccessful grafts, it is necessary again to mention unfavorable conditions *emanating from man* whose vicious blood (syphilis, diabetes, etc.) can work against the taking of the graft."

Too late, says Niehans, he realized that *he* had been wrong; that he should have taken Niehans' advice to use bulls as donors rather than monkeys; that his patients had been in perfectly good health upon arrival at his castle-clinic, but that they were leaving it victims of mankind's ugliest, most insidious venereal disease— syphilis. His monkeys had infected his clients.

Immediately after making this appalling revelation to Niehans, who tried determinedly but unsuccessfully to cheer him, Voronoff vanished. A couple of months later he was reported dead, at age eighty-five, of complications resulting from a badly set fracture.

CHAPTER FOUR

"Un Grand Monsieur"

We live as long as God has decided, but it is a big dif-
ference whether we live miserably, like old dogs, or
well and fresh, and in this respect a wise physician can
help a lot.
    PAUL NIEHANS, paraphrasing Goethe's *Faust*

It is a great shuttered loaf of a chalet, planted on a slope of the
rock basin encircling Lake Geneva. There are flowers all around,
goats and sheep grazing on a thick green alfalfa carpet in back.
The only sound is the whispering of maples entertaining breezes
from the Alps above.

When I first saw La Prairie clinic, it made me uneasy. Nothing there fitted my bizarre preconceptions. Until that moment
even, I had had trouble believing that it was anything but rumor.

La Prairie is the atelier, the laboratory, of the most famous youth
doctor of our day, a black prince who has treated an international
Who's Who with injections of cells scraped from the still-warm
flesh of unborn lambs.

I dwelt on what I had heard, the many tales, the gossip, the
wild speculation about what went on in this improbable hospital.
It was impossible to reconcile the man of legend with a flesh-and-
blood person. For this man was reputed to hold the secret of rejuvenation. He was said to be rich beyond counting. He was supposed to have sacrificed thousands of beasts to the voracious God

of Eternal Youth. His grateful potentate and millionaire patients
were alleged to have filled his palatial home with treasures that
could stock a major museum. His mind was thought to hold secrets which, if divulged, could have overturned several govern-
ments.

His name was known to every gerontologist, but few had ever
met Paul Niehans. Most said they had tried at one time or another, in vain. The usual complaint was that Niehans hadn't bothered to answer their letters. Few believed that I would ever get
to talk to the Great Rejuvenator—even if he *was* still alive, which
many doubted.

In Vienna, while attending the Seventh International Gerontological Congress in July, 1966, I tried to find someone who
knew how to get to Niehans. On the very last day of the conference, I noticed in the program a paper entitled "A Critical Survey
of Cellular Therapy and Therapeutic Application of RNA in Degenerative Endocrine Disorders with Case Histories," written
by a Dr. Wolfgang Goetze-Claren of New York. I caught him at
his hotel just before he checked out.

He was tall, dark-haired, and spoke with a soft Prussian accent.
His costume seemed perfect for a courtly role in a Transylvanian
operetta, but odd for a doctor. He wore a white shirt with blue
candy stripes, Buster Brown collar, tie to match his turquoise
eyes, gilded leaf cuff links, dernier cri chunk crystal timepiece on
his wrist, gleaming black boots, crimson waistcoat, Tyrolean
spruce-green-trimmed gray flannel suit with saber-sharp trouser
creases.

He introduced himself as a colleague and friend of Niehans.

Would he help me see Niehans? Yes, of course. But seeing Niehans was never easy unless one was a patient, and that, he
admitted, might be expensive and, even then, one still might not
be received. The only way to contact Niehans was for me to go
to Zurich, take a room at the posh Baur-au-Lac Hotel, tell the
concierge that Dr. Goetze-Claren had sent me, bribe him for Niehans' phone number, and pray that Niehans would be in a good
mood.

I followed Goetze-Claren's prescription exactly and did manage to reach Niehans. He set an appointment for the very next day

at his home in La Tour de Peilz, between Vevey and Montreux, which was some two hundred miles from Zurich.

Niehans lives ten minutes from the Vevey railroad station, and every cabdriver knows his home. It is a magnificent white two-story affair overlooking the lake on the south and underlooking the Alps in every other direction. Majestic, billowy cypresses line the path from the road up to the door of Sonnenfels, which means "rock in the sun" and formerly belonged to Emperor Haile Selassie.

A maid answered the doorbell. With a tiny key she unlocked a mammoth iron grille door with the gold initials PN wrought into the upper half. My steps echoed across the white Italian marble floor of the foyer, until I reached the magnificent needlepoint carpet of the waiting room. Vast Gothic chairs upholstered in deep Burgundian reds matched the drapes. On the walls were a Van Dyck, a Dürer, and a painting attributed to the Sienüa School (supposedly Niehans' favorite): a portrait of the Holy Family which art scholars have photographed in great detail.

His office is a bright, cheerful room adorned with mementos of his career. He strode briskly into the room, shook hands firmly, and sat down at his desk. With his hands folded in front of him, he explained the surroundings.

He spoke an elegant French, apologizing for his English, which was, he said, irregular. He was the tallest (6-foot 3-inch) octogenarian I've ever met, and he looked the healthiest. The proper epithet for him is the one his associate, Dr. Walter Michel, uses: *"Un grand monsieur."* The constant twinkle in his eyes can, with equal ease, express mirth, mockery, spite, or incomprehension. He is quite purposefully ambiguous.

He wears a dark blue suit every day. He speaks simply, quickly, forthrightly, often ignoring the questions being asked him. His memory is bad—perhaps a sign of age. The upward tilt of his nose is a warning not to try his patience or ask foolish questions. The more personal the questions, the higher goes the nose. No, there would be no tape recording.

He was maddeningly imprecise at times, impossible to pin down, evasive of delicate questions, often dropping an innuendo that he would refuse to complete or substantiate— "Ah, I for-

get the date and other details . . . forget what I have said because it might hurt an innocent person"—usually in connection
with persons he believed were out to do him in or destroy his business.

The clinical work is done almost entirely by his assistant, Dr.
Walter Michel, these days. Niehans thus has time to answer correspondence and promote research into his pet projects: the cur-
ing of diabetes and cancer by means of his famous cell therapy.
He walks a good deal, going hatless (and coatless except for the
past three winters) in the coldest weather. His diet is mundane,
without fancy sauces or heady wines—"I wouldn't take three steps
for a good restaurant, but I'd go anywhere for good conversation
and interesting company."

In a sense, he seems to be holding death at bay in order to make
a mark upon the academic world, which has derided him bitterly
and treated him as a spoiled child. He is an acknowledged "outsider"—"I am, first and foremost, a revolutionary and you must
understand this"—and refuses to brawl with academic medicine
—or even to engage in a dialogue with anyone but his Creator.
He is snappy and curt with doctors who try to "teach" him. Truck-
ing with Niehans means doing things his way.

Dr. So-and-So thinks cell therapy is a fraud? *"Moi, je m'en
fiche,"* says Niehans with a shrug of the shoulders. He does not
attempt to refute criticism. "If So-and-So is happier believing
that, then let him believe it. But it's not true."

His desk is a beauty—a long, sturdy Louis XIV piled high with
correspondence from the curious, the critical, the helpless, the
hopeless, the thankful, the irate. There is no secretary—"How
could I possibly have a secretary? My work requires absolute discretion. I prefer to do it all myself." *All* letters, he claims, are answered by himself or by Dr. Michel. Even his intimates admit
—though Niehans denies it—that in bygone times unrewarding
or upsetting mail (such as requests for charity) was swept into
the circular file with an intentional slip of the elbow. Friends were
urged to print their names clearly on the envelope.

At his left hand is a large bronze medallion portrait of his
grandfather, Frederick III of Prussia. One of the carved chairs
across the room is a gift of Alfonso XIII of Spain. Two swords lie
on a small table. One belonged to his grandfather; the other,

which he describes as "a more modest piece," is a small treasure, its silver blade inlaid with gold, given to him by the late Austrian emperor.

Opposite stands a vast, grandiose, gilded Louis XIV commode, which houses his monographs. The newer ones he hands out freely; the older he keeps hidden since some are quite passé.

His single most valuable treasure is an 8 by 10 photograph. It hangs on the wall to his right. The subject: Pope Pius XII in prayer. It is inscribed (in German) to Niehans and his wife Coralie "in gratitude" for the rejuvenator's ministrations that cured the Pope in 1954.

Another picture, farther away on the other side of the door but also on the right wall, is a wistful photograph of the pale, delicate Coralie wearing a fur stole (vintage 1920).

Niehans is his most articulate when he recounts anecdotes about his gay youth, the old army days, his rare—and always victorious —engagements with cynical, disbelieving physicians and scientists. Occasionally, he interrupts his narrative to evoke a figure or a name by running a large, powerful hand through his coarse white thatch of hair. His skin is thin, chalk white, remarkably clear, thanks largely to his avoidance of the sun's rays, which he considers poisonous.

Paradoxically, this apparently quite healthy old man is not, as is so often stated, a living testimonial to his rejuvenation treatment. In 1949 he injected himself with cells to cure a prostate condition, and several years before that he almost died from a frozen-cell experiment on his own body (discovering, in the process, that only rapid *deep*-freezing to $-75°$ C. prevents autolytic breakdown of the cells into toxic substances). But until now he has relied on his own constitution rather than cell therapy to ensure a hearty old age.

If the promise of cells holds no special charm for Niehans personally, it has seduced thousands of people in their middle and late years who can afford the $1,500 fee for his cell (or "cellular") therapy injections.* Niehans claims to have performed over fifty

---

* Niehans prefers the English "cell therapy" to "cellular therapy," or the French *"thérapie cellulaire,"* or the German *"Zellulartherapie"*—although the latter terms, less precise as they are, have gained greater currency in the literature. I prefer "cell therapy" and use it throughout except where another term is used in quotations. CT is the abbreviation.

thousand successful CT injections, mostly on very rich and celebrated people. Whereas in his early years, according to Dr.
Joachim Stein of Heidelberg, who worked with him, up to one-
third of his clientele was charity work, the number of charity patients has dropped to virtually zero. During the two weeks that I
stayed in a chalet next to La Prairie clinic, every one of the hundred-
odd patients was a paying customer.

The list of celebrities who have been treated by Niehans over
the past fifteen years or so is staggering. The ones who are commonly associated with his treatment are merely the peak of an
iceberg. Most patients are afraid to let it be known that they have
had cell injections, and several celebrities have threatened to
sue writers who associate their names with the Niehans treatment.

The list of celebrated cell therapy patients includes Pope
Pius XII, Konrad Adenauer, Theodor Heuss, King Ibn Saud,
Thomas Mann, Sacha Guitry, Yvonne Printemps, Aga Khan, vari-
ous members of the Japanese Imperial family, Gayelord Hauser,
Lillian Gish, Somerset Maugham, Wilhelm Furtwängler, Chris-
tian Dior, Georges Braque, Alan Searle, Bernard Baruch, Cobina
Wright, Sr., Ann Miller, the Imam of Yemen, Gloria Swanson,
and many others.

According to Raymond Jaussi of the Montreux Office of Tourism, the three biggest assets of the area are:

(1) The Swiss bank secret
(2) Tourism facilities
(3) Paul Niehans

Niehans is probably the best-known Swiss of all time. At the
Swiss Consul General's office in New York never a week goes by
without a prospective patient inquiring how he can get in touch
with him. The only other inquiries which top those about
Niehans (except during the winter sports season) have to do with
Swiss medical service and abortions.

While I sat with Dr. Michel in his office one day, a nurse interrupted our conversation to announce that the Cuban Consulate
was on the phone.

"Excusez-moi, docteur," said Michel, who calls everybody *"docteur."*

He listened at length, then said: *"Bon, ça va . . .* but I won't be able to do it till the twenty-second or the twenty-third of the month. Yes . . . by São Paulo, then on to Havana. I understand . . . No, I *don't* have to know who the patient is. Don't worry about that . . . No, listen, I don't even *want* to know who he is. Yes, total discretion . . . of course . . . I understand."

It was clear that the patient was a top-ranking Cuban VIP, if not *the* top-ranking Cuban VIP. Two pregnant ewes were shipped (as a precaution in case one proved to be infected) in the pressurized compartment of a specially chartered plane.

I mentioned the conversation to Lee Lockwood, author of the book *Castro's Cuba, Cuba's Fidel*. A few weeks later he sent me a clipping from the New York *Times* dated October 12, 1966, about the state funeral of Captain Leonardo Quintana, chief of the permanent mission in Cuba of the Venezuelan pro-Castro faction. In an accompanying note, Lockwood said: "The Cubans would certainly spend the money for something like this—believe me."

When a man knows that he is about to die, he often will grasp desperately for succor from the most unorthodox healer. Since regular medicine can offer nothing more, why not try CT? Most "respectable" rejuvenationists, however, dislike treating terminal cases because it lowers their batting average (if, that is, they do any such totting up). Some, though, give CT for virtually any condition at any stage. Niehans customarily turns down a patient with any infection or cancer, especially if it looks as though he might expire in the clinic. Fatalities on the premises, he says, have never occurred.

Niehans is careful to see that none does take place. A young Manhattan doctor had recommended that one of his celebrity patients see Niehans for possible CT. So great was the VIP's reputation and achievement, Niehans went out to the airport in Lausanne to meet him. For hours the two men talked about their common passion: music. (Niehans credits his most enduring and valid inspirations to the influence of music.) Finally, Niehans sent his patient to a colleague, who conducted extensive diagnostic tests, including the Abderhalden (which is performed on every Niehans patient at additional cost as part of the course). The doctor's findings confirmed what had been discovered in Manhattan —the patient was suffering from primary polycythemia (a chronic and sustained high red blood cell count that often causes a greatly swollen spleen), which is incurable. Niehans decided —with apologies—not to risk trying CT on his patient—composer Igor Stravinsky.

A word about the Abderhalden test, the scientific detective that ferrets out ailing organs. Among the orthodox cell therapists who slavishly copy every detail of the master's technique, the complicated urine enzyme reaction test invented by the late German physiologist Emil Abderhalden is considered de rigueur. It is believed that the Abderhalden, when properly performed, indicates the presence of protective ferments in the blood specific for the various proteins that stimulate their production. It reveals individual organ and tissular malfunction per se, but does not indicate whether the malfunction is due to over- or underactivity.

The Abderhalden enjoyed a certain vogue as a pregnancy test —until Kaiser Wilhelm playfully submitted to the laboratory urine samples from his private guardsmen in bottles labeled with girls' names. When word came back as to which of the donors were expecting blessed events, the name Abderhalden was never again mentioned in respectable medical circles except derisorily.

Indeed, the Abderhalden is so complicated that only a handful of youth doctors perform it. Its ostensible advantage is that it gives a reading on the health of tissues for which there are no other tests. Manhattan youth doctor Max Wolf, whose rejuvenation techniques aim toward reactivation of worn-out organs, states that he has perfected the Abderhalden (by pre-digesting the animal substrates) to a point where only Abderhalden's widow can do it as accurately. "If it's done right, it's wonderful," says Wolf. "I swear by it."

The results are customarily given on two cards, one for the physician and one for the patient, on which ratings of 1, 2, or 3 are given for each tissue, depending upon the intensity of violet color resulting from precipitation of the respective substrates. The higher the number, the more serious the malfunction. It should be noted that even many cell therapists doubt its precision.

Niehans fixes the beginning of his fabulous cell therapy practice as April Fool's Day, 1931. The case he treated with cells that day had nothing to do with rejuvenation as such, but involved a new technique for transplantation that would eventually become one of the great medical fads of all time.

Niehans tells the following story about his discovery of cell therapy:

The young Swiss surgeon was new to the blade—so new that he did not realize what he had done, even immediately after the operation. The patient's name was Madame Volman.

It was the nurse who first noticed something strange: "She is still unconscious, Doctor, but her hands and forearms have taken on a strange, unnatural position. A kind of cramp."

The surgeon had removed not only the elderly peasant woman's goiter, but also, quite accidentally, part of the adjacent vital parathyroid glands. The chances of repairing this disastrous slip were practically nil. Without functioning parathyroids—four tiny oval glands located just behind the thyroid which control vital blood calcium levels—the patient would probably live no more than a few hours.

The body on the table began to twitch. Minutes later the woman was possessed by heaving, thrashing convulsions.

Tetany.

The significance of what followed next on that first day of April, 1931, would be debated for decades to come.

Hastily, the surgeon summoned the Lausanne clinic director Professor DeQuervain into the operating room. DeQuervain decided that only a transplant could save the woman. But transplants were very tricky. Could one be performed? Indeed, if it could be, *who* could do it?

What *was* his name? The surgeon-endocrinologist who had written that book on rejuvenation? His clinic was in Vevey, just down the road . . . Niehans! That was it. Call Paul Niehans in Vevey!

At La Prairie, there was no Niehans. The nurse on duty called the homes of each of the three patients listed in Niehans' datebook under April 1. Still no Niehans.

An hour after the surgical misstep, the patient's convulsions became increasingly violent. Another agonizing twenty minutes passed. Finally DeQuervain reached Niehans and quickly told him what had happened. Yes, Niehans would drop everything and come over. Before going to the hospital, however, he drove to the Clarens abattoir, where his experimental animals were slaughtered. He deftly snipped the parathyroids from a freshly killed steer and proceeded with them to the hospital.

As he strode toward the operating room, he passed the patient's family. Calmly, confidently, they thumbed through the magazines in the waiting room, unaware of the drama unfolding nearby. So much the better, thought Niehans.

Niehans saw that the patient was almost gone. The next spasm, he thought, might well be her last. There were two reasons for not attempting the ordinary transplant DeQuervain had in mind. The first was that at least two hours were needed to graft the gland—and that was possible only if the patient were absolutely serene, which this one was not. The second was that, according to Swiss law, a surgeon may not cut into a dying patient. "This law," explains Niehans, "is based on the belief that one's death should be respected."

Suddenly (because of the utter hopelessness of the situation, thinks Niehans) something "awakened" in the tall, handsome young surgeon. To the amazement of the clinic staff, Niehans removed the patient from surgery and had her wheeled into a private room. Then he seized a surgical knife and began paring the tiny steer glands he had picked up at the slaughterhouse into fine pieces, taking pains not to mash the cells. He called for a physiological solution and began to irrigate the small clumps of parathyroid cells. Then he loaded a large hypodermic syringe with the mixture.

If the onlooking DeQuervain had been perplexed by Niehans' unorthodox behavior, the rejuvenationist's next move positively chilled him. Without a second's hesitation, Niehans injected the strange fluid into one of the patient's pectoral muscles.

Was this a mercy killing? The others in the room believed that foreign protein injected into the body would inevitably produce a lethal, anaphylactic (allergic reaction) shock. But in this case, they were wrong.

Almost immediately the woman's cramps became less violent. Two hours later they disappeared altogether. In some mysterious fashion, Niehans' weird concoction had revived her parathyroid glands.

In the end, nobody was more surprised than Niehans himself.

"I had thought," says Niehans, "that the action would be no more than that of a hormone injection, with a brief relief and a need for repeated treatments. But, surprise! Not only did it fail to provoke any unpleasant reaction in the patient, but it acted in a lasting way, longer than any extract or synthetic hormone, hormone crystal—or even a surgical transplant."

Eventually, the woman died. But she died as few of us can: in her nineties, some thirty years later.

The technique used by Niehans to save that peasant woman was certainly a precursor of cell therapy. Yet, the curative effect was definitely not the one that is supposed to result from cell therapy. Normally, the effects of CT are not experienced for at least three months from the time of injection. What saved Madame Volman was, in all likelihood, a hormonal reaction. Whether the cell injection actually regenerated the severed parathyroid gland is anyone's guess. One has only Niehans' word as to what occurred. He says it did.

In any event, cell therapy as such—used to revitalize a senescent patient or to cure specific diseases—did not become popular until many years later. In 1937, Niehans published a book entitled *La Sénéscence et le Rajeunissement*. Few people have seen it. I found a copy in the Institut Pasteur in Paris. In it, Niehans explores the gamut of rejuvenation techniques he believed useful at the time, and CT is curiously *not* among the elect. In fact, there is not a single word on cell injections.

In view of his subsequent preoccupation with CT, it is interesting to note how many other modes of rejuvenation he considered valid six years after he says he invented CT.

He did perceive the healing promise of cells, calling them those "animated building blocks of the living citadel." Interestingly enough, in this early monograph, he freely uses the word "rejuvenation"—a term he later dropped in favor of "revitalization," which was more acceptable in medical circles. Here he explores the value of nature therapy (sunbaths, fresh air, sea voyages, and swimming); organotherapy ("absorption of young fresh testicle material in sandwich form [sic] or dried and pulverized in tablet form"); hormone therapy; young or "activated" blood serum, saline injections (with or without hormones); infrared irradiation of the testicles; heat treatments; X-raying of various glands; an assortment of "wave treatments"; and gland transplants and ligatures. It is not until 1949 (in *Traitement biologique des maladies organiques par injection de cellules vivantes*) that Niehans discusses cell therapy in any manner whatever.

What was apparent in his 1937 treatise was his obvious preference for transplants over all other rejuvenation modes—despite what he termed the "geniality" of Eugen Steinach's ligature of the sex glands, which was supposed to employ energy sources from within the organism itself. "Gland transplants," he wrote, "have the incontestable advantage of being able to be repeated."

When CT began to become popular and profitable to Niehans, he began to think about protecting his process against infringement by other would-be rejuvenationists. This wish was frustrated when German doctors informed him that a surgeon named Kuettner in Breslau had published his experiments with a technique that greatly resembled CT in the *Central Journal of Surgery* in 1912, and as late as 1929 had publicized the manner of injection with wide-caliber syringe needles.

"I am glad," said Niehans gallantly, "that the stupid question of priority has been cleared up. This question has always seemed unimportant to me because I consider priority claims, especially in medicine, as of dubious value."

As "stupid" a question as he may have considered it, Niehans fought vigorously to assert his preeminence in the field of cell injections. In 1948 the anatomist Karl Frederich Bauer visited the Niehans laboratory for the purpose of creating artificial tissue cultures *in vitro*. The laboratory product never quite made the grade, and to this day only the cells of freshly slaughtered animals are used in cell therapy preparations. Although Bauer failed to contrive an acceptable way of manufacturing cell magic in the petri dish, he swore that he, not Niehans, had invented CT. This immensely perturbed the normally imperturbable Niehans, and the two former friends tangled for months in the courts. Finally, in December, 1956, a Swiss court decided that CT was properly Niehans' baby.

Thereafter, Bauer tried to "unmask" Niehans as a charlatan and incompetent. In an article in the *Deutsche Medizinische Wochenschrift*, Bauer criticized Niehans' old-fashioned record-keeping and pointed out discrepancies among the rejuvenator's published accounts of cures. It failed to undo Niehans. Heavy artillery was needed to dent the armor of a giant, and Bauer was fighting with a slingshot.

Other attempts to discredit Niehans have—to date—been equally ineffectual, notably those of the American Medical Association. JAMA's occasional foray, like Bauer's, has always been distressingly superficial, and nakedly biased. Unlike his hapless predecessors Brown-Séquard and Voronoff, who eventually fell into disgrace, Paul Niehans has enjoyed continuing success at the trickiest of trades for more than forty years.

Niehans is unique. He is neither a naïf, like Brown-Séquard, nor a hell-bent opportunist like Voronoff. He has tidily turned the mystique of his noble origins, his formidable medical talent (as surgeon, endocrinologist, physician, diagnostician, and rejuvenator), his glittering manner, his compelling personality, and total confidence in himself into a multimillion-dollar payoff.

The key perhaps is his self-confidence. While other "outsiders" struggle to win approval by academic medicine (like moths batting their wings in a suicidal rush toward a bonfire), Niehans plainly doesn't give a damn. He snubs all "authority." "If they want to come to learn from me," he says, "I'll show them whatever they want to see. I have no secrets. My only concern is for the welfare and health of my patients—not for other doctors."

Unknown to most people, including many of his friends and patients, Niehans is of royal blood—a Hohenzollern. But neither Niehans nor the Hohenzollerns have ever officially disclosed the facts concerning his mother's recondite origins. As with so much of the mystery surrounding his life, Niehans prefers to let his chroniclers speculate, perhaps only because he would hate to end public speculation and interest in himself.

Of the liberal aesthete Frederick III of Prussia, who is represented in the large bronze medallion on his desk, Niehans says no more than: "That is my grandfather. He was a great man."

A great man, indeed, whose early days would make Hugh Hefner look like Bert Bobbsey. Spawning children of nature was the sport of kings, and of kings-to-be, such as the young Frederick. And while it was implicitly accepted as a divine right, publicity on such goings-on was closely censored. In later years, Frederick and his court successfully covered up the more infamous liaisons, scandals, duels with irate husbands, and other splotches on the royal escutcheon which once filled the gazettes.

Niehans' maternal grandmother is said to have been the Countess Fürstenberg, half-sister to the Prussian King Wilhelm II, who was detailed by him to mend relations between the Hohenzollerns and their English cousins. (Frederick III eventually married the royal Princess Victoria, sister of Edward VII, in 1858.) Using a Swiss passport, the Countess shuttled back and forth between Prussia and England on missions beclouded by intrigue and delicacy. When she became pregnant (allegedly by Frederick III) the truth of the old popular saying "The emperor fights no great battle but a Fürstenberg falls" was amply demonstrated. The king quickly procured a one-way passage for her to the frontier of her choosing.

Picking Switzerland as her country of exile, she used the new title Countess of Wiesbaden. Then in 1853, or thereabouts, she gave birth to a baby girl whose name went onto the hospital register as Anna Franziska Kaufmann.

Frederick, who appears to have been remorseful about his mistress' sad plight, took a lifelong interest in the winsome, blond Anna. Upon word of her betrothal to a young surgeon of the straightlaced Bern bourgeoisie named Paul Niehans, Frederick III sent her a long, affectionate letter, a box of jewels and a substantial dowry. It was her first inkling that her father was not, as she had been led to believe, an undercover Prussian diplomatic agent whose cloak-and-daggering had kept him far from home.

The staid, terrifyingly respectable Niehans family weighed scandal negatives against Hohenzollern positives—and quickly decided in favor of promoting the union.

In time, there came a Paul Niehans, *fils*, whose boyhood was marked by enormous talent and charm. He was a top student, a sure marksman, an agile and inveterate equestrian, a champion mountain climber. Anna and Paul, *père,* strove constantly to draw their impetuous son away from the adventurer's life he seemed headed for (he talked of becoming a soldier) and into more respectable pursuits.

"We take the liberty," wrote a professor to his parents, "of suggesting that you push your son as far as possible in the direction of mathematics. His imaginative power can rapidly carry him to the limits of human knowledge."

Neither parent saw Paul as a mathematician. Mama would have had him don a Reform cleric's collar, Papa a surgeon's smock. The thing both feared was that Paul might accept his uncle's offer of a Prussian military education at the cadet school in Potsdam, thereby abdicating his Swiss citizenship. Young Niehans was greatly tempted. But his parents finally prevailed upon him. After penning a long, thoughtful "thanks-but-I-can't" letter to his uncle (Wilhelm II), Paul enrolled in divinity school. In three years he was given a doctorate in theology. His father never abandoned the hope that he would go into medicine one day. All during his divinity studies, Niehans *fils* received a steady stream of medical books from his father. The hint was not without consequence, for after a brief but eloquent *pastorat* Paul Niehans, Jr., began to study medicine in Bern and, eventually, in Zurich.

His youth was not all work. One of his intimates describes him as having been the number one playboy of Zurich in his day. "I *did* have a superb youth," confesses Niehans.

Deftly—and occasionally not so deftly—he eluded the eager clutches of would-be mothers-in-law. Points of honor raised by angry or jealous or cuckolded males were settled under torchlight with flashing sabers. His towering height and long arms gave him a considerable advantage over his opponents. But today he carries engraved on his throat the memorandum of a jealous rival's blade that found its mark during *sine-sine* combat at Menzour.

"Ah . . . girls . . . girls," he says, "I was always ready to cross swords for a girl."

In 1912, Niehans was appointed honorary aide-de-camp to his visiting Prussian uncle, whose so-called "peace offensive" was causing Europe to tremble in its boots. It was a high point of his military service. For a full week during maneuvers in the Jura, the dashing cavalier never left the side of his beaming uncle.

The prewar European scene was Niehans' oyster: debutante balls in Budapest, trysts along the Danube with any number of fair young maidens, six weeks on horseback from Hungary to Adrianople, mountain climbing (he has mastered every Alpine peak deemed worth conquering). He scorned soccer: "Running after a ball," he says, "is for children."

Once, while bedded down for the night on a farm in Bosnia-Herzegovina, he was startled by an infant's cries. The scene he happened upon appalled him. A child was obviously convulsed by acute appendicitis, and a village healer was preparing an herb infusion treatment. Finally, he convinced the child's parents that surgery should be performed. It remained only to convince the healer, who indicated that his "rights" to his patient would have to be purchased. Outraged, Niehans paid off the rustic quack with an uppercut and then calmly proceeded to remove the appendix with a kitchen knife.

His tour with Wilhelm II brought the two Hohenzollerns very close to each other, a fact that complicated Niehans' ambiguous national loyalties. He did not want to compromise his fidelity to Switzerland, but at times his Hohenzollern blood proved thicker than the waters of Leman. When the Emperor requested that he return to the Balkans, Niehans volunteered to equip a Swiss medical mission (financed in part by his own purse) and went immediately to Sajckar, which had been severely ravaged by a typhus epidemic.

The old saying that the Holy Roman Empire was neither holy, nor Roman, nor an empire was convincingly proven at Sajckar. The stench of war almost overcame Niehans. Total chaos had gripped the Bosniacs, Albanians, Serbs, Hungarians, and Bulgars, many of whom had been led to believe they were fighting alongside—not against—the Russians. Every hideous degradation wrought by war's devastation met Niehans' eyes in Sajckar: starvation riots; unburied, putrefying cadavers; rampant lice and crabs feasting upon the living—as well as an assortment of diseases and mutilations.

His first job was to persuade the apathetic, shell-shocked Serbs to bury the dead. Then he competed with the rats for the lives of the remaining men. In all, Niehans spent twenty months in the Dolomites and treated fifteen thousand patients.

Niehans' camera became a veritable necrophage, recording lifeless horror after horror. As he turns the pages of his photo album, Niehans, the octogenarian rejuvenator, recalls the times of his greatest happiness: his own youth. The enthusiasm of his descriptions of the illustrations is spontaneous, seemingly more vital than that he shows when discussing medical matters.

"I remember this fellow well," says Niehans of a rifleman sizing up his quarry from behind a sandbag barricade. "He was so gentle, a great animal lover. Just before I snapped this picture, he picked up a centipede crawling near his firing piece and carefully removed it from harm's way. Then he shot an Italian dead in his tracks."

As a Swiss medical corps officer, Niehans was required to remain aloof from displays of partisan passion. With his temperament and Hohenzollern blood, however, neutrality was an impossibility. He proudly boasts of being able to blank the eye of an enemy target at 300 meters.

Niehans has his own favorite tale to add to the world's collection of accounts of Italian war prowess and heroism.

"Once," he relates, "at three-thirty in the morning at Rauchskoffel, I was asked to take command since I was the only officer—even though I was Swiss—left among an Austrian detachment of two hundred men. I accepted. But I told the men: 'I warn you, if I take over, I shall never surrender.'" The Austrians accepted his terms.

"The Italians outnumbered us by at least five hundred men. I knew that I had to use my head to win. I figured that, since it was Italians we were up against, our lungs could be as lethal as our rifles. We were low on ammunition. I ordered the men to make one grand assault on the Italian camp, firing everything at the enemy and—most important—yelling and screaming.

"I was amazed. The Italians, thinking the whole Kaiser's army was upon them, surrendered immediately."

Niehans became that rare object: a Swiss war hero. He was mentioned twice for bravery, was twice wounded, and was awarded the Order of Saint Sava by the King of Serbia. He is said to have saved fifteen lives a day among the wounded working with Professor Tixier at the Hôtel-Dieu hospital in Lyon.

Then word of his origins leaked out, and irate Frenchmen accused him of being a spy for the Prussians. While his pro-German sympathy must be assumed, espionage does not seem to be his style. He declares that he left the hospital only to sleep. Disgusted by French ingratitude, the surgeon returned to Switzerland, where he apprenticed himself to leading specialists in (successively) ophthalmology, gynecology, and urology.

This catholic approach to medicine was far from orthodox, but the liberty afforded him by his brains and money made it possible. A look at Niehans' biography suffices to indicate that he was on his way to becoming a great something-or-other. In surgery or endocrinology he would most certainly have made a good name for himself. But, too, he might have been bored silly.

Instead, he chose to become a rejuvenator. And while one may dispute the sophistication of his science, no one can gainsay his qualities as physician and healer. As Dr. Ivan Popov, of Opio, France, described his colleague:

"There are not ten people who really know what the problem of rejuvenation is. It requires a very strong erudition . . . an experience difficult to transmit to others. . . . Only Niehans cures everybody."

The praise is exaggerated. Niehans does not cure all of his patients. But he does have an impressive roster of satisfied customers. One can only guess how many of his "cures" are due to CT, how many to placebo effects, and how many to the sheer power of his personality.

How does one account for Niehans' fabulous success? The answer lies, at least partially, in a great source of strength that is probably simultaneously his most grievous failing. Niehans possesses an infantile "believer" quality, a trust in others and implicit confidence in his own righteousness, that has made him immune to criticism that would have discouraged anybody else from going on.

Niehans simply ignores his critics. They are either "misguided" or "uninformed" or "mischievous." In any case, unworthy of notice. He, Niehans, is never—or hardly ever—wrong. His attitude toward the press is ambivalent. He is tolerant of some newspapermen, brushes off others haughtily. He was gracious to me.

Journalists often overstate what Niehans says (it is not difficult to misinterpret him), and while almost every article on him evokes a flood of queries and new business, sometimes it gets him into trouble.

Before developing cell injections, Niehans performed many "tissular transplants" to bring about rejuvenation. When he came to New York in the 1930's, newspapers played up the success he had had in stimulating growth in an eighteen-year-old dwarf by means of a pituitary (acidophile layer from the anterior lobe) tissular graft.* Apparently, according to Niehans, his press notices pictured him as able to add or subtract inches at will. What he had done was amazing enough (if true): After four years during which the young dwarf had not grown an inch, Niehans grafted a thin sliver of pituitary tissue onto the dwarf's gland and, within another four years, added 9.5 inches to his height.

After fourteen years, the dwarf grew from 4 feet 3 inches to 5 feet 8 inches.

On Niehans' first day in New York, a dwarf came to his hotel room and boisterously demanded that Niehans sell him whatever it was that could make him tall. Niehans refused, explaining that he treated no one without extensive diagnostic tests beforehand.

The next day, three dwarfs and a giant showed up. Exasperated, Niehans told them he could do nothing for them.

The day after that, twenty-five dwarfs, four giants, and several midgets took his room by storm.

Finally, the hotel management asked Niehans to leave. "If you're signing up circus acts," the manager said icily, "you'll have to meet somewhere else. Just what do you think this monster parade is going to do to our clientele?"

Apologetically, the Swiss physician checked out—still pursued by his colorful menagerie.

The year 1948 probably marks the actual debut of CT as such, for it was then that Niehans began to inject *fetal* cells into his patients. It was the nontoxicity and regenerative power of these fetal cells that made CT safe and, if one believes the lore, effective.

Slowly, cell therapy began to catch on among the International Set. At times Niehans' clinic was so mobbed that he found himself rejecting applicants. He turned down the candlestick-maker and accepted the pianist, rejected the rancher in favor of the diplomat or writer. It was (and still is) as elite a clientele as a physician has ever had. Industrialists, financiers, literati, painters, musicians, theologians, heads of state swept into the little town of Vevey.

For a moment, it looked as if George VI would be his first major sovereign. When the king fell ill, Niehans was immediately con-

---

* In *Cellular Therapy from the Viewpoint of Doctor and Patient*, Niehans gives the date for the graft as 1927; in *Vingt Ans de Transplantation de Glandes Endocrines*, he gives it as July 3, 1928.

sulted. But when word of the possibility that a foreigner (and a Hohenzollern rejuvenationist at that) would attend His Britannic Majesty leaked out, court physicians, buttressed by public opinion, quickly vetoed the idea.

One of Niehans' longest (in distance and in time) house calls was to the palace of a powerful Indian maharajah who had fallen victim to asthenia. Specialists called in from the four corners of the world failed to revitalize the fabulous, bejeweled old roué. Treasure-counting and wenching—once his favorite pastimes—no longer excited him. The maharajah challenged the implication of his electrocardiogram, which read normal, and insisted that he had heart disease—in addition to dizziness, fainting spells, insomnia, and, most bedeviling for a swordsman with a well-stocked harem, neither the lust nor wherewithal to make love.

Niehans diagnosed the potentate's condition as neurovegetative dystony, a luxury ailment of the idle rich. After treatment with Sertoli (testicle) cells, the Swiss rejuvenator prepared to leave. A palace aide informed him that he would have to wait out the cure. And, should there be no cure, he would, pity, lose his head "like the last doctor."

Nervously, Niehans explained that certain types of neurasthenia did not respond to cell therapy. And if the maharajah failed to get well, he could not take the blame. If Niehans had logic on his side, his host had other persuaders. Niehans was forced to stay on. Eventually, the ruler recovered his former appetites. One day the bahadur's spirits rose so high that he took time out from his routine to oversee the execution of some political prisoners. Niehans knew that his treatment had proved itself at last. Gratefully, the maharajah scooped up a fistful of precious stones and showered them into the physician's hands. A few days earlier, Niehans would have been content just to leave the palace. This was probably the severest test to which CT has ever been put.

Luminaries from assorted professional and social galaxies began to stud Niehans' client roster. Most of them have managed by one device or another to conceal the fact of their Vevey visits. Celebrities commonly boast of seeing the Great Rejuvenator to their friends, but deny it in public. It is hard to ascertain who has had CT and who has not.

A few years ago, Niehans was called into a case so fraught with serious consequences that it would have been impossible to have hidden his connection. The resultant publicity, in fact, conferred upon him an enduring notoriety and rocketed CT into a million-dollar business within the next few months.

The patient was Pope Pius XII.

The Pontiff's sickness is one of the most confused episodes in the history of modern clinical medicine. Niehans has been reluctant to talk about it.

After conversations with a number of people involved in the affair, I believe I have managed to piece together the picture of what actually transpired in this case.

The idea of the seventy-seven-year-old Roman Catholic Pontiff allowing himself to be treated by a Swiss Protestant rejuvenationist is not as farfetched as it might sound at first. The Pope had always been a friend of Germany. As nuncio in 1917 he had engineered complicated diplomatic concordats for the Vatican between Bavaria and Prussia. Again, in 1933, he had worked out an agreement with Adolf Hitler. He probably learned of Niehans through his nurse, Sister Pasqualina, Prussian by birth, who was fascinated by Niehans' resemblance to Wilhelm II.

The actual introduction, however, was made by Wilhelm Furtwängler, conductor of the Berlin Philharmonic (although credit is sometimes given to Phyffer von Attilhofen, chief of the Pontifical Swiss Guard, who acted as the direct intermediary). Furtwängler had fled defeated Nazi Germany when American occupation authorities accused him of collaboration with the Nazis. For nearly a year, until he was absolved of the charges in 1946, Furtwängler was given a cozy refuge at Sonnenfels by melomane Niehans.

In a private audience some time later, Furtwängler strongly advised the Pontiff to see Niehans. The Pope was suffering from chronic insomnia, a condition Furtwängler had had when he met Niehans and which had been cured by cell therapy. Niehans, he explained, considered insomnia to be caused by a disruption of the body's organic harmony. Redressment of faulty organs by fresh cells was Niehans' standard therapy.

The year was 1953, and the Pope had been driving himself relentlessly. Normally he slept from four to six hours a night. Now he was getting barely one fitful hour. In addition, he was suffering from constipation and a weakened heart rhythm.

On October 14, 1953, Niehans met the Pope for the first time. It was the most important conference of Niehans' life. The Pope took kindly to him, but categorically refused to countenance the suggestion that he take a week off.

As is true of most prudent cell therapists, Niehans usually treats only healthy patients. Cell injections tend to increase any existing bacillary activity. CT seemed contraindicated here on two counts: first, there was evidence of infection; second, lactic acid produced by the Pope's fatigue could have caused undesirable reactions if cell injections had been given. In his run-down condition the Pontiff would have been far less than an ideal test case for CT. And test case it would have been, thanks to the Vatican's overnight metamorphosis into a hive of *paparazzi* and newshounds eager for every scrap of information dealing with Pius' illness.

Niehans decided to postpone treatment, but implored His Holiness to get some rest. After consulting with other Vatican specialists, Niehans retired to his home in Burier-La-Tour-de-Peilz.

Just before Christmas, 1953, Niehans wrote to the Pope, asking him if he felt prepared to undergo treatment. His letter was answered by Dr. Galeazzi-Lizzi, Pius' personal physician, who had dabbled in rejuvenation and once used the ironic, improbable name of "Mahomet" as a racing car driver. He informed Niehans that the Pope was weakening, thinning, growing paler day by day —and was still as insomniac as ever. The Pope was definitely not ready for cells.

On February 12, 1954, Niehans received an urgent request by telephone from a Vatican official. Ready or not, the Pope was in an extremely critical condition. Niehans raced to the airport, enplaned for Castel Gandolfo. When he entered the seventeenth-century summer papal palace seventeen miles from Rome, he found the Pope far worse than when he had seen him the first time, confirming Galeazzi-Lizzi's assessment. The Pope was vomiting, spitting up blood, unable even to keep down a drink of water. He was being fed intravenously.

Was it cancer? Niehans biographer Gilles Lambert (an ardent Niehans apostle) suggests that Galeazzi-Lizzi had made such a diagnosis. *Time* magazine reported on August 31, 1959, that Niehans himself mentioned the possibility of cancer, and when the

word was mentioned he was "hustled out of the papal presence."
Time's interpretation is unlikely for several reasons, but basically
because there is no other evidence that the friendship between the
two men was anything but consistently vigorous from the day they
met.

The Pope's condition worried Niehans. The normally frail body
was a specter. He was hiccuping, with each bout amounting in se-
verity to a seizure. In addition, the rejuvenator detected a hemor-
rhagic gastritis. Specialists—all of them Roman Catholic—had
tried their hands at relieving the Pope's distress. All had failed.

Niehans quickly tackled the hiccups. He asked the nurse to turn
the patient on his side. Gently, he began to massage the chest
right above the stomach. In ten minutes the hiccups were gone.

On the second day, Niehans proposed giving the Pontiff cell injections.

"Do you really want to take the responsibility?" he was asked.

"Yes," said Niehans firmly.

The secrecy cloaking the Pope's treatment gave rise to a host of
rumors. The only certifiable fact was that Pius was seriously ill,
and that Niehans was at his bedside.

Was he being treated with cells from freshly slaughtered sheep
fetuses? Every little squeal and grunt from the papal farms was interpreted by the press as a sign that the Pope was getting fresh-
cell therapy, which Niehans was known to prefer to the bottled
cells.

Was something new and unheard of being tried? Every conceivable treatment—from massive dosages of royal jelly to chick embryos—was reported in the press.

Fresh cells? No, says Niehans.

"I gave the Pope lyophilized [deep-frozen, dried, vacuum-
packed in ampules] cells because I couldn't take my own sheep
into the Vatican."

(A physician very close to Niehans told me, however, that Niehans had flown two pregnant ewes to Rome in preparation for
fresh-cell therapy. Whether they had been used or not, he didn't
know.)

The lyophilization process, similar to the instant coffee process,
was developed by Niehans, with the help of a Nestlé Company en-

gineer in Vevey, and is said to preserve some of the cells' regenerative powers. The lyophilized cells were at least better than nothing, Niehans thought.

Cell therapists have conjectured as to just *which* cells were given
to the Pope. Niehans says: "I gave him hypothalamus and placenta
among other things which I cannot tell you, since I had promised
to keep it a secret. I treated him as Cushing taught me." (Harvey
Williams Cushing, the great neurosurgeon and Pulitzer-Prize-win-
ning author-teacher, once invited Niehans to work with him at
Yale, an invitation Niehans declined. In informal get-togethers,
the two men discovered common ground in their esteem for the
pituitary and hypothalamus, which, they felt, medicine had unjustly
ignored.)

Liver, stomach, and other endocrines including testes were also
given, according to a French cell therapist who says Niehans told
him so.

The thought of giving fresh cells in the Vatican struck Dr. Joachim Stein, who personally prepared the dried cells for the Pope
in the Siccacell factory in Heidelberg, which he operates for Niehans, as absurd. "You cannot kill a sheep in the Vatican. I was
there. I've seen the layout. It is unthinkable. For another thing,
one is not allowed to kill a living being in the Vatican."

For eight weeks, Niehans (accompanied by Coralie Niehans,
whom the Pope repeatedly called "Caroline") stayed on at Castel
Gandolfo, chatting with the Pope, strolling in the gardens surrounding the Palace, the Villa Barberini and Bernini's Church of
St. Thomas of Villanova.

Once the Pope asked Niehans if he were still "a religious man."

"I told him 'yes and no,' " recalls Niehans. "I had to tell him the
truth. I *am* a religious man, but my conception is astronomical
rather than ecclesiastical. Kepler took off his hat when he talked of
God."

"Do you believe in life after death?" the Pope asked Niehans.

"I *know* that we live after death," said Niehans with certainty.
"And I have two witnesses who can testify to the fact." Niehans
told the Pontiff of two men who had been snatched from death
whom he had been able to interrogate immediately afterward.
Niehans' father, who was chief surgeon of the city of Berne,

watched a patient succumb after chloroform had been improperly administered.

"The man was dead," says Niehans. "They had already put the white sheets over his body. Then my father intervened, first putting on his sterile gloves. He made an incision and massaged the man's heart for a very long time. Finally—after being dead for an hour—the man opened his eyes. 'How was it?' I asked him. 'There was no pain,' he said. 'I felt as though I were going through a tunnel at the end of which I saw a clear light. I wasn't anxious at all. On the contrary. Suddenly I felt somebody grab me by the neck and pull me backwards away from the light. Then I woke up.'

"The other witness had drowned in Lake Geneva in 1920 after getting entangled in the algae. He had been out of the water thirty minutes by the time I had got to him. I worked artificial respiration on him for a half hour. Finally he revived. I asked him what his sensations had been. Do you know what he told me? Exactly what the other man had told me. The complete absence of pain, the tunnel, the light . . . everything.

"Since then," Niehans told the Pope, finishing his story, "I haven't given death a second thought."

During the fifth week following the injections, the Pope's condition had visibly improved. He began to eat normally, take walks in the garden with Pasqualina, Galeazzi-Lizzi, and Niehans. He worked sitting up in bed.

By April 15, he was back to his former weight and he indulged Niehans by resting for two full days. A second series of injections was administered. Shortly thereafter, the Pope returned to the Vatican, and Niehans, now very much a celebrity, returned to Sonnenfels.

For the rest of the year, Niehans was besieged by would-be biographers and journalists. The Swiss rejuvenator, who has always treasured his privacy, registered under aliases at hotels and wore dark glasses.

His work in Rome seemed eminently successful. The Pope was feeling much better, and gave full credit to CT. "I find it incredible, though," Niehans quotes him as saying.

In November of that same year, while lifting a heavy safe containing secret papal documents, the Pope was suddenly afflicted with a harsh, suffocating pain in the chest.

Niehans was summoned to the Vatican once again. Both he and Galeazzi-Lizzi decided to call in Professor Paolucci, a distinguished Italian surgeon, and Professor Gasbarrini, a well-known Italian diagnostician. Paolucci seemed very sure of himself: surgery immediately. Niehans rejected the idea. So did the Prussian-born, Bavarian-raised Sister Pasqualina, who ruled Vatican affairs under Pius with Bismarckian firmness. Gasbarrini couldn't seem to make up his mind.

The Pope's pain was excruciating, causing him to gasp for breath and moan constantly.

The X rays showed that he was suffering from a diaphragmatic hernia. Niehans' prescription was so simple it evoked spite from the other specialists: Novocain injections to assuage the pain on the phrenic nerves, which in turn, said Niehans, would relax the diaphragm—followed by ingestion of mashed potatoes, whose weight and bulk might liberate the temporarily strangled portion of the stomach.

Paolucci continued to opt for surgery.* As he told Niehans: "The consequences of your unorthodox treatment would be highly uncertain."

"Surgery, at any rate," retorted Niehans sharply, "would have consequences with which I am all too familiar!"

Niehans' proposal at least had the advantage of being more innocuous. It was adopted. What's more, it worked. The Pope recovered.

The whole affair was faintly ironic. With access to the full range of modern medicine's most sophisticated techniques and the greatest medical minds in the world, the Pope had been cured by a Swiss rejuvenationist branded a slick, gouging quack by official medical circles. Even more paradoxical, the cure did not arise from the youth doctor's mysterious, exotic cell therapy of diced sheep embryo glands and tissues—but from a liberal dose of mashed potatoes!

With its customary opacity, _Il Osservatore Romano_ snippily

* Cecil and Loeb's _A Textbook of Medicine_ (10th Edition, 1959, Saunders) on surgical treatment of diaphragmatic hernia: "Surgery . . . is indicated if . . . the hernia is with reasonable assurance considered to be the source of the bleeding . . . In a sliding type, the outlook is less encouraging; in about one-fourth of the cases symptoms persist or recur, either because the hernia could not be corrected or because gastroesophageal reflux persists in spite of successful fixation of the gastroesophageal junction at the diaphragmatic hiatus."

stated that Pius had *not been cured by Niehans' cells*. It, however, did not bother to say what *had* relieved the Pope's distress.

Ever since, it has been fashionable to deride the affair as *opéra bouffe*. I asked Fritz Verzar, a leading figure in Swiss and international gerontological circles, what he made of Niehans' cure of the Pope.

"Niehans?" bellowed Verzar. "Cured the Pope? Yes . . . cured him of constipation. Hah! But that's all. And with what? With mashed potatoes! No, I will not discuss Niehans with you. Either one discusses serious things or things that are not serious. Niehans is *not* serious."

I mentioned Verzar's comment to Dr. Joachim Stein, who, while critical of Niehans' theories, admires his clinical ability.

"Make no mistake," said Stein angrily, "the Pope was really dying. Scientists, doctors, academicians from all over the world gave him a very pessimistic diagnosis. I was working with Niehans in Vevey at the time, and took over the clinic in his absence. No matter what Verzar says, the Pope had more than constipation. You don't die of constipation. Six or seven doctors from Catholic countries did not give fatalistic prognoses because he was constipated!"

Stein went on to describe Niehans' manner with patients:

"Niehans has not been accepted by academic medicine because he expresses himself in a simple, seemingly naïve way. But he is a scientist in the real sense of the word. As far as intuition goes, he is one of the best physicians I have ever met in my life. You ought to see him at the bedside, how he gets his diagnosis, how he treats his patients. He has an enormous *Fingerspitzengefühl* . . . fingertip touch sensitivity. With a few questions he immediately finds out what's what. He has a *Klinischeblick,* a clinical view, and from the patient's expressions and gestures he can draw excellent conclusions and arrive at a diagnosis. He finds the right tone for each patient, addressing simple patients simply, and sophisticated patients in an academic manner.

"I remember a little girl, eight or nine years old, who had bone sarcoma. Previous specialists who had seen the girl had overlooked the condition, but Niehans knew precisely how to talk to a little girl, and drew from her information that told him exactly what was the matter."

Galeazzi-Lizzi's role in the Vatican affair has never been clear. He did not oppose Niehans in principle—only toward the end for personal reasons. A product of the Salerno Medical School, known during the Renaissance for its rejuvenation studies, Galeazzi-Lizzi not only gave a ringing testimonial for CT shortly afterward, but eventually went into the CT business himself, choosing the Franco-Italian border town of Menton in which to hang up his shingle. Gilles Lambert, in *Niehans ou La Viellesse Vaincue*, quotes Galeazzi-Lizzi as saying: "When an organ is sick, as from old age, its cells seem to be tired of reproducing themselves; the cadence varies, the form changes. What else can one do against this degeneration except bring fresh cells to the tired organ? That is what is done today."

Pope Pius XII rewarded Niehans on April 5, 1955, with a fellowship in the Pontifical Academy, filling the empty chair of the late Sir Arthur Fleming, discoverer of penicillin. Whenever Niehans returns to Rome, as he does frequently, there are rumors that he is treating a pope with CT. More likely, he goes to Rome to attend sessions of the three-hundred-sixty-four-year-old Pontifical Academy of Sciences. What he does at these sessions is anyone's guess. I suspect that he listens a little, but, most of the time, he probably instructs the assembled Nobel Prize winners, professors, academicians, and divers geniuses on how the little cell can cure and rejuvenate.

CHAPTER FIVE

Inside Cell Therapy

Cell therapy is far and away the hottest contender in the rejuvenation popularity sweepstakes.

This may surprise Anglo-Saxons, who—incorrectly—tend to regard CT as the exclusive elixir of a legendary Swiss rejuvenator who treats only Popes, millionaires, and potentates. But CT is actually much more than this. It is practiced all over the world, on every continent (although more or less covertly in Britain and the United States). Europe has, however, had a big head start.

In West Germany, for example, lyophilized cell production is strictly controlled by the Ministry of Health and the University of Heidelberg. Some CT treatments are reimbursed by social security. Three hundred and ten MDs have gone into CT on a full-time basis, and another four thousand five hundred use it occasionally. A half million German patients have received cell injections since the Heidelberg cell factory opened its doors in 1954. Two hundred thousand more have had fresh or frozen cells.

National societies to propagate CT have been established in Argentina, Belgium, France, Holland, Italy, West Germany and the United States.

Despite prohibitions on importing the cells into the States, a handful of therapists play cat-and-mouse with authorities and smuggle in ampules from abroad or, failing this, ship their patients out to overseas sanitoria. At one time, a few clinical experiments were sanctioned by the FDA. Although they were supposed to have been done free of charge, one cell therapist concentrated on treating diamond-laden dowagers, Hollywood movie stars, and

Wall Street bankers. It turned out that he did in fact give the cells to his patients "for free," but charged fees for "his time" in the neighborhood of $1,000 per visit.

Getting around the FDA's embargo on lyophilized cells is easy. The small glass ampules are mailed from Switzerland or Germany as "gifts" to the patients, or simply shipped to a mail drop in the Bahamas, and from there forwarded to the rejuvenationist's office in the United States.

One youth doctor naïvely invited visiting FDA inspectors into his laboratory to show them his stock of lyophilized cells. The entire cache, worth about $3,000, was confiscated on the spot. Realizing how the wind was blowing, a former Madison Avenue cell therapist now uses his New York office exclusively to recruit clients for his European clinics.

Why is CT becoming so popular all over the world? One can cite such contributing factors as the Niehans mystique, the Pope Pius publicity, man's insatiable appetite for anything that conceivably might—just might—help him cheat death, as well as the recent decline in the prestige of orthodox medical practitioners. But so far, both *in vivo* (on live animals or human patients) and *in vitro* (on laboratory cultures) research has been glaringly inconclusive. The glowing empirical results boasted of by youth doctors are not scientifically controlled or programmed, and therefore must be taken with a hefty grain of salt.

In a sense, cell therapy is merely a novel twist to the old medical idea that failing organs and tissues should be treated biologically—not chemically—with corresponding living material from another animal.

This notion appears as far back as the Eber Papyrus, the oldest known medical document, which mentions the curative power of animal organs. Some therapists regard CT merely as a highly sophisticated form of transplant. In the classical sense of grafting an entire organ from one animal to another, transplants were begun by the Scottish anatomist John Hunter in the eighteenth century, and then revived a hundred years later by A. A. Berthold of Göttingen, who restored the hen-chasing urge to capons by affixing sex organs to their gizzards. Ever since, testicle transplants have figured prominently in the repertoire of the "Erector Set."

The basic principle of rejuvenative cell therapy was expressed in the sixteenth century by Paracelsus:

The heart heals the heart, lung heals lung, spleen heals spleen; *similia similibus curantur*.

Paracelsus' "like cures like" philosophy was a medical milestone, but great doctors had applied the concept previously with varying degrees of success. The fifteenth-century B.C. Hindu physician Susrata prescribed a tiger's testicle appetizer for his impotent patients. For youthful get-up-and-go, Achilles ate lion bone marrow, according to Homer.

The historical precedents for the basic biological therapy mystique fill a long list, but they cut little ice with scientists today. The youth doctors become more persuasive in citing the more recent work of the nineteenth century Prussian politician-pathologist Rudolf Virchow, whose concept of the "life-bearer" cell as the key pathological unit revolutionized medicine.

In the 1930's, the magnificent (if eccentric) French genius physiologist Alexis Carrel further demonstrated the rejuvenating power of the cell—especially that of the young cell. He showed that tissues *in vitro* could be kept alive and vigorous indefinitely if they were nourished on live, young substance. Niehans attributes his own inspiration for CT to Carrel's rejuvenation of a dying cell culture by the addition of healthy young cells.

Niehans was not the first to employ cell therapy, even though he is responsible for its notoriety. The process was performed by the Breslau surgeon Kuettner before World War I, and by the monkey- and goat-gland master Serge Voronoff in the late 1920's. It really was not until the 1940's that Niehans began using the technique extensively, and it was, in fact, Dr. Franklin Bircher of Zurich, not Niehans, who gave it the name *Zellulartherapie*.

The cell therapist today uses the cells of sheep fetuses approximately one month before their scheduled birth. Sheep are preferred to other animals because of their resistance to disease. For injections of pituitary, testes, ovary, adrenals, and parathyroid, mature animals are used because these organs are not sufficiently developed in the fetus. For other organs, fetal cells are used because of their sterility and low-grade anaphylactic (shock reaction) quality. This means that they are better tolerated by the patient. The cells must be prepared quickly. Within minutes of the animal's death, autolysis, the breaking down of cell material into potentially toxic substances, sets in.

Niehans is one of the few cell therapists who continues to use "fresh-cell therapy"—injection of the cells immediately following slaughter of the animal. He believes that the cells lose some of their regenerative properties when they undergo preservation. Therefore, he considers frozen or lyophilized cells inferior to the fresh. Unless conditions of optimum asepsis (absence of germs) are observed in the slaughter and dissection of the animal, risks of infection are incurred.

The so-called "fresh-cell therapy," which is done at the Clinique la Prairie in Vevey and at a few other clinics in Europe, is executed with great speed and dexterity. With curved scissors, the fetus' tissues are cut into small cubes and placed in a dish to which 20 cc of Ringer's (salt) Solution is added. Then the cubes are minced more finely with a special chopping knife—named after its inventor, Paul Niehans—until the morsels are no more than 0.3 mm long. If the suspension has been properly prepared, no more than 10 percent of the cells have been destroyed by the chopping.

Ideally, a maximum of one hour should elapse between the death of the animal and injection of the cells into the patient's buttocks. In practice, however, up to two hours sometimes intervenes. Niehans contends that the more severe the organic malfunction, the greater the quantity of cells required for treatment.

With fresh cells, there is always the danger of infection. One hour does not allow enough time to make a complete microscopic inspection of the animal's tissues before treatment. This is one reason why most cell therapists prefer to use only preserved cells, where the sterility of the injections can be more rigorously assured.

The best method for preserving tissues and their specific biochemical compounds is lyophilization, according to Joachim Stein and F. Schmid, authors of Cell Research and Cellular Therapy. Strictly speaking, lyophilization means removing water from frozen material. Normal drying, or desiccation, denatures the protein. Lyophilization doesn't. Microorganisms, yeast cells, bacteria, and viruses which have been lyophilized and stored for decades show no change in vitality and reproductive capacity.

Niehans first developed lyophilization for his cells in 1949, and since 1954 his Siccacell factory in Heidelberg, which markets some sixty varieties of organ preparations, has been the largest manufacturer of lyophilized cells in the world. Niehans' assistant, Dr. Walter Michel, runs a competitive plant called Cellorgan, near Montreux.

The University of Heidelberg's Hygiene Institute and the West German Ministry of Health control asepsis of the Siccacells. Experiments show, say cell therapists, no therapeutic differences between the lyophilized and fresh cells, although Niehans confides that he prefers the latter. When the ampule is broken, the cell debris is mixed with a salt solution and in ten minutes the liquid is ready to be injected into the patient.

Simple deep-freezing (without drying) is another way to prepare the cells, although it is considered inferior to lyophilization by Stein and Schmid. Other doctors suspect, however, that some therapeutic benefits may be lost in the drying process—benefits that are retained in simple deep-freezing.

In freezing, tissues are treated with coolants containing acetone and carbon dioxide snow, which lower the temperature to —80 C. Just prior to freezing, the tissues are scissored into small pieces to increase the surface area, then smeared onto the inner wall of a small Pyrex flask. The flask is then sealed and immersed in the cooling solution. After sampling the tissue for sterility, the flask may be thawed and a suspension prepared for injection.

The CT fraternity has set up a number of rules. Although there is some variation, in general practitioners try to observe these commandments:

1. Animals must undergo a preliminary serological examination to determine whether they are free of infection. If infection is present, they may not be used.

2. In fresh-cell therapy, the slaughterhouse should be as close to the hospital as possible, and no more than one hour should elapse between slaughter and injection.

3. Patients must take a thorough clinical examination, including the Abderhalden urine enzyme reaction test (which determines which organs need treating).

4. Usually, more than one organ is needed to treat a patient (as indicated by Abderhalden).

5. No more than one organ's cells should be placed into any one syringe.

6. Hypofunctioning (underactive) organs are generally treated by injections of the same organ. Hyperfunctioning (overactive) organs need cells of "antagonistic" organs.

7. Patients should spend a few days in bed following the injection.

8. The patient should avoid all alcohol, tobacco, vaccines, X rays, overheating the body by saunas, steambaths, sunbaths, diathermy or shortwave therapy for several months following treatment.

The gamut of conditions for which cell therapy is indicated (*i.e.*, recommended) as well as specific contraindications (where CT could be dangerous) are listed in the following chapter. At one time, Niehans believed that CT could cure homosexuals of their "aberrations." In fact, he still believes this, although his colleagues in cell therapy refuse to support him. Their skepticism dates back over a decade, when Niehans was anxious to follow his successful treatment of Pope Pius XII with another sensational triumph. For some years he had treated sexual inverts with transplants of police dog and steer testicles. CT, he was convinced, would be an even more effective remedy.

Sertoli (testicle) cells would provide the formula's operative agent, with pituitary and hypothalamus added for good measure. Lesbians would be treated with the same formula, except that ovarian cells would be substituted for the testicle cells.

The year 1954 belonged to Paul Niehans. A free-thinking Protestant, an outsider, anathema to orthodox medicine, he managed to resuscitate a fast-failing Roman Catholic Pontiff after the most renowned Catholic specialists had given up. Niehans and cell therapy were spectacularly launched and in orbit.

Doctors everywhere wanted "in" on Niehans' medical magic. With the availability of easy-to-administer Siccacells from the recently-built Rhein-Chemie factory in Heidelberg, the miracle treatment was being tried by doctors on many different human ailments.

On June 29, 1954, from his white manse overlooking Lake Geneva, Niehans answered a letter from Dr. Hans Giese, director of the famed Hamburg-Eppendorf Institute for Sexual Research in Germany:

Dear Colleague:

Your letter has been on the way for some time, but I have finally received it. Many thanks.

Testes-cells seldom fail to influence homosexuals favorably. Any doctor can obtain dried cells from Rhein-Chemie in Heidelberg . . .

With collegial greetings.   [signed]
Niehans
La Tour de Peilz, Switzerland

Giese was dubious about *anything* altering male homosexuality, on which he is considered one of the world's leading authorities. For one thing, his experience led him to believe that sexual inversion was strictly an environmental and psychic phenomenon, having little or nothing to do with the body's hormonal output. In his book *Homosexualité de l'homme,* Giese explores critically various therapeutic measures, including hormonotherapy, punishment, castration, and psychotherapy, all of which, he says, are ineffective. He was, nonetheless, curious to see just what effect cell therapy might have on various homosexuals, and he advised Niehans that he was ready to try it.

Correcting antisocial behavior with cells was an old dream of Niehans, one he had practically abandoned when prison authorities all over Europe turned thumbs down on his repeated requests to experiment on prisoners. During World War II, the famous neuroanatomist Professor Oskar Vogt, of Neustadt, who later dissected Hermann Göring's brain, had been given access to the brains of deceased prison inmates by none other than the Führer himself. One day Vogt brought Niehans two sets of brain cells mounted on slides and asked the cell therapist to compare them. Although the first set of cells seemed entirely normal, Niehans observed that the second were "badly developed." The second set, explained Vogt, were taken from the brains of executed criminals.

Niehans asked Vogt if his new *Wundertherapie* could conceivably revitalize such brains in order to eliminate their antisocial aberrations. The German replied that it was at least worth a try. Therefore, when Giese offered to experiment with the Siccacells on his flock of homosexual patients, it struck Niehans as the fulfillment of a long-postponed ambition.

Giese, a familiar figure on West German television, is frequently called upon to comment on deviant sociology and psychology. He presents an unforgettable Charles Addamsesque figure: well over 6 feet tall, skinny as a fly rod, his skin the color of fresh coconut milk. As one colleague described him, "When Giese turns around he often gives the impression of a cadaver vanishing into thin air."

Thirty homosexuals, ranging from relatively inexperienced teenagers to men over sixty, were treated over a period of one year. A fifty-three-year-old, described by Giese as "particularly perverse," had a long criminal record. He was given a placebo; the others were given various combinations of testes, hypothalamus, and pituitary Siccacells.

Although each of the men volunteered for the project because he hoped to become "normal," Giese tried to keep concepts of success or failure out of his discussions with patients, who were casually asked to describe and analyze their dreams, their responses toward all sorts of people and stimuli.

Niehans' theories received a crushing setback when the results of the experiment were compiled. Twenty-nine of the thirty patients reported absolutely no change whatever in the direction of their sexual activity. Most, in fact, stated that their homosexual drives and moods were noticeably *intensified* following the treatment.

The only subject reporting a successful return to heterosexuality was the "particularly perverse" ex-convict—whose "therapy," unknown to him, had been merely saltwater injections. Giese inferred that the man was probably a "particularly perverse liar" as well, since the patient had hoped to have a pending prison sentence reduced as a result of his sexual rehabilitation.

"Cell therapy," concluded Giese dryly, "is not recommended for homosexuals." When Giese informed Niehans of the negative results, Niehans broke off all correspondence with him. Instead of admitting that CT was probably ineffective in this area, Niehans simply ignored Giese's experiment entirely.

Niehans' closest associates believe that he's deluding himself equally when he says that: (1) he can cure *diabetes mellitus,* and (2) CT is a successful *cancer* prophylaxis.

Niehans would have us believe, however, that in addition to pioneering with CT, he will also be remembered for accomplishing these cures. Should he be proved right at some future date, his success would dwarf everything else he has done to date.

Diabetes mellitus is described in *Stedman's Medical Dictionary* as "a metabolic disease in which sugar is excreted intermittently or continuously in varying amounts in the urine and is elevated in the blood. The quantity of urine is greatly increased, causing the patient to have increased thirst. There is also increased appetite and weight loss." It is considered a chronic and incurable disease. When insulin was developed, it was believed that the problem of diabetes mellitus was solved. Today, however, the disease seems considerably more complex and a malfunctioning pancreas is not, in most cases, the primary cause.

Niehans, however, has ignored this trend of medical thought and reverted to the single hypothesis that malfunctioning beta cells of the islets of Langerhans in the pancreas are the trouble. Get the beta cells to function properly again and diabetes mellitus will be cured. According to the CT catechism, almost any organic cellular disorder can be fixed by injections of similar cells from an embryo animal.

Niehans has spent $50,000 of his fortune assigning to five research teams tasks of acquiring beta cells (which in most animals are inseparable from the alpha cells which counteract beta activity) that could be used on diabetes patients. The rejuvenator believes that his supply of pure beta cells may have to come from fish such as the bony *Pholis Grunellus,* the *scorpaena scrofa,* or the *Selachian Scyllium canicula,* in which the islet cells are completely separated from the digestive cells. Although Niehans has often mentioned his diabetes experiments in his writings, he says piously, "I am waiting for my thousandth cure of diabetes mellitus before publishing anything on cell therapy's ability to cure it."

On the cancer question, again, Niehans is ready with simple answers and simple diagnoses. He believes that CT is a cancer prophylaxis because the sheep cells he uses are "cancer-resistant."

"A sheep raiser in Australia who owns a flock of more than forty thousand sheep," declares Niehans, "told me that over a period of thirty years his veterinary surgeons had never found a single case of cancer."

Apparently, it has never occurred to Niehans that the reason sheep rarely succumb to cancer is that they are slaughtered young. Cancer is principally a disease of older organisms.

To buttress his thesis, Niehans surveyed former patients to determine how many of them were cancer victims. Of the first one hundred "reliable case histories" of patients from his 1931-1954 period, when various donor animals were used, only one patient had been operated on for cancer, and six others had died of the disease. This gave him a 7 percent average. Then he queried nine hundred patients he had treated from 1954 through 1964, when only sheep cells were used. Of them, five had been operated upon and six others had died of cancer. This gave him a 1.2 percent average.

Niehans compares these figures with the Swiss national average cancer mortality rate of 20 percent and concludes: *"Therefore cellular treatment with cancer-resistant cells affords to the human organism the greatest protection against cancer hitherto known."*

Niehans does not pretend to know precisely how CT acts as an anticancer agent, but he suggests it may have something to do with the "revitalizing effect," which increases oxidative metabolism and decreases fermentative metabolism, according to his chief researcher, Dr. Alfred Kment, a Viennese veterinarian. This theory leans heavily on the work of the German biochemist Otto Warburg, who theorized that carcinogens hamper normal oxidative metabolism and stimulate an inefficient fermentative oxidation process in its stead, thus liberating the body's cells from normal controls and causing them to become cancerous.

The only other evidence to corroborate CT's effectiveness against cancer is Niehans' rejuvenation therapy of over a thousand women patients with sheep ovaries for menopausal disturbances. Of them, he observed, "how very seldom a carcinoma developed subsequently. This allows me to surmise that cells from cancer-

Paul Niehans, M.D., Cell Therapist.

Patrick McGrady Jr.

Niehans' office
in Sonnenfels.

Patrick McGrady Jr.

Patrick McGrady Jr.

Clinique la Prairie.

Max Wolf, M.D.,
Rejuvenator-generalist.

Patrick McGrady Jr.

Mr. Peter Stephen in his
London office.

Patrick McGrady Jr.

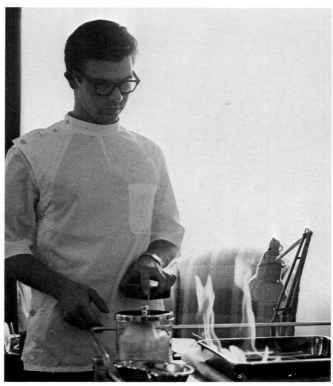

Serge Voronoff's Château Grimaldi on the Italian Riviera. Below the château, in a vast hillside *singerie,* he kept the hundreds of monkeys that were the source of his transplants.

George Van Tassel's "Integratron" stands in the middle of the desert near Giant Rock, California.

Patrick McGrady Jr.

Cora Galenti in her Tijuana apartment with a considerable supply of her special formula.

Patrick McGrady Jr.

Cora Galenti's luxurious House of Beauty was located right in the heart of Hollywood.

Dr. Ana Aslan, the *grande dame* of Rumanian rejuvenation.

Patrick McGrady Jr.

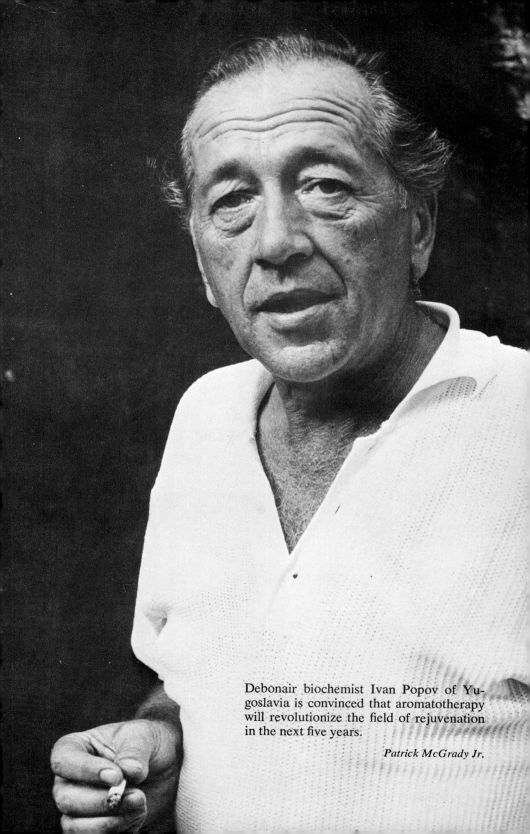

Debonair biochemist Ivan Popov of Yugoslavia is convinced that aromatotherapy will revolutionize the field of rejuvenation in the next five years.

Patrick McGrady Jr.

Dr. Alex Comfort, Medical Director of the Medical Research Council Group on Ageing in Britain.

Patrick McGrady Jr.

One of biochemist Denham Harman's important contributions to gerontology is his "Free Radical Reaction Aging Theory."

Patrick McGrady Jr.

resistant animals transferred to human beings will protect the latter from cancer."

These data are all that Niehans advances to support his cancer prophylaxis claims—and they are dismally inadequate to persuade the scientific community of the inferences he has drawn from them. Niehans' confreres try to avoid contradicting him, however, even though they are extremely skeptical about CT's effectiveness against the disease.

Unhappily, one cannot find any comprehensive, intelligent criticism of CT. Attacks from academic medicine on the whole have been largely obscurantist and nit-picking. Few critics have taken the time even to read the CT literature. Most are unaware that such a literature exists.

In behalf of the enlightened, modern gerontologist, Dr. Alex Comfort presents the most rational case against CT:

"Until these people," he says, "produce proper statistical results and publish them in scientific journals, I think we shouldn't take them seriously. There is no 'effect' to investigate. I'll wager that each time an advance in scientific terminology or diction, let alone knowledge, comes along, the cell therapists will incorporate it into their literature. In other words, failing contrary evidence, I think it's simply a fad, and entirely phony. If they can produce a decent experiment, even a single one, which suggests that their remedy produces objective effects other than by suggestion, I shall be happy to start thinking about how it does so. The air of hanky-panky, instant cookery, and big money about the whole Niehans system strikes me as pathognomonic. He probably sincerely believes in what he is doing, but his unwillingness to try to convince others by proper publication is, in effect, an unwillingness to subject his work to the dispassionate examination of the scientific community."

The cell therapy spokesmen answer this objection by declaring that they are blackballed from official publication because the "serious" medical journals are directly or indirectly controlled by drug interests which fear that the European success of CT might be repeated in England and the United States.

Some of the severest criticism comes from the cell therapists themselves. Dr. Karl Heinz Neumann of Cologne points out that

CT has aroused antagonism from medical circles because it is the *patient,* by and large, who has brought the remedy to the *doctor,* and not the other way around. Patients obsessed with the desire to receive CT usually won't take No for an answer, and will drop a reluctant physician in favor of an obliging one. This popular enthusiasm has convinced more than one nonbelieving doctor to go into CT.

Critics who argue that cell therapists do not publish their work obviously have not looked very hard for CT literature. Although some national medical association journals may be closed to them, others are not. The *cellular therapy bibliography* lists seven hundred and fifty-three separate monographs, fifty-five of which are attributed to Paul Niehans. Niehans, however, is not CT's most articulate advocate. When powered by his own pen, his books are quaint and charming, but they fail to meet his critics' major objections. When ghosted by his erudite colleagues, the writing seems technically correct, but dryly irrelevant and trivial. The best basic text on cell therapy is the compendium *Cell Research and Cellular Therapy,* edited by Schmid and Stein. As cellular biologist Paul Weiss once observed when a colleague charged that nothing had been written on a particular scientific matter: "He said there is no literature on the subject. According to that definition, literature is not what is printed but what is read."

Unfortunately for the CT case, most of the research into its specific mechanisms and clinical value has been financed directly by Niehans. This means, fairly or unfairly, that even work done by highly competent investigators is suspect in the eyes of official and academic tribunals.

If Niehans cannot control the research with an iron hand, he has no interest in it whatever. His old friend Max Wolf, who believes in CT's effectiveness against certain ailments and as a rejuvenating agent generally, once aroused the enthusiasm of several millionaires for a CT research foundation. The sole condition behind their $150,000 grant, Wolf informed Niehans, was that the operation would have to be audited and supervised to allow the philanthropists their tax deductions. For some time, Niehans had talked of starting such an institute to convince a doubting medical world of CT's value. "My desire," he wrote in 1948, "is to be able to create an Institute for Biological Research and Therapy, with a biological division and a medical division, in order to put the science of tissue culture at the service of suffering humanity."

Yet, when it was made clear that the institute would operate independently of Niehans' whims, Wolf says, Niehans vetoed the entire project.

Now that Niehans' Heidelberg cell-lyophilization plant is showing signs of turning a profit, some of the overflow will be directed to research heretofore financed by Niehans' personal fortune. Meantime, the International Society for Research into Cellular Therapy's treasure is annually sweetened by the rather modest sum (from Niehans) of $30,000—most of which goes directly into lab work.

These projects were supposed to bear out his theories and support rejuvenationists who had been practicing CT for years with only fragile "empirical results" behind them. And while some animal studies appeared to confirm CT's pretended validity, others did not. Thyroid function improvement tests, for example, have been a complete failure. Still others have pointed to a distinctly *negative* relationship. Rats trying to learn a T-maze are more befuddled than ever after cell injections. The researchers' dismay at discovering that their miraculous treatment had succeeded only in *lowering* the rats' learning ability was partially mitigated by follow-up observations that indicated that the CT rats *remembered* better (what they had learned so slowly, that is) than the control group.

Placenta cell suspensions were implanted into female rats working a treadmill. It was found that the injections increased their activity for the next five days.

The Siccacells also seemed to have a rejuvenating effect on tissue homogenates (cells blended to a creamy consistency). With most tissue homogenates, oxygen consumption goes down with the increased age of the tissues. At first, testes Siccacells were added to heart, liver, and kidney homogenates. Nothing happened. But when placenta cells were added, the homogenates suddenly began to "breathe" at a faster rate, like far younger tissues.

All of the experiments were done with lyophilized cells. Whether results would have been more impressive with fresh cells (which Niehans prefers) is not known. Stein, who runs the Siccacell factory for Niehans, thinks not. He says: "Greater amounts of lyophilized cells are used than would be used in fresh-cell therapy. In one Siccacell ampule there are hundreds of millions of cells —in one fresh-cell syringe only a million or two. Neumann, Kment, and I conducted experiments eight years ago and found no difference in animal experiments between fresh and dried cells."

Could CT help relieve arteriosclerosis, that great bugaboo of old age? In 1949 Ahrens and Kunke had reported favorable empirical results with human patients. In experimenting with rats, Kment found that the aorta's primary extensibility (stretchability) was unaffected by cell injections, whereas the vessel's *residual* extensibility (ability to resume its original shape) was significantly improved.

Can cells actually rejuvenate the skin? Many European aesthetician-cosmeticians think so, and use thousands of cell ampules monthly for skin rejuvenation alone.

Alfred Kment has experimented on connective tissue, which is the seat of many geriatric diseases such as chronic rheumatism, arthritis, sclerosis, and many other skin changes. From his studies on rat-tail collagen, Kment determined that: "Extensibility of the skin can be influenced with cellular therapy in the sense of a revitalization. Also, the strength of the skin remained significantly higher after injections of placenta and testes Siccacell."

When asked why they do not test out Niehansian theory definitively with laboratory tests of their own, scientists critical of CT usually reply that CT is low on the list of biomedical notions worth testing. Cellular biologists are an exception. From time to time, distinguished researchers in cellular biology have expressed genuine interest in pursuing studies of CT's effectiveness. The cellular biologists and cell therapists have at least a lexicon in common and can talk the same language. Both groups intone the word "cell" with reverence. When Niehans says *"la cellule"* one can practically see him kneeling on his prie-dieu, his eyes closed in solemn contemplation of its divine mysteries. His faith in cells is total, as witness his statement: "When I cannot cure a patient with cells, it is I, Niehans, who am to blame—not the cells."

One of the few independent studies of the rejuvenating power of the cell was conducted by the eminent cellular biologist of Rockefeller Institute Paul Weiss, who, with his assistant A. C. Taylor, discovered that cells, alone and unassisted, have the capacity to reconstruct an entire organ—even after "complete isolation, dispersal and random recombination" in "an indifferent environment from which they could have received no cues as to how to do it." These isolated cells formed complete tissues, with each tissue component completely normal, viable, robust, and functional! In the Weiss-Taylor experiment, published in the September, 1960, *Proceedings of the National Academy of Sciences,* eight-to-fourteen-day-old chick embryo kidney, liver, and skin cells were used. Each organ was separated, pooled, minced, and incubated for a half hour in a mixture of trypsin and pancreatin in a calcium-magnesium-free Earle's solution. The resulting cells were washed, strained to remove residual clumps through a nylon strainer, concentrated by mild centrifugation, and then deposited by pipette onto chorioallantoic membranes (the membrane which normally lies just underneath the eggshell) of eight-day embryos, left to develop for an extra nine days, giving them an age of from seventeen to twenty-three days. The organs were then located, cut out, fixed, and examined.

However encouraging it may be to the cell therapists, it is not fair to assume that the Weiss-Taylor study automatically may be extrapolated onto the human clinical level. The difference between effects obtained on a chick embryo at the Rockefeller Institute laboratories and on a human patient bedded down in La Prairie is obviously enormous.

Weiss is the first to admit this. After having been cajoled by financier Barnard Baruch, a Niehans patient, Weiss consented to see Niehans in Vevey. When he had seen the whole operation, from the slaughter of the ewe to the cell injections in the clinic, Weiss declared: "It wasn't just primitive—it was totally unscientific in a way. And Niehans was absolutely honest about it. He told me: 'I'm not a scientist. I don't understand any of this. I'm just a surgeon, and the idea is right.'

"But," continued Weiss, "the idea of cell specificity of course *is* right . . . I'm not in favor of throwing the whole thing out because I'm convinced that my own line of work confirms the presence of organ-specific effects on the growth of homologous organs. Whether it improves or impairs [however] depends on all kinds of balances."

Organ specificity, explained Weiss, means that an injected substance (such as sheep liver cells) bears a message in its structure which, if delivered to the addressee (the human recipient's liver), can be opened, read, and used for the recipient's benefit or harm. This would be, he suggests, the first contention about CT that ought to be settled. In other words, even granting vague therapeutic benefits from cell injections, one should know whether positive results are due to first-class routing of particular letters or to the arrival of ordinary junk mail.

Independent research in fact does confirm certain dicta of the gospel according to Paul Niehans.

Heinrich Wrba (pronounced Vruh-bah') is director of experimental pathology at the German Cancer Research Center in Heidelberg. He is not a cell therapist. Of stout build, medium height, sporting a round-the-clock five-o'clock shadow, Wrba admits that, while Niehans' philosophy is vague and crude, his own and others' research bears out the old man on several critical points, namely, that:

• Injected *embryonic* tissue has the greatest effect upon mitosis, or cell division, in the recipient's liver.

• Moreover, this effect is definitely (as Weiss contends) *organ specific* and not *species specific;* in other words, the combination of a donor sheep and a recipient human is not incongruous.

• Every known growth factor in animals is also organ specific.

• Superfluous or unwanted injected cells do no harm, but are simply rejected by the body. ("There is now the theory," says Wrba, "that the cells' RNA messenger which determines the particular kind of protein to be manufactured acts only if the recipient's specific organ is malfunctioning.")

Concludes Wrba: "These mechanisms *do* seem to act as Niehans believes."

What, then, is indicated by the wealth of available research, from both the cell therapists' own studies and those of outsiders?

One can safely say, first of all, that there is no evidence that conclusively *disproves* the major tenets of CT.

Second, there is some laboratory and animal research that is highly supportive of Niehans' main contentions regarding organ specificity, increased organ metabolism, the relative innocuousness of embryo cell injections, and so forth.

Third, there are no scientific tests on human patients that either bear out or refute Niehans' contentions—with the exception of Hans Giese's demonstration that lyophilized cells have no positive effect on reversing homosexual behavior in men.

One bothersome point, often swept under the rug by practitioners, is CT's safety. There most definitely *are* risks involved.

When word got out that Pope Pius XII had been given Niehans' cells, the life of every pregnant ewe in Europe was directly imperiled. Physicians quickly leaped onto the CT bandwagon, and overnight, jerry-built clinics sprung up next to slaughterhouses. Doctors and nondoctors alike made pilgrimages to Vevey to learn the new CT rejuvenation and healing techniques. Everyone was getting into the act. Including the undertaker.

The ten years following Pius' widely publicized recovery in 1954 were the blackest in CT's history. Thirty-five deaths at the hands of incompetent cell therapists using fresh cells were reported in Germany alone. Hundreds of other deaths caused by unscrupulous physicians went unreported.

Admittedly, there was a difference between Niehans and his successors. Niehans was no fly-by-night tyro in this field. He nearly had lost his own life while experimenting with frozen cells in 1949. He had watched his entire clinic population come down more than once with galloping infections that proved to be very expensive when patients filed successful lawsuits against him in Swiss courts. He knew from personal experience that CT could be a high-risk venture, and he proceeded cautiously.

But the attitude of the opportunist physician with his eye on a windfall profit was: What the patient doesn't know can't hurt *me*.

Soon, the medical and popular press were filled with scandalous accounts of abuses by cell therapists. Many accidents were hushed up.

One apprentice doctor confessed to me that he had treated two women simultaneously for menopausal disorders with pituitary cells. His first injections were followed six months later with a second series. The women, who had developed pituitary antigens from the first shots, immediately went into anaphylactic (shock) reactions and died. These often fatal reactions are the nemesis of the cell therapist. Some doctors give antihistamines as a precaution with every cell injection. The risk is considerably less when embryo tissues are used, but embryos cannot supply every organ. Testes and pituitary, for example, must be taken from adult animals.

Asepsis is difficult to assure, even under ideal circumstances with the most qualified therapist. But during the "black years," the circumstances were far from ideal. In Paris, according to Dr. André Picouret, a short, crew-cut cell therapist operating the Villa Borghese clinic in Neuilly, a Fifth Arrondissement pharmacist advertised the "Niehans therapy" with handbills passed out in the street and "carted the patients off to the slaughterhouse in a bus."

Often patients paid exorbitant prices for cells cut to a fraction of the normal dosage.

"I once gave a king's physician from a former French colony cells with which to treat a patient," says Picouret, "but for every single dosage I gave him, he treated *six* patients. So I cut him off from my supply. Now he gets them *en contrabande* from Germany."

The sort of physician who seeks to pick up CT methodology at La Prairie is not always highly qualified and is sometimes downright incompetent. Dr. Walter Michel tells the following anecdote about one MD who had come to watch the slaughter and resection of the sheep: "When I removed the thyroid from the fetus," this doctor said, 'That's the liver, isn't it?' I said, 'No, that's the thyroid.' Then I brought out the adrenals, which are not hard to find since they're right next to the kidney, and he should have been able to recognize them. Then he said, 'Oh, *that's* the liver!' "

The frenzy to treat every condition with cells went so far that, according to Picouret, in scheduling sheep tissues to be implanted into a patient, one therapist marked down *"blood"* on his card. "I *saw* his medical card," says Picouret, "and *blood* was indicated. . . . It's been several years now since *he's* done any more cell therapy." A sheep blood injection into a human patient, of course, would be disastrous.

Another youth doctor once insisted on treating a feverish child over the objections of the nurse on duty that night (infection and fever are classic contraindications for CT), says Picouret. The next morning the child died.

Two deaths in France attributed to fresh cells were reported in the French National Academy of Medicine Bulletin by Dr. Jean Olmer of the Therapeutic Medical Clinic of the Marseille Medical Faculty. The first involved a sixty-three-year-old man suffering from arthritic leg pains. A blood test and cardiogram taken before treatment were normal. Then, on four occasions between March, 1957, and July, 1958, he received injections of hypothalamus, liver, spleen, placenta, and testicle cells. In October, after his last injection, he began to tire quickly and lost his appetite. Then his liver and spleen swelled to alarming proportions. He was admitted to Conception Hospital in Marseille, where tests showed a proliferation of white blood cells. He was then sent home, where he died shortly afterward.

The second case was that of a sixty-two-year-old man who had tried cell therapy to remedy a chronic respiratory condition. Over a period of ten months he received three series of cell injections. Each time he was given heart, liver, nervous system, pituitary, adrenal, lung, testicle, and hypothalamus cells. At first the injections seemed to benefit the patient, then his condition declined until, three months after the last treatment, he became anemic and died.

Eventually, France passed a law controlling the practice of fresh-cell therapy. The "manifest dangers" of anaphylactic reaction and the impossibility of preventing infection were cited. Legislation, however, did nothing to contain the popular enthusiasm for Niehans-style cell therapy. Dr. René Basile Henry, a Paris cell therapist, describes the attitude of would-be rejuvenates: "So many patients come to us in the hope of rediscovering the vigor and pleasures of their youth, that it is more difficult for us to convince them of the limits of our help than of its usefulness."

Rejuvenation?

Probably not, says Henry. "It is grotesque to say that cell therapy can prolong one's life . . . but it is certain that it can help man age more comfortably, and only this certitude ought to account for the interest in cell therapy."

Although it is Niehans' boast that he has yet to sign the first death certificate at his clinic, occasionally things do go wrong. Take the case of a middle-aged woman who sought out Niehans to end a host of chronic complaints, including insomnia, liver attacks, gall bladder trouble, fatigue, nervousness, faulty short-term memory (her long-term memory is, by contrast, excellent), tardy and complicated menses, and various sequels to an adolescent case of rickets.

When she was twenty, her mother's Italian doctor, a student of the famous Swiss surgeon DeQuervain (with whom Niehans had worked), gave her monthly injections of a kind of a cell "cocktail" of rabbit and sheep organs, often as many as twenty organs represented in a single syringe. Of the hundreds of physicians she saw subsequently, she recalled these treatments as having done her the most good. Other doctors would stare unbelievingly at her charts and test results and express surprise at seeing her alive. Still others would pinpoint a gland, and prescribe some kind of hormonotherapy. Her cortisone bill alone over the years had mounted well into four figures. Still others told her she was suffering mainly from hypochondria.

In 1961, she decided that only Niehans could put an end to her persistent afflictions. For two days she filled his ear with a blow-by-blow account of her medical history. Patiently, he heard her out and then had her send a specimen to the late Abderhalden's widow in Basel for examination.

When the results from the Abderhalden test were returned to Niehans, he told her, "Madame, you never had anything wrong with your pituitary. You never had anything wrong with your thyroid. You never had anything wrong with any part of you—except with the hypothalamus and the brain. When you were quite young you were poisoned by something. Either you swallowed poison or somebody tried to poison you."

Try as she could, the woman could not recall a possible incident of poisoning. Niehans continued his diagnosis:

"This poison cut off oxygen to your brain as a child and did cellular damage. In your case, it damaged the hypothalamus. That, of course, paralyzes the pituitary. It's true it doesn't function—although it may function spasmodically. But when the Abderhalden was done, it was *not* functioning, since there's a '3' next to it. Then there's a '2' next to the thyroid. But your heart and arteries are all right. The liver, ah, yes, the liver . . . always weak—"

Suddenly the tall physician interrupted himself, looked up from the card, and recalled what his patient had told him three days previously about her medical history. "I think I know what poisoned you," he said. "When you were young, you had an overdose of chloroform when your tonsils were removed, and this was followed by your long-standing liver trouble."

This analysis made sense. Now she recalled that she had spent six months recovering from her tonsillectomy, while her sister had been out of the hospital within ten days following a similar operation.

"You'll need eleven injections," said Niehans.

The next morning, about 10 A.M., a nurse entered the room with a trayful of labeled syringes. Eight fearsomely thick needles were poked into her upper gluteals and attached to the syringes containing the watery cellular debris. As each plunger was depressed, filling her muscles with sheep embryo cells, she began to sneeze violently.

"I think, Professor," she called out, "that might have been an allergic sneeze." But Niehans was already out the door and did not hear her warning.

That night, a nurse dropped in to see her. When she looked at the patient's face and arms, stitched with chintzy, wavelike raised welts, she gasped, "You're allergic!"

Only the year before the patient had reacted similarly to a meal in Athens. She assumed it was the lamb entrée. At that time, an ambulance rushed her to the hospital, where ACTH injections brought the allergic reaction under control and probably saved her life. She suggested to Niehans' nurse that the hormone would probably help her now.

"But we *can't* give you ACTH," protested the nurse. "It will kill the cells."

"Well," retorted the patient, "you would give it to me if I were dying."

"Your face is turning very dark," said the nervous attendant. "I'm going to call the Professor."

At 2 A.M., Niehans raced into the room and took the woman's

pulse. Until daybreak, three and one half hours later, the Great Rejuvenator, plainly worried about his patient, stayed with her, asking her to breathe deeply while the nurse alternately cranked the upper part of the bed up and down. Finally she slept. To this day, she is not certain whether she was given ACTH or not.

"You know," the nurse told the patient's daughter later, "I saved your mother's life that night. Her heart stopped beating three times."

Despite the apparent danger, the woman told Niehans that she wanted the three remaining injections. Niehans refused, saying he had never lost a patient and had no intention of spoiling his perfect record.

"But, Professor," she complained, "it's the pituitary and the hypothalamus . . . for cancer . . . Look at my poor nails. I haven't got any. Look at my poor bones. My twisted legs. Look at my tiny chin. I've had rickets. I've needed these cells all my life."

Finally, Niehans agreed to give her the remaining organs, using a calf, not a sheep, as donor. This time there was no reaction. Even though eight months later the CT had failed to relieve her insomnia, the main reason for treatment, her liver attacks, had stopped. Most benefits from therapy are supposed to take place in three months, but it was not until six years later that she began to sleep regularly.

"Can you imagine," said the credulous patient, "those grafts took six years to take?"

Since Niehans' retirement in 1965, there has been considerable speculation as to who would succeed him as spiritual leader of CT. It is an explosive question, as I quickly found out when I brought it up at a luncheon during the Cell Therapy Congress in Bad Homburg in July, 1966. My query brought the conversation to a standstill. Finally, one of the leading cell therapists gathered at the table, Dr. Franklin E. Bircher of Zurich, a physician who long ago had given Niehans the name for his new technique, blurted out, "I am perhaps the *one* man here of whom you should not have asked *that* question."

Finally, someone broke the resulting embarrassed silence by suggesting that whoever the new leader would turn out to be, it would definitely *not* be Dr. Walter Michel, Niehans' present assistant. The others agreed. Their unanimity may have been no more than unanimous jealousy of the man who seemed to be way ahead in the race. While it is possible that no one may fill Niehans' shoes, Michel holds unassailable trumps. One is that he treats all the old Niehans carriage trade, except for the few individuals competitors have been able to wean away from Vevey. A second is his private Cellorgan (lyophilized cell) plant in Vevey, which allows him an advantage few cell therapists possess —that of being able to practice CT at actual cost. Still another trump is his own swelling clientele, for whom Niehans is no more than a legendary father figure and Michel his visible reincarnation. Moreover, Michel seems to be Niehans' personal choice of successor.

Michel has done much for Niehans, turning the Clinique la Prairie into a modern, cost-accounted, well-run institution with a contented staff. The files are up to date and complete, and one day—Michel willing—may provide the surest indication as to what CT actually can and cannot achieve for a patient. Still, this does little for *other* cell therapists, who need someone who can make CT more exciting, more exploitable, and more acceptable to youth-hungry consumers around the world.

Bircher is seventy-two, son of the late dietician Dr. Max Bircher-Benner. An orthodox Niehansian, Bircher is one of the few who still gives fresh-cell injections. "I do not believe the cells can retain their full powers unless they are absolutely fresh and living," says Bircher. As a convinced fresh-cell man, however, he is unable to guide the practice of thousands of German, Austrian, and Swiss cell therapists who are obliged to use the freeze-dried cells for convenience.

The flamboyant Goetze-Claren has two strong advantages. He is young—forty-six, and, if nothing else, an innovator. While few of his colleagues pretend to understand precisely what his mutant, Genetic Therapy (GT), is all about, it has entranced a new generation of prospective rejuvenates. When the FDA evidenced its lack of enthusiasm for claims of GT's alleged efficacy, Goetze-Claren gave up his New York practice and began to fill the Clinica Mater Dei in Rome with his American patients.

The former Luftwaffe pilot dreams of a genetic therapy empire, in which clinics would be established under his aegis in the

Tyrol, the Bavarian Alps, on the French Riviera (preferably Monaco), and at other plush oases. GT is based on Goetze-Claren's theory that it is the RNA fraction of the sheep cells that reactivates the organ. His treatment involves alternating series of yeast RNA extract and diluted lyophilized cell injections, spaced over a twenty-eight-day cure, entailing a less strenuous regimen than Niehans prescribes (*i.e.*, cigars and moderate alcohol intake are permitted). Goetze-Claren also recommends an 80 percent vegetable diet with lots of raw milk, steamed string beans, squash *au jus,* and "clean, clear proteins" such as fish.

Although he speaks of genetic therapy as the successor to "old fashioned" CT ("Niehans was right in his time. He isn't now"), his self-styled mentor Niehans is acidly dubious about any newfangled twists to the old idea. "Don't let yourself be influenced by Goetze-Claren," Niehans told me just before I left Vevey. "His ideas aren't very good. You cannot mix biology and chemistry. Add chemistry to biology and you destroy biology. Goetze-Claren will fail. He is too complicated."

Another candidate for the CT crown is Dr. Adolphe Mocquot, a fortyish Midi practitioner, and one of France's few cell therapists. Mocquot, a conservative, rejects the idea that cell injections can have any beneficial effect against cancer. (Goetze-Claren parts company with Mocquot on this point.) Mocquot goes along with Niehans' ban on vaccinations following CT, but doesn't believe that whisky or saunas have even a slightly deleterious effect on the injections.

Despite the strong personalities and undisputed charm of both Goetze-Claren and Mocquot, neither has published extensively on his CT experience. Mocquot's most noteworthy contribution to the CT bibliography was a paper on the allergic, bacteriological, and viral problems associated with the injections.

Goetze-Claren is striving, above all, to endow CT (and GT, of course) with respectability. In 1966 he broke with the cell therapists' "outsider" tradition to appear at the International Gerontological Congress in Vienna to deliver a paper. In addition, he has published privately *Cellular and Genetic Therapy,* a popularized explanation for his patients.

If deep, academic dedication to the CT cause counts, Paris' René Basile Henry, author of a clear, concise, and serious account of CT (*La Thérapeutique Cellulaire*) may become the new sovereign. Henry declares that CT merits "better treatment than the exaggerated enthusiasm of journalists and patients or the suspicion of numerous physicians." The fluent Frenchman has translated most of the important papers on CT from German into French (a task performed in the United States by Dr. Hyman Goldstein of New York, President of the inactive American Cellular Therapy Association).

What CT is really all about is still unknown. It is, as the AMA has reiterated time and again in its journals, a relatively untested medical therapy.

Pending the ultimate verdict on his work, Niehans has probably earned himself an honored place in the history of rejuvenation. Unfortunately for him, the projects in which he has placed the greatest hope appear destined for the trash heap of medical history. No reputable scientist is convinced that CT has any appreciable curative or prophylactic effect against cancer (except possibly to accelerate its progress) or diabetes. But by dint of his obsession with this singular idea, his curious brand of showmanship, his impressive *noblesse,* and his fabulous financial success, Niehans has kept alive the idea of biological therapy in medical circles. Many brilliant minds in medical science outside of CT believe that treatment of biological ailments with biological measures deserves much more intensive exploration. Niehans' application of the lyophilization process to his sheep cells has universalized a treatment which otherwise would have been impossible to contemplate. Finally, Niehans, himself an MD and proficient surgeon-endocrinologist, insisted on performing CT only under the most aseptic conditions after careful diagnosis and observation of his patients. His claim of fifty thousand injections without losing a single patient is an impressive claim for any physician.

CHAPTER SIX

The Rejuvenation of a Master Storyteller

Rejuvenation, like dollar bills, is unquestionably "in." All the Beautiful People are having it done. It's the ultimate in health fads, an extravagant and entrancingly wicked self-indulgence. It's your initiation into a very fast circle.

Yet despite its high-flying status, most rejuvenates simply don't talk about it—except with other rejuvenates. People talk your arm off about their operations. They'll gleefully propagandize their latest diet to anyone who will listen. And they'll force you to relive with them every second of the extraction of their impacted wisdom tooth. Not so with rejuvenation. The world of the newly young does not proselytize. It does not boast. It does not wish to talk about it. It is a little bit ashamed. It often denies it ever happened.

Dr. Paul Niehans' dossier of VIP patients is well-known, yet only a handful confess to having had cell therapy.

Former Chancellor Adenauer, from about 1958 on, took CT injections every year from a clinic in Buehler-Hoehe. But he publicly denied it.

Gloria Swanson, whose friendship with Paul and Coralie Niehans is too well-known to be denied, admits having had the cells from Niehans, but insists that the treatment was only to get material for a UP feature story (the story, incidentally, never went out on the wire)—*not*, repeat, *not* to be rejuvenated. She doesn't believe in it.

Pope Pius XII tried to salvage a modicum of privacy during his illness in 1954 by requesting Niehans not to reveal *which* cells he'd been given.

Noel Coward, often mentioned as a Niehans rejuvenate, brusquely rejects the contention. "I told you," he once answered a reporter, "that I was too much of a coward. And I still am, if you will forgive the pun. I believe he uses a bloody great syringe about the size of a rolling-pin and he injects a horrifying solution made from an unborn ewe. As I said then, judging from the effects on some of my friends, it's a very non-U ewe . . . I am prepared to grow old as gracefully as I can without any help from the animal kingdom." However, during a recent television program on aging ("Don't Count the Candles"), Coward admitted that he had had a "rejuvenating shot," but added, "It had no effect on me, except that it made me sleepy."

After naming Niehans' *crème de la crème* of celebrated patients in his book *Gayelord Hauser's Treasury of Secrets,* the noted nutritionist plugged CT as having "great promise for people who want to keep their tissues young." Possibly out of humility, Mr. Hauser pointedly omitted his own name as an occasional visitor to La Prairie. One is left to infer the fact of his treatment by his reference to "over 40,000 other important people" who have been sold new youth for their declining years in Vevey.

In bold contrast to these coy rejuvenates was W. Somerset Maugham, whose admiration for Niehans as a doctor was as great as his personal regard for him. Maugham was a persuasive testimonial for cell therapy.

It was through another rejuvenationist and medical outsider that Maugham got to Niehans. He is Max Wolf, a peripatetic Viennese intellectual who saved Maugham's life twenty-some years ago. Wolf is five feet five and amazingly alert and energetic for his now eighty-three years. Like Niehans, he is a living endorsement of his ability to keep mind and body young in the later years.

Maugham had been afflicted with a brutal, recurrent malarial condition he had contracted in the Far East fourteen years earlier. A hundred doctors (including Wolf) had treated the great writer without success.

"The fever and chills would disappear, then come back again," recalls Dr. Wolf. "He also had a huge gelatinous tumor in the pylorus, at the end of the stomach, which had blocked the stomach. It was benign, but bigger than the head of a baby. All of the other doctors had given up on him."

"Since you are too weak to be operated upon," Wolf told Maugham, "I will try my enzyme treatment on the tumor. I probably can get it to recede in about two months. As for the malaria, if you want to take a chance, I'll give you one hundred and twenty-five grains of quinine in one injection [twenty times the normal dosage]. I have done this only once before. The patient survived. But this will either kill you or cure you."

"I'll take it," said Maugham. "I've been getting chills every other day. I cannot live this way. If you don't cure me, I shall take my own life. I have not been able to work for the past two years anyhow."

Maugham went through two days of absolute hell following the injection, but he lived. The malaria never returned. And, in two months—just as predicted—the tumor disappeared as well. (Garson Kanin inscribed a copy of *Remembering Mr. Maugham* to Wolf thus: "To Max Wolf, without whom this book would have been much shorter.")

"None of Maugham's other doctors ever understood how the tumor disappeared," says Wolf. "In America enzymes just don't exist."

Maugham detested the circumstance of his age (he died at ninety-one on December 16, 1965) and spent much of his later life bemoaning his increasingly "Chinese" appearance. It is said he stared at himself in the mirror for minutes on end, deploring his pathetic flesh.

Once, Maugham and a companion went into a dance hall. He was dying to dance, but feared that no girl would accept his invitation. Knowing how timid Maugham was, his friend approached one of the girls and said, "There's a gentleman over there who would just love to dance with you, but he's afraid nobody would want to dance with him."

"Don't worry," confided the girl, "I'd be delighted. I just *love* old men."

Maugham beamed with pleasure when the girl asked him to dance. After one turn around the floor, however, she inquired of Maugham, "Are you too tired to go round again?"

"You filthy bitch!" spluttered Maugham, and with that he stalked off the floor.

On another occasion, after a tennis match (Maugham had been Perry tennis champion years before) he petulantly broke his racket over his knee when he heard a bystander comment, "He didn't play a bad game for a man of his age."

Maugham's five years in the Orient were probably his most blissful. He wondered what the secret of his pleasure was. He asked a Chinese why life and manners in the Orient should seem so much more pleasant to him than anywhere else.

"In the Far East," the Chinese told him, "we have great respect for age." Maugham was furious.

When they were living in the United States, Maugham and his constant companion and secretary Alan Searle kept in close touch with Max Wolf. Aware of his patient's chronic anxiety about his craterlike pores, deepening wrinkles and unflattering slack skin, Wolf told him about cell therapy. Maugham was intrigued. Wolf was highly skeptical about Niehans' theory of *how* the cells rejuvenated the organism—but he had seen too many people, both his own patients and those of other cell therapists, given a new lease on life by them to reject the therapy itself and not to think it could be beneficial for some people. At first Maugham wanted Wolf to administer the cells. But Wolf convinced him that, since Maugham was often in Europe, he might as well have CT from Niehans himself.

For the thirty-six years (with but three days of vacation) that Searle secretaried for Maugham, the two were inseparable. At least a half dozen of Maugham's stories can be attributed to Searle (including "The Bigamist," "The Kite," and "The Episode"). He is sixty-three, but looks ten to fifteen years younger. Courteous, soft-but-pithily-spoken, he is of medium height, has naturally black hair growing in ringlets, baby-pink skin. One is struck by a frequent, impish grin revealing perfect teeth. He loves company, which, to his somewhat surprised dismay, he has much less of since Maugham's death. I talked with him on the terrace of his apartment overlooking the Mediterranean on the Avenue de Grande Bretagne in Monte Carlo. It must have been a heartbreaking sequel to the splendid, sprawling Villa Mauresque in St.-Jean-Cap-Ferrat from which he was evicted by the Maugham family two years ago.

He told me that Maugham had wanted rejuvenation treatments for one reason: to enjoy a happy old age. He also vaguely hoped that they might help other specific conditions.

"Maugham spent two years in a TB clinic in Scotland, starting in 1916," recalls Searle. "He recovered, but like all creative men he was a mass of nerves. He was never a truly happy man. He had a terrible stammer (not with me, but with other people). He had a fund of marvelous stories which he loved to tell. In relating these stories—right in the middle—he'd begin to stammer and completely ruin the effect. And then he hardly slept at all."

When Wolf described what was entailed in the CT treatments (the slaughter of the pregnant ewe, the chopping up of the organs, the injections through gigantic syringes, the risk of shock reactions), Maugham, who had had an extensive medical background before going into writing, told Searle, "I don't like the sound of it, but we'll go see Niehans anyway."

After a preliminary meeting with Niehans in London, Maugham was convinced he could benefit from CT. So he and Searle packed and departed for Switzerland.

Niehans is, as Searle put it, "celebrity-conscious." He especially likes creative people. He considered Maugham eminently stimulating. Therefore, the writer and his secretary were given the red-carpet treatment in Vevey, including frequent lunches and dinners in Niehans' palatial home in Burier-La-Tour-de-Peilz.

"Meals took such a long time," Searle relates. "We were always told that we were eating off of something from such-and-such a place or sitting on a gift from so-and-so. Their artistic taste is rather Germanic, but I liked them both."

After a visit to the slaughterhouse and clinic, where the whole process was performed for them, Maugham turned to Searle and said: "You have it first!" Searle, who was a bit shaken by the show, blanched at first, then—with the fidelity of a bygone era—bravely acquiesced.

Niehans did not bother to tell them that there might be an

unpleasant temporary reaction to the cells. And Maugham's physical distress, due to the normal body reaction to the injection of foreign protein, was multiplied by the stress of doing without alcohol or tobacco for the first time in many years.

"The treatment," says Searle, "wasn't at all difficult for me. I'm a nonsmoker and I don't care if I haven't got a drink. But it troubled Maugham. He was a creature of habit. He couldn't begin work till he'd had a couple of cigarettes. I watched him carefully, and always knew when he was about to begin to work. He needed inspiration." Nonetheless, Maugham religiously abided by Niehans' prescription to abstain from all alcohol, tobacco, medicaments, X rays and sun's rays for three months.

Then, quite abruptly, Maugham began to feel what he deduced to be the effects of the therapy. "I have never felt better in my life," he announced to Searle one day. And, just as abruptly, Maugham's latent creativity reawakened. He began to write again.

"Maugham," notes Searle, "always wrote everything out in longhand. He'd rewrite it. A second time. A third time. A fourth time. Then he'd fill out the proofs with endless corrections. After Niehans' treatment, his imagination worked overtime. He didn't have the physical strength to keep up with it."

What effect did the therapy have on the Master's sex life?

According to Searle, Maugham's proclivities were always "predominantly for women," but his libido was of no consequence after he had reached eighty. So he was quite surprised to find himself "with very distinct urges . . . usually in the bath."

"He had wanted to forget all about sex," says Searle. "It was rather tragic in a sense. Maugham said it this way to me once: 'One loses one's looks and figure and desirability . . . but the desire remains.' "

Searle was told he might reap some quite concrete benefits from CT himself. Ever since puberty, he had suffered from an excruciating psoriasis which covered his entire body except his face. The effects were psychological as well as physical. He was continually melancholic and nervous.

"I'll give you a new skin," Niehans promised him. Searle was skeptical, having tried scores of doctors and "every conceivable remedy, including rays, ointments, massages, pills, lotions, potions, and whatnot." Doctors had given him up. It bothered him acutely that he could not expose his skin to the rays of the magnificent Riviera sun because of his rash. His account of his therapy bears telling in his own words:

"We were ignored at the clinic for three days. Then, on the fourth, we got the injections. When Niehans came into the room with that big trayful of horse syringes full of pink, swarming cells I asked him: 'Where are *those* going?' 'Into you,' he said. 'I'm glad you have some curiosity.'

"After I'd had this blasted treatment I didn't feel well at all. I woke up in a *tent* every morning, feeling randy as could be. Here I was with all this bull and lamb and whatnot in me . . . and I didn't know *what* to do with it. As a matter of fact, I'm still frightfully ardent. And at my age one ought to be thinking about the grave, don't you think?"

One French newspaperman quoted Searle as saying: "Ever since I have followed this marvelous treatment, I defy anyone to come climbing in the trees with me."

A surprise bonus was a rapid memory improvement. "This astonished me," says Searle. "No, I do not think there was any placebo effect, because I hadn't much faith in cell therapy at all. I went through with it to please Maugham."

If Niehans treated his guests cordially, even royally, he apparently dunned them accordingly. Searle reckons the fee to have been in the neighborhood of £1,000 apiece.

"We were stung," he says. "Maugham told me it was my Christmas present for the next three years. And at that price we were disappointed at its being over so quickly."

Ten days in the modest but modern clinic was the maximum Maugham could stand. Thereafter, he and Searle settled into the rambling, stately comfort of the Hôtel des Trois Couronnes in Vevey. Stung or no, both were quite satisfied with their treatment. Miraculously, Searle's skin regained its preadolescent clarity, his nervous condition vanished, and Maugham began to sleep again. Most important of all, he began to write again. He was inspired.

There is no better advertisement than a satisfied customer. Maugham unhesitatingly recommended CT to anyone he thought needed it or could benefit from it—except for women, upon whom it seemed to have no effect whatever, according to Searle. Gloria Swanson, for one, agrees with him. She says her bout with the embryo cells gave her nothing more pleasing than a headache. As for rejuvenation, she claims that only a proper natural diet—minus the insecticides, preservatives, and chemical poisons that modern supermarket shelves are stacked with—can restore lost youth to the body.

Two years later, the author of *The Razor's Edge* and *Of Human Bondage* decided to have another go with CT. Once again, for both, the results were good. This time, however, there was no unpleasant aftereffect whatsoever. Apart from the vulpine bickering with his family, which eroded him considerably, Maugham hung onto much of the serenity and creativity that his injections appeared to have restored to him.

"His old age was very healthy," says Searle. "He was extremely strong, and used to take long walks around Cap-Ferrat. He was an ardent sightseer and enjoyed long trips. He continued to work extremely well."

Beverly Nichols' published memoirs of Maugham described Maugham as "all charm, all bonhomie . . . with . . . positively alarming energy . . . after a second course of rejuvenating injections . . . and it was evident that these were working overtime. He [Maugham] had suggested a 'little walk'. . . [which] proved to be a miniature version of the Everest expedition—a scramble among the gorse on a steep cliff-face."

It is frequently alleged that Maugham introduced his old crony Winston Churchill to Niehans and that the statesman was treated by the Swiss doctor. The allegation is false. The truth is that Churchill had been treated with CT years before the famous author made his first trip to Vevey.

Niehans could not have treated Churchill for at least one and possibly two reasons. The story goes that the rejuvenationist rejected Churchill because of his wholesale consumption of brandy and cigars. Alcohol and tobacco are supposed to poison the injected cells and destroy any conceivable benefits. While Niehans encourages belief in this tale, it is without apparent foundation.

The more likely cause for their not getting together is the old Hohenzollern's avowed hatred for "the man who was responsible for the "inhuman" *bombardment à tapis* [blanket bombing] of German cities during the war"—as Niehans expressed it in conversation with me.

The cigars-and-brandy excuse is unconvincing because Churchill neither drank nor smoked excessively during his last decade. Or so maintained his rejuvenationist, Dr. Jean-Baptiste Durand-Boisléard of Eze-sur-Mer, who gave him CT over the staunch objections of his personal physician, Lord Moran. If one inspects the later newspaper photographs of Churchill, one notices that the cigar is always freshly lit. Durand-Boisléard contended that the cigar pose was merely and exclusively a symbolic gesture for the benefit of photographers.

Dr. Durand-Boisléard was reputed to be an excellent surgeon-physician as well as a competent cell therapist. He practiced in Paris and on the Côte d'Azur until his death, in 1955, at age seventy-four. It was after Churchill's first stroke, during 1953, that he first received Durand-Boisléard's ministrations. The doctor used Siccacell placenta, heart, testes, and cerebrum (frontal lobe) lyophilized cells from Heidelberg prepared especially by Dr. Joachim Stein to treat Churchill's sclerosis of the cerebral vascular system. The results, according to Stein, were excellent and without side effects. In the two years following, Churchill received at least two, and perhaps three, more treatments.

Some writers, among them Garson Kanin, attributed Maugham's penultimate miseries to cell therapy. Kanin conjectured that the injections may have "disturbed [Maugham] mentally" and caused him to be "jumpy, irrational, and unstable" and brought on the troubles with his kin. On the other hand, while readily admitting that Maugham became increasingly difficult to abide, Searle is convinced that Niehans' treatments were in no way responsible for the writer's extreme irritability in his last few years.

One afternoon, greatly chagrined and anxious because of his employer's bizarre behavior, Searle made a desperate, furtive call to Niehans. "There are signs," he told Niehans, "that I simply do not understand. I think Maugham is going insane. Is there anything you can do for him?"

Searle described the symptoms carefully. Niehans replied that he thought he could help him. It would require a third CT series. This time Searle refused to take the injections because he felt he did not need them. Maugham took them, but, for lack of will, neglected to obey Niehans' strictures on abstinence. Plainly, Maugham was not improving at all.

"Immediately afterward," says Searle, "Maugham started in again on his double scotches on the rocks, his cocktails, and after-dinner brandy. He smoked eighty cigarettes per day. That, of course, killed the cells and the value of the treatment."

"I know my mind is disturbed," he told Searle, "but I must have a drink and a smoke."

Whether Maugham was actually out of his mind before he died is questionable. Dr. Max Wolf insists that Maugham retained his sanity to the end.

"Insane? Oh no! Though he was senile, he was perfectly clear. He was deaf and couldn't hear anything, but nine months before he died he was quite sane. I know because I dined with him then in Munich at the Vier Jahreszeiten. He was far from crazy. He had difficulty concentrating and his memory was poor. But the explanation for this was that he suddenly had become senile."

Maugham believed deeply in the worth of rejuvenation by cell therapy. He thought much good could come from it, and he willingly spoke of it to his friends. Toward the end of his life, however, he failed to evoke the willpower necessary to make the Niehans magic, whatever it consists of, work.

CHAPTER SEVEN

The Youngest Rejuvenator

Peter M. Stephen is the only professional rejuvenator in the history of the art who doesn't prize his very youthful appearance.

The best-known and perhaps the only cell therapist in London, he is, therefore, very busy and very rich. I was struck by his remarkable physical preservation. He looked like a young man. I asked him how old he was. He answered with a drawn-out, nervous "Heee . . ."

"I ask this of everybody," I assured him.

"Why do you want my date of birth? I've got a reason for asking this."

"For reference. It makes it easier to describe a person. I always ask the ages of people, even those in their seventies and eighties, where it might be a little embarrassing."

"Well, mine *is* a little embarrassing . . . from the other end. I'm pretty young. I'm probably the youngest practitioner."

"You're thirteen and a half."

"No."

"Why should youth be embarrassing?"

"People are very funny."

"Nobody's refused to give his age to me yet."

"I'm not refusing you. I simply ask your motives for a specific reason. I'm twenty-three. You see, at twenty-three a person who is studying medicine is still at university. I've been practicing since I was seventeen and I worked with my father from fifteen on."

With hard-core rejuvenation, as with serious gambling, the English have been liberated. No longer does a fling require a trip to the Continent. They now have a home-grown, English-speaking therapist who propagates the ideas of Switzerland's most glamorous recluse. Not only does Peter Stephen save his clients air fares, but he performs Niehansian cell therapy for a few bob—indeed, quite a few bob—less than Niehans.

True, he is no doctor. But his father was. Dr. Ernest A. Stephen (MD from Leiden and PhD from Zurich) first visited Niehans in 1950 and immediately parlayed the connection into a flourishing CT practice. For personal wealth, Stephen *père* was obliged to pay a professional price: exclusion from the British Medical Association, albeit a voluntary exclusion, says his son, because of the MA's stuffy, ungenerous attitude toward cell therapy. The exclusion apparently did little or nothing to dent his practice. It has been booming ever since. Naturally, Stephen *fils*, who took over his father's practice at seventeen (the father died in 1964), is ineligible for the MA anyway, since he is not an MD (he dropped out after one year of medical school), so the question of *his* expulsion has never arisen. He manages, however, to keep *au courant* of the Association's activities through regular contacts with its members who, he says, are happy to send him patients and sometimes suggest to him that he would be wise to go into business with them since *they* have MDs.

Young Stephen probably needs no one. Not when he can drive a convertible Bentley Continental and work out of a poshly decorated apartment-clinic—stereo hi-fi tweeters and woofers throughout, two Siamese cats with tinkle-bells and jeweled collars, African game rugs, Oriental antiques, a very "with-it" mod (and former model) wife named Jacquie, who doubles as his nurse, and assorted electronic gadgetry and gimmickry that bespeak the owner's hipness. Stephen uses only the latest, shiniest, most aseptic everything in treating his patients: disposable plastic hypodermics, electric-eye systems, an expensive pulsemeter that takes a reading in two seconds from the fingertip. The powder rooms are cheerful and spacious, with gilt mirrors, crystal chandeliers, combs and brushes carefully laid out for the fastidious. The appointments, the colors, the styles go harmoniously together, and the visitor is made comfortable. He even has his choice of pastel-colored waiting rooms (if there is hesitation over the choice, Stephen chooses for the patient). Some six to forty patients per week try his brand of cell therapy—a fraction of the number he *could* treat (over two hundred, he says) if he "went all out."

Stephen has blue eyes, his black hair is brushed straight back, and he wears staid black horn-rimmed glasses. He argues earnestly and uses plain, nontechnical language. His conversation appears to combine a kind of cool with recurrent defensive reflections on his "outsider" status. He is always congenial, at moments desperately honest, and only rarely seems evasive. He speaks slowly, occasionally surrendering to expansive elaboration which propels him smack into discrepancies.

Sensational tabloid publicity has left people with the idea that Stephen claims he can whisk almost anyone back as many years as he wants. He regrets this.

"What I'm endeavoring to do here in England is to get away from this youth drug business. Let's be honest. It's impossible to make a man of eighty, fifty. No matter what treatment you give that man. At least . . . not at the moment. You restore and you regenerate—but not rejuvenate—whatever hypo- or hyper-functions there might be. In other words, you restore balance. But he's still eighty. A better eighty, admittedly. People of fifty or sixty come to me. All right. Their idea is to go back. You can go back to the extent that you can restore that which you've lost, to a degree. But you'll never be twenty again."

I asked him how he had acquainted himself with Niehans' rejuvenation technique, and whether he had actually met the master himself. No, but he'd met Michel and seen the whole operation, from the slaughter of the ewe to the injections. He thought he had been rather inhospitably treated, in view of both his (self-proclaimed) status as "the representative in England," and as a therapist with a large international clientele.

"All this snooty business in La Prairie drove me mad. I'd been traveling. When I arrived I was tired, I was hungry. I *said* I was hungry. So I had a couple of sandwiches and a cup of coffee. Michel looked me up and down. All right, fine, he's a great man . . . but . . .

"We went to the slaughterhouse. In a jeep. Helluva ride, isn't it? Then we did the dissection. And my French is terrible! But

it's all in French there, you know. There was a Doctor [X] from
Paris there. And I was standing there. And this Doctor [X] was
terribly condescending. He translated a little bit for me occasionally . . . but that was all. And I was trying to figure all this out.
Then we got back to the [operating] theater and I watched the
[cell] preparation. And just as I was leaving the nurse tapped me
on the shoulder and said: 'That'll be so-and-so much.' And I said:
'For *what?*' She said: 'For your coffee and sandwiches.' So you
might imagine how I felt. I was a little bit disgusted."

I asked him his opinion on how CT's rejuvenating mechanism
actually works.

"Well, *think* about it. That's all I can say. Just *think* about it.
It's the most logical, the most basic, the most sensible treatment
there is. If you sit down and *honestly think* about it. Look around
the world. Forget the people who are using it. What are they
working on in America? Cells! They're talking about cancer . . .
about transplanting tissues . . ."

"Do you really think it cures cancer?"

"One doesn't talk about cancer. Unfortunately, one can't. I
agree with Niehans . . . that it probably acts as a prophylactic.
But one can never be sure, of course."

"Do you turn down cancer patients?" I asked him this because,
with practically no evidence to support cell therapy's value against
cancer, most of the therapists I had talked to treated cancer patients, and led them to believe it would help their condition.

"I never treat the condition of cancer. I treat them—it—as a
general condition. It depends. I would obviously have a long discussion with the patient, and explain to him that I would not
treat his cancer, but what I *would* attempt to do is strengthen
the parts of his body that were *not* affected to give him that little bit extra . . . you know what I mean?"

"You don't believe, then, [as some doctors do], that the injections could give a cancer patient that little bit extra that would
give an extra push to the cancer . . . that is, start it off on a faster
course . . . spread it?"

"Yes, I think it might. . . . But cancer is something one just
doesn't talk about. And if I started talking about cancer, they'd
be on me like a ton of bricks, the MA. It's one of those conditions
you just *don't* treat."

"Would you treat a patient who seemed near death and thought this might do him some good?"

"*I* would. Because if the patient thinks it might help him, it might. Whether it helps him organically or not . . . So far, nobody is known to have died from [the cells]."

"That's not true, several are known to have died from them."

"From *fresh* cells . . ."

"From fresh cells *and* lyophilized cells."

"Give me a case of a lyophilized death."

"[Dr. Joachim] Stein himself told me about them." (Stein and Schmid detail several such deaths in their book.)

Most of Stephen's patients who are seeking rejuvenation do so principally to restore their sexual abilities. This is far from uncommon. Indeed, most rejuvenators get their business from men who find themselves increasingly impotent with age, and from women who find themselves less attractive to the opposite sex.

"Is it the testes cells that help restore sexual potency?" I asked Stephen.

"In order for a man to have an erection, it's not only the fact that *his testicles* must function. It's the fact that his nervous system must be in balance, his glandular system must be balanced."

"What about your female patients who are worried about their breasts?"

"Fear plays a very great part. They feel they're losing their husbands once they reach a certain age. I can do quite a lot for the female breast. If the treatment is given correctly—don't misunderstand what I mean by correctly—then the muscle tones, and strengthens, and becomes more firm. It's the same with a man. Instead of half an erection he can have a full erection."

"Can you really . . . ?"

"Put a little life back into it? Yes, I've done it. Not every time. About fifty percent success for the breast. Ninety percent for the penis."

"Can you *really* make something out of a pancake?"

"Now let's be logical . . . absolutely perfectly logical about it . . . there are drooping breasts and there are drooping breasts, are there not? I mean, don't give me an impossible case. Let's have a sensible case. A woman of fifty. All right, so they're drooping a bit and she has to wear all kinds of supports. *That* you can *help*. If they're pancakes, as you call them . . . *no*."

"Can you get a breast to upturn?"

"I've done it."

"What about other kinds of rejuvenation treatment besides cells?"

"I'm dead against hormone treatment. All right. So you give a man an erection every morning, so he can cope with all the dollies he's managed to pay for because he's got so far in his profession and his financial status. But what about his heart? What about his digestive system? What about a dormant ulcer that's been there all those years? All right, so you can bang testosterone in as much as you like . . . Admittedly, it acts upon the rest of the system to a degree . . . but . . . that's it. [Other rejuvenation treatments] have all got their place. They've all got their patients."

"Since you're not an MD how far can you go in medicine?"

"There's no law in this country that says I can't perform a major operation . . . if I've got the patient's consent. But if I make a mistake I'm up for manslaughter."

"A mistake in surgery?"

"A mistake in anything. Of course they've got to prove that I did it."

Presumably to explain the complexities of cell therapy to his patients, and possibly to reassure them, Stephen keeps a large book of newspaper clippings, which his father began and he updates, on the subject.

Before showing it to me, he mentioned that he'd been on a Granada TV, Ltd., film on old age and rejuvenation with Dr. Alex Comfort. Knowing I was lunching with Comfort later that day, he asked me to get his reaction to cell therapy, and to his own performance on the program. I did. Comfort is highly critical of all cell therapy, and said so. I informed Stephen of Comfort's attitude. The cell therapist replied that there probably was a good answer to Comfort's criticism that youth doctors rarely publish their papers in orthodox journals—but he did not say what it might be.

Then he leafed through the clippings. Typed onto one page was a caution that read: "This is an account, in the language of

the layman, of the Niehans cell therapy. The wording is somewhat florid, but the essential data are correct. The cell therapy is
available at the Clinic for RegenerativeTherapy. Interested patients are requested to discuss the matter with Doctor Stephen."

The clippings were, on the whole, misleading in substance and
detail. Cell therapy was always referred to as harmless, which it is
not in every instance. Stephen, in an old clipping (referred to only
as a "Harley Street doctor who was getting wonderful results with
a new Continental treatment of animal cell injections"), was
quoted as assuring a patient "that although there had been some
failures with cell therapy, there had been no deaths."

One journalist wrote that the elder Stephen had been "fully
trained at the Neihans [sic] clinic to treat patients."

Headlines showed a powerful appeal to age-conscious women:
THE DOCTOR WHO MAKES WOMEN YOUNG AGAIN; THEY SEEK THE
SECRET OF BEAUTY; THE ASTONISHING STORY OF A HARLEY STREET
SPECIALIST WHO CLAIMS HE CAN GIVE MEN AND WOMEN BACK THEIR
LOST YEARS.

One lone item, dated February, 1959, told how the former
British lightweight boxing champion Eric Boon, at age thirty-
nine, was applying for a license to fight again after a seven-year
ring absence. Once known as the "Golden Boy of British Boxing,"
"The Chatteris Thunderbolt," and "Boy Boon"—and now billed
as "Animal Gland Boon"—the pugilist maintained that Dr. Stephen's therapy had knocked exactly eight years off his age. His
physician explained to the press:

> I cannot imagine that the [British Boxing] Board [of Control]
> have turned down Boon on physical grounds. Normally, of course,
> a man of his age would be too old to return to boxing. But he has
> been given therapy consisting of organic cells of newly-born or un-
> born animals which are introduced into the human body. This sets
> off a continual production process of new body cells which revitalize
> and rejuvenate the entire human system. And Boon is now the
> equivalent of a man in his early thirties. He is a man in extremely
> good physical condition.

There is no follow-up on Boon's progress. The cynical reader
can draw his own conclusions from the omission.

Most of the cuttings were about the usual celebrities reported to have been treated by Niehans (Maugham, Pius XII, Adenauer, and Chaplin) and success stories among Dr. Stephen's case histories. Among the rest:

A London woman who presented herself as "living proof" of cell therapy's success. The treatment, she said, banished wrinkles, ugly fat, menopause disorders, old age, fatigue, weakness, inability to ski, and thoughts of suicide.

An aging millionaire who told a reporter he had nearly lost his business out of despondency resulting from the death, two years previous, of his wife. Three months after cell therapy he stopped visiting his wife's grave and announced to his doctor: "I'm getting married again."

A middle-aged woman, whose husband had run off to Italy with a pretty young thing, who found cell therapy a more powerful means of getting her husband back than the courts. After cell injections, and some considerable expenditure on haute couture, a hairdo, and a few fashionable accessories, she succeeded in making her husband so jealous that he asked for her picture "to take on business trips." Concluded the article: "She knew she had won him back."

In an age when most practitioners tend to lean away from Niehans' rigid, primitive (albeit charming) theory of the therapeutic process and to explore more sophisticated biochemical explanations for CT's healing phenomena, Stephen remains an ardent dyed-in-the-wool Niehansian, a member of the old school. He believes that the cells travel, intact and alive, directly to the specific corresponding deficient organ (that is, sheep embryo liver cells make their way to the human liver).

Stephen, Sr., on the contrary, was of the opinion that the injected cells did not travel, but instead created miniature organs right in the buttocks of the patient, which substituted for the failing originals—a theory the son rejects because if it were true "one would feel" the new organs in the buttock, which he, after trying a few, failed to do.

The young Stephen also shares Niehans' preference for fresh cells, which are supposed to have more zing in them. The use of dried cells is *faute de mieux*.

His belief in the viability of the cells after injection is the more touching and optimistic since the Siccacell manufacturer claims categorically that they are as dead as dodos. Stephen uses the classic Abderhalden diagnostic reaction test to determine which glands and tissues and organs are malfunctioning. He sends urine samples to Cologne (at £15 each) for analysis, and receives airmailed or cabled results, depending on the urgency of the request. While many therapists "cut" the normal Siccacell ampule on the theory that small dosages may be as effective as large ones, Stephen states that he always gives more than one ampule of any organ in a syringe.

Stephen has always dreamed of establishing a bona fide Niehans *fresh*-cell operation in the United Kingdom. England appears out of the question since English law forbids slaughter of a pregnant ewe, and there is also the nightmarish prospect of British antivivisectionists parading around the plant with placards. His recent failure to locate a plant near home was a deep disappointment. "I tried last year," he said. "I had everything set up . . . *everything* . . . my own flock of sheep . . . a slaughterhouse laid on . . . right out in Kent." Presently he is considering an offer of financing for an operation in Ireland.

While the medical profession publicly pooh-poohs Stephen as an upstart, know-nothing outsider, many doctors quietly send him —or, more often than not, are *obliged* by their youth-bent patients to send him—business.

"It's still under the table," he explains. "Like this doctor now [who had just called]. He'll send [a patient] in an odd way. He'll say: 'We *know* it won't work, old man, but . . . you know . . . have a go.' Knowing England . . . I wouldn't be surprised if it goes onto National Health in ten years."

While doctors' recommendations and regular patients account for half of his clientele, the other half is drawn to him by newspaper publicity. In the initial session, the awkward business of financing the therapy is always discussed, the total treatment costing anywhere from £150 to £200.

"When you come across an Arab king, does the bill come to a little more?"

"This," he replied, "is something I *don't* do."

"Why?"

"Because a man has got a little bit more money, why charge him more? Do you know what I mean?"

"Maybe then you could make it easy on the people who don't have as much?"

"Yes, but you can't really run a practice like that."

"Don't you have any charity business?"

"You know, people are funny. You start running a charity business, as you call it, then every one of your patients becomes a charity patient. Do you know what I mean? If somebody really can't afford the fee, then I say, 'Right, we'll come to some arrangement.' And if I think the treatment is *really* going to help them, and if I think they're going to be *sensible* about it . . . You know, some people expect the moon . . . and they say: 'My financial situation allows me such-and-such.' Then what I do is say: 'The fee for the treatment is this. What we can do is draw up an agreement between us—and this may sound terribly businesslike, but it's the only way to do it. You'd pay a deposit and pay as you can, monthly.' But the moment you cut that out and say: 'All right, I'll give you the treatment for fifty guineas,' the next man who comes in says: 'Why should I pay the additional for the person who can't afford it?' It's not fair. Do you see? I've treated a lot of rich people. But I wouldn't charge them more."

Once in his office, the patient would have to know a little bit about doctoring to know that he is not in the hands of an MD (though Stephen does not hide his lay status). Customarily, he goes through the patient's case history, insists that a regular GP give him a thorough examination before seeing him, then runs him through routine diagnostic tests of his own. He shies away from treating patients still suffering from infections or severe cardiac conditions. The appearance of the clinic is spotless.

"Everything is absolutely sterile here," Stephen said. "I have to be more careful—I'm 'underqualified.' A, it's necessary. And B, I can't take chances."

Using the results of the Abderhalden and his other diagnostic tests, he determines which organs are deficient and, therefore, which to administer to the patient. Treatment usually consists of twenty ampules of some five or six different organs. On occasion he will use Regeneresen, which Stephen describes as sheep embryo cells with the protein removed, recommended for weaker patients who cannot stand the stress of foreign protein in their systems; or H-3, the procaine rejuvenation treatment promoted by the Rumanian woman doctor Ana Aslan; or nerve manipulation, used for any purely physical condition, insomnia, or stress and strain.

After the shots, the patient is directed to remain at home in bed for the customary three days, then to return for a visit after a week. Another visit is in order after the third month, and a fourth in six months' time, when more tests will be done to determine if the patient needs additional cells.

In principle, the treatment should, Stephen claims: (1) improve memory, (2) relieve fatigue, (3) improve skin, hair, and nails, (4) provide a natural face-lift for those who need it, and (5) instill a feeling of alertness.

Several times Stephen mentioned his preference for the Heidelberg Siccacells over Michel's Cellorgan dried cells—both essentially the same, but the former processed in a much more elaborate factory. I asked him if his personal feelings against Michel had influenced his choice of supplier.

"We just don't get on. Two people."

"He probably feels," I conjectured, "that only an MD is qualified to do this thing. He feels strongly about that."

"I use a helluva lot of cell preparations . . . a thousand cell preparations per month. They come from Stein's factory [Siccacell]. I don't know Stein personally. I get mine through Dr. Griffel, Stein's associate. Tall, always gay, full of life, very powerful, always smiling, on top of the world, always running about. . . . He's a little bit overbearing at times, but he is really brilliant and the kind of man you can sit down and have a straight talk with. But if you're talking about medicine with him, he talks about it . . . sort of, I don't know how to explain it . . . not in a *condescending* way. Doctors have a way of doing this. Talking *down* to you. But he doesn't do that. He lifts you *up*. All the time. You know what I mean? Which is very *good*."

Because of the official prohibition upon BMA physicians against using cellular therapy, patients who want to be treated in England are forced to resort to Peter Stephen. His has all the earmarks of a bootleg business. While my conversation with Stephen shed a good deal of light on one sector of the rejuvenation field, it also shed light on the hypocrisies of official orthodox medicine and its practitioners. Somewhere along the line the patient seems shortchanged.

CHAPTER EIGHT

Doctors of Last Resort

Do not go gentle into that good night,
Old age should burn and rave at close of day;
Rage, rage against the dying of the light . . .

Grave men, near death, who see with blinding sight
Blind eyes could blaze like meteors and be gay,
Rage, rage against the dying of the light. ·

DYLAN THOMAS

I learned of Henry Wallace's rare nerve disease quite by chance. I had acquired a long shelf of cell therapy literature, including a few pages which Dr. Max Wolf had given me. Although I'd had them in my possession for a week or so, I had previously overlooked the typewritten note at the top of the first page, inquiring whether Wolf was equipped to administer cell injections. It was signed "Henry A. Wallace."

I was curious. My maternal grandparents had been diehard Wallace boosters for as long as the man cared to hold or run for national office. Frank and Libbie Robinson of Lilliwaup, Washington, accounted for two of the 1,157,063 votes Wallace received in his unsuccessful bid for the Presidency in 1948.

Wolf told me that the Wallace note was one of many written to him over the course of their friendship which dated back to the forties. Most of them, unfortunately, had been thrown out.

But the few that remained told an interesting story, Wolf said, one which Wallace had hoped to see published in one form or another one day. He believed that others might benefit from his account of his struggle against a malady for which orthodox medicine held out no hope of a cure.

After reading the letters, I realized that they constituted important and dramatic witness to this man's restless curiosity, his will-to-live, and his protracted encounter with one of contemporary medicine's unresolved enigmas.

By the mid 1960's, the impassioned turmoil of his middle years was well behind him. Single-handedly he had made the New Deal's dream of an agricultural revolution a reality. If in the 1960s the American farmer held his head high, he could thank Henry Agard Wallace for it.

After leaving politics, Wallace retired to his South Salem, New York, farm Farvue, where he spent his days profitably hybridizing gladioli, strawberries and corn. He was rebellious, leathery and callused, a son of the soil. He lived in the fields with his plants. Every day he ran a half mile and did twenty-two push-ups. He enjoyed Indian wrestling, volleyball and squash. On weekends he played tennis. He was an inveterate traveler and made frequent trips to Haiti and Mexico to rummage in the mountains for various strains of grasses and corn to improve his superb corn hybrids, for which he was famous. Once, on a high-altitude flight from Alaska to Siberia, he shocked the plane crew by declining an offer of oxygen, for no more compelling reason than to prove that he could survive without it.

His energy amazed his friends—and, at times, appalled his family. His wife constantly cautioned him about overdoing it. He was, after all, in his seventies. Gently she criticized him for "doing too many push-ups" and for "running up and down that pyramid in Guatemala" during a Central American tour in 1963.

He was careful about his nutrition. With the proper diet and exercise, he felt, he might live to be one hundred—possibly even more. But in 1963 he began to slow down. Perhaps, it occurred to him, his wife had been right. At seventy-five he might well be overdoing it with all those sports and exercises.

Suddenly, after a tennis game in July, 1964, the former Vice-President of the United States perceived that something was wrong with his left leg. It could not be attributed to mere strain or over-exertion. He could not lift it off the ground; the leg muscles simply refused to work. Normally, he had the strength of a bull. This debilitation was decidedly peculiar.

Several months previously he had suffered a nasty streptococcus throat. But that had cleared. The nose polyps? They were nothing new; he'd had those since boyhood. Recently, however, he had been having some trouble with his voice. It was huskier than usual; the sentences emerged from his throat almost as they had always come from his pen—in a kind of scrawl.

Perhaps, and more probably, his incapacity had to do with his asthma. Due to a long-standing allergy, his nose and mouth tended to fill with mucus. He already had had a sinus operation. And even though his tonsils had been taken out, the stumps were still there and easily became infected.

Then an even more frightening thought occurred to him. Perhaps his symptoms reflected something much more serious. Could the pesticides he worked with, day in, day out, be affecting him? He had tried to avoid direct contact with them, but that was impossible. Wallace knew all too well how DDT worked on bugs. After one blast, they would go on for a moment or two as though nothing had happened. Then they would suddenly flip over onto their backs and frantically claw the air until they died a few seconds later.

Had the DDT affected his own central nervous system?

Wallace was not the only one concerned for his health. Almost a year before the tennis game that had left him lame, Wallace's old friend Dr. Max Wolf had observed a certain awkwardness in his movements. The family, too, were uneasy.

In August, 1964, a Danbury, Connecticut, hospital performed several tests, including a brain scan with mercury 203 and an electromyelogram with olive oil and iodine. Diabetes was suspected. Unfortunately, that was *not* Wallace's trouble. The condition the tests revealed was far more serious—amyotrophic lateral sclerosis, an uncommon neuromuscular degenerative disease for which there is no known cure. At most, he was told, he could expect to live for another two years. In effect, Wallace had been given a death sentence from which doctors held out no hope of a reprieve. Even the cause of the disease was a mystery.

But Wallace and his family never gave up hoping. His wife and daughter insisted that he see a neurologist at the Harkness Pavilion of the Columbia Presbyterian Medical Center. He did, but there, too, he was told he was a dying man.

Wallace wasted no time in appealing his sentence. He made a November reservation at the single remaining appellate tribunal —the famed Mayo Clinic in Rochester, Minnesota. "Here there were whole batteries of doctors specializing in different things," Wallace recalled. "They were efficient, but their final answer was the same as at Danbury."

Meanwhile the disease was spreading, fiber by fiber, throughout his body. Wallace kept track daily of the number of push-ups he could do and the distance he could run. His diminishing strength was a source of great anxiety to him.

Wallace was not the first celebrated ALS victim to be diagnosed at the Mayos'. Another was the famous "Iron Horse" of baseball, Lou Gehrig, who had established an all-time playing record of 2,130 consecutive league games. The blow hit Gehrig, as it had Wallace, from out of the blue. In the middle of the 1938 season, Gehrig began to slow down. One day, when he realized that he was being applauded by fans for an elementary put-out at first base, his fierce pride obliged him to leave the playing field, never to return again. From the Mayo Clinic on his thirty-sixth birthday, on June 19, 1939, the public was given the official verdict on the famous infielder. It read, in part:

"He is suffering from amyotrophic lateral sclerosis [which] involves the motor pathways and cells of the central nervous system. . . . The nature of this trouble is such that Mr. Gehrig will be unable to continue his active participation as a baseball player."

It was one way of stating the brutal truth: Gehrig was not going to get better. The beloved athlete lived out his allotted two years, the standard period from onset of the disease to death, serving as parole commissioner for New York City until he died in 1941.

Even though the odds seemed insurmountable, Wallace was not about to give up. "I am going to live to be a very old man," he had said once. "Every year I know I have to be around the next year to see what's going to happen in my garden, with the sort of interest with which we can hope God looks down on us."

Russell Lord, who wrote the biographical *The Wallaces of Iowa,* once described Wallace's undauntable determination to win thus:

"His only expressed chagrin was that he could not, by nature, take tennis or any game lightly; he had to be good at it; he had to win. And he did win, most of the time, over the then opposition, by sheer determination and driving vigor. But his game did not improve."

A friendly physician in nearby Ridgefield, Connecticut, Dr. Ed Ochsner, brightened Wallace's outlook. He would at least attempt to help him. He tried out some crude liver extracts and vitamins. Two or three times a week, Wallace drove the five miles to Ochsner's office to receive his injections.

"I measured my declining strength by my ability to climb his stairs," he later noted. Still, his condition showed no improvement.

On February 16, 1965, Wallace called his old friend Max Wolf, and asked if he knew of anything that might help him. Wolf knew that ALS was incurable, but promised to find out all he could about the disease. "If you really want to fight," Wolf told him, "I'll do everything I can to help you."

Wolf and Wallace had known one another for many years. They shared a common interest in mutations. Wolf had been working with fungi, enzymes, and bacteria, Wallace with plants. When RNA and DNA first began to be talked about in the scientific community, Wallace felt the need of a tutor in the New Genetics. Someone recommended Wolf.

Both men had long been interested in rejuvenation, particularly in the sense of living beyond the normal life-span. Each had set for himself a minimum goal of a hundred-year longevity. When Wallace learned that Wolf specialized in treating patients for disorders associated with aging, he established a close and lasting relationship with the venerable youth doctor. Wolf described for him his work with enzymes, cell therapy, Bogomolets (see Chapter Fifteen), serum, and so forth. Wallace, who was deeply interested in unorthodox medicine, listened with enormous interest.

In many respects, Max Wolf is the most interesting of all the practicing rejuvenators. Niehans, for example, is an open book beside Wolf, who has assiduously avoided all publicity on his rejuvenation work. Operating in almost clandestine serenity out of his beautiful one-hundred-and-twenty-three-year-old, five.story office-home brownstone on Manhattan's Upper East Side, Wolf has been family doctor, youth doctor, and doctor of last resort to an unbelievable number of the United States' top two hundred families, including the *crème de la crème*. His blue-chip clientele consider him a "find" and, for fear of being crowded out of his schedule, only reluctantly recommend him to outsiders.

"Wolf's great virtue as a physician," said a friend recently, "is that he feels a compulsion to get to the bottom of everything he undertakes."

Wolf's office walls are bare. There are no diplomas, no honors, no plaques, no photographs, no paper whatsoever. Stout green plants from Florida swamps soak up the sunshine cozying in through his windows. His visible equipment is minimal: an old-fashioned doctor's scale, a couch (he catnaps), a sanitizing apparatus, and a plug-in gadget resembling an unboxed pioneer superheterodyne radio set.

He is cheerful, confident, alert. He wears a polka-dot bow tie, a knit sweater under a tweedy sports jacket (whose shoulder padding makes his slightly stooped five-feet-five frame seem even smaller), trousers hitched high over his loafers. His smile is personal, not professional. His speech is rapid-fire, slightly accented. He and his wife are his best patients, and both are surprisingly vigorous octogenarians. Miraculously, at eighty-three, he has never had a single filling or lost a tooth. His secret is simply flushing his teeth with saliva after eating. A fluoridation foe—"it mottles adult teeth"—he began to brush his teeth only three years ago, "mainly to please my wife."

A twentieth-century Cornaro, Wolf admits having done all the wrong things until he was sixty. Now, with regular tests, exercise and diet, application of cell therapy whenever the Abderhalden so indicates (he's received two CT treatments from Niehans, six from himself), regular injections of Bogomolets serum and his own Wobe-Mugos enzymes to keep his vessels clean, he expects to reach one hundred at the very least. His annual trips to Europe enable him to use there substances that are not imported into the United States.

It was Wolf's "yeast protein" that first caught Wallace's eye. By carefully directing mutations of an airborne yeast by means of ultraviolet lamps and addition of protein culture (they said it couldn't be done), Wolf produced a mutant that was not 18 percent protein, like the original yeast, but an astonishing 75 to 80 percent protein. Using much the same fermentation process as is used to make beer, Wolf began to manufacture a "yeast meat" at low cost. The most expensive element was the air, which had to be pumped up through aluminum grids into the water—to which minute quantities of molasses, sulfuric acid, and ammonia were added. The result was a substance that could be altered (by varying the glutamic acid content) to resemble chicken, veal, beef, or pork. The cost was less than 20 cents per pound. Moreover, it was a complete food. Rats fed yeast protein and water doubled their normal life-spans. Since Wolf's work with "yeast meat," other such foods have been produced in various parts of the world. Soya protein is produced even more cheaply.

Wolf's insect nucleus transplantation experiments also captivated Henry Wallace's scientific curiosity. If yeast cells could be genetically altered to be more useful to man, why couldn't man himself eventually be genetically reprogrammed? Theoretically, this is possible. Technologically, however, science is many years away from achieving any such profound metamorphosis. The obvious technological hurdles, however, did not prevent the two men from musing about the changes they would like to effect in Homo sapiens.

"Wallace," recalls Wolf, "used to fret about man's unkindness to his fellowmen. He felt that man does not possess enough sympathy in his makeup."

When Wallace telephoned Wolf in February, 1965, the physician promised to make inquiries all over the country and of colleagues in Europe to locate any possible cure for ALS. For lack of anything more promising, Wolf wanted to try his Wobe-Mugos proteolytic (protein-dissolving) enzymes on Wallace in the meantime. In European trials, Wobe had produced surprising remissions in several multiple sclerosis cases. Perhaps it would do some good for ALS.

The Wobe-Mugos enzymes come in several varieties. Each contains a mixture of enzymes of plant and animal origin that depolymerize (break down into smaller molecules) protein and some fats which are not protected against the action of these enzymes. The protein in living, healthy tissue is protected by the intact cell membrane and other inhibitors. Not protected are fibrin and proteins in necrobiotic (normally dying) and necrotic (pathologically dying) cells. Cancer cells seem to have little protection against Wobe, probably because their membranes are more permeable and retain fewer inhibitors. Wolf has experimented extensively with Wobe at his Medizinische Enzym-Forschungsgesellschaft factory in Grünwald, near Munich. It has been used in treatment of various protein deposits, inflammations, and cancers. According to Wolf's Munich associate Karl Ransberger, Wobe has been tried on 52,000 patients at twenty-two institutions throughout Europe.

In correspondence, several neurologists reported "excellent" results in 40 percent and "good" results in 35 percent of their clinical trials in eighty-four cases of multiple sclerosis and amyotrophic lateral sclerosis. Later reports, however, showed further progress of the disease after twelve to eighteen months of marked improvement. Plainly, Wobe was no lasting cure.

"My colleagues and I," reports Ransberger, "feel that the physical and mental improvement in more than two-thirds of these patients is a very high degree of success [and the therapy] should be offered and made available to all patients concerned."

Although Wobe-Mugos cannot presently be imported into the United States by the FDA, an experimental permit was granted at the time of Wallace's treatment. The permit has since been withdrawn, however.

With nothing to lose, Wallace decided to leave as soon as possible for the Continent. He would headquarter himself in Vevey, at the home of his sister, Mary Wallace Bruggmann, wife of the retired Swiss minister to Washington.

Available information on ALS is not terribly enlightening. It is a rare disease. Few clinicians have had any breadth of experience with it, and therefore know next to nothing about its origins or cure. In the main, it is an older man's disease. It begins in the legs usually, working up to the arms. The end comes shortly after the breathing and digestive functions are arrested, usually two, sometimes five, and very rarely up to twenty years after the onset of symptoms.

ALS's most prominent symptom is a strange erosion of the fatty myelin sheaths surrounding the nerve fibers of the central nervous system. Many doctors believe that the disease is caused by a virus. Others regard it as a kind of autoimmune disease, in which the body regards its own tissue as an antigen.

Recently, it has been found that a significantly high percentage (10 percent) of ALS victims have also had cancer. This fact has led Drs. Forbes H. Norris, Jr., and W. King Engel (who later treated Wallace at the National Institutes of Health Hospital in Bethesda, Maryland) to hazard the guess that cancer "in some way" might be "producing the ALS syndrome."

Wallace's physicians were encouraged by his rabid desire to live and his willingness to endure any inconvenience or pain to brake the progress of his disease. "I look on myself as an ALS guinea pig, willing to try out almost anything," noted Wallace, as he embarked upon his quest for cure. "Fortunately I have the resources to pay for it without Medicare. . . . After a year of feeling like a disembodied spirit . . . the sensation of the walls closing in on me has disappeared."

The following letters were written by Wallace to Max Wolf. The first is dated just prior to his discovery that he had ALS. Before he was through with his "doctors of last resort," all of whom were full- or part-time rejuvenationists, he had tried out every major "miracle" therapy known to man, including lyophilized cells, procaine with caffeine (Impletol), Wobe-Mugos enzymes, Bogomolets serum, a host of vitamin compounds, shark liver extract—as well as more orthodox, if still experimental, drugs.

I feel that these letters bring into sharp, dramatic focus a major, still obscured problem of twentieth-century clinical medicine— that of the terminal or supposedly incurable patient. They also show how the youth doctors tend to become doctors of last resort when traditional medicine throws in the sponge. Time and again, Wallace expresses his gratitude toward those doctors who were willing to slug it out with him against the mightiest of adversaries. The youth doctors, to a man, were hugely impressed by the magnificent stamina and iron will of their patient.

Each letter is preceded by notes which provide an explanation for references in the letters that otherwise may be obscure.

The diagnosis of a degenerative spinal cord illness made at Danbury Hospital was purposely withheld from Wallace pending confirmation from another source. Even two months after his visit to the Connecticut hospital, Wallace is still under the impression that his malaise might be due to "a very, very mild form of incipient diabetes."

FARVUE FARM ·   SOUTH SALEM   NEW YORK
October 29, 1964

Dear Dr. Wolf,

I doubt if there is anything of value in the enclosed but the summary is fairly good and I thought you might like it.

I trust you had a good summer in Europe and that you return to find that the F and D people in Washington will let you carry on your good work.

Since I last saw you I have developed a weakness in my left leg which seems to be hooked up with a very, very mild form of incipient diabetes which is now being controlled by one tablet of Orinase every morning. No pain. Feel fine. Can still do 20 pushups although for a time before the Orinase I was down to 17. Left leg is still weak but not painful.

The second week in November I am going out to Mayos' at Rochester, Minn. Let me know when you have a green light to do to me what you wanted to do.

Sincerely yours,
[signed]
Henry A. Wallace

Could the leg be hooked up with my allergy? The allergy is now getting better as is always the case in late fall.

Wolf's reply was casual. A minor nerve dislocation or malfunction might be at the root of the trouble, he speculated. Wolf suggested, however, that Wallace see Dr. Hellmut Haubold, a beefy, congenial Munich internist who, like Wolf, abandoned a career in architecture to take up medicine. As is true of a startling number of therapists specializing in the treatment of mongoloid children, Haubold was the father of a mongoloid child, a boy who died in his early teens. Since then, Haubold had devoted most of his time trying to correct this genetic disorder in other children, using vitamins and hormones and, at times, CT. On the wall of his study, the visitor sees hundreds of blue and red pins dotting a map of Europe, each pin representing a young retarded patient. Haubold is regarded as having worked wonders with mongoloid children, many of whom he has enabled to compete spectacularly well with their schoolmates.

Although he had much experience with CT, Haubold felt it would do nothing for ALS. On the other hand, he thought that Impletol, a blend of caffeine and procaine, might help Wallace. According to Rumania's Dr. Ana Aslan, procaine is indicated in nerve conditions, since it breaks down into para-aminobenzoic acid, which is neurotropic—that is, it has an attraction for certain nerve centers. Haubold was convinced that DDT, which Wallace had used profusely in his plant work, had probably damaged his nerves and was implicated in the ALS. "As the patient had been working for many years with insecticides, despite all precautions, a chronic damaging of the central nervous system may be assumed," he reported.

Wallace's overwhelming dynamism deeply impressed Haubold, just as it had all of his physicians. Rarely had he met a man so eager to do battle against the inevitable. "I should like to stress the astounding stout-heartedness of the patient and his will to live," said Haubold. "His attitude and his energy are to be [considered] as positive factors for all further therapy attempts."

The second letter (undated) is typed on a copy of an article on cell therapy. Strangely enough, while at his sister's home in Vevey, Wallace did not visit Niehans personally. He knew he had ALS, and he was curious about CT, yet he didn't think it worth going direct to Niehans to find out about it. (Niehans' estate is but a couple of miles from the Bruggmann villa.)

Dear Dr. Wolf, Are you in position to give me the proper adaptation of the Niehans treatment as described here? Haubold gave me some Impletol as put out by Bayer, based apparently [on] Procain[e] and [caffeine] to be given very superficially, pricking the skin lightly in many places along my left leg. He gave me one treatment. Per-

haps a momentary stimulation. Of doubtful value I am inclined
to think. Yours,

[signed]
Henry A. Wallace

Could I mail blood and urine in to you 3 months hence to measure
again the level of proteolytic enzymes?

While dubious about any benefits CT might offer Wallace, Wolf
knew that his patient was toying with the idea of having the cell
injections. In any event, the cells could do him no harm. The best
thing, he felt, would be for Wallace to have treatment directly
from Niehans in Europe. As it turned out, Wallace waited until
he returned to the United States before getting the cell injections.

The next letter, from Vevey, was written between operations.
Haubold had recommended that Wallace consult Zimmermann, a
leading European ear, nose, and throat specialist whose name is
sometimes misspelled in these letters. Ransberger and Barry were
Wolf's associates.

March 22, 1965 Chapponeres, Vevey, Switzerland

Dear Dr. Wolf,

I just received your letter of March 9 here at my Sister's home
in Vevey, where I am [recuperating] after the sinus operations [pre-
paratory] to the [tonsillectomy] about April 9.

We leave here to go back to Starnberg on April 7 and then await
Dr. Zimmerman's [pleasure]. At the moment he is at his home in
the Ticino (the German heaven) for a couple of well earned weeks
of rest. I have never known such a hard working man.

At the Airport I met by accident Karl Ransberger and Mr. Barry.
They both seem like two such fine young men. So young—so full
of promise. I shall not get back in the USA until about April 22
but when I get there I shall get in touch with you.

I feel fine with occasional pains in the left sinus where they had
to probe very deep.

I wanted my tonsil operation right away but Zimmerman would
not hear of it . . .

It was a great blessing that I phoned you the morning of Feb. 16
and heeded your warning to move fast. Everyone has been very nice
to me and I am sure that this is largely due to you.

Cordially yours,
[signed]
Henry A. Wallace

In the following letter to Karl Ransberger, Wallace explains that he has been on a full Wobe schedule for several months. Although such unorthodox remedies are normally forbidden to be imported into the United States, I have been told by Ransberger that an exception was made in Wallace's case.

The "Greek and the Czech experience" refers to experiments on MS and ALS patients with the enzymes in those countries.

FARVUE FARM   SOUTH SALEM   NEW YORK
                        April 27, 1965
Mr. Karl Ransberger
Mucos, Munchen, Germany.

Dear Mr. Ransberger,
This is to thank you for your many courtesies. I phoned Dr. Wolf and have made arrangements to see him on May 7.

My local Doctor, Edward Ochsner, was trained in Switzerland and speaks and reads German. You might send him any relevant material, especially the Greek and the Czech experience. Or send it to me at the above address and I shall take it to him. Also please return the Mayo Clinic report.

I bought a large amount of the Wobe candy, Wobe suppositories and Wobe injections and am making up a schedule with Ochsner. So far my leg shows no improvement but Dr. Wolf tells me that that is not surprising.

I have taken a full dose of Wobe in one form or another every day since Feb. 23.

Ochsner gives me injections twice a week and I shall take the suppository and candy forms on the other 5 days.

We had a smooth trip back and we are now adjusted to the time zone change.

Sincerely yours,
[signed]
H. A. Wallace

Could you give me Mr. Barry's first name or initials? It would seem you have a very nice partner.

Wallace's doctors of last resort proliferated fast. At this point he had tried Wolf's enzymes, Haubold's Impletol, and Ochsner's liver extract.

The "material which reduces hardening of the arteries" is

Bogomolets serum. His doubts about Niehans persisted for a while, but eventually he tried CT.

FARVUE FARM   SOUTH SALEM   NEW YORK
                     May 8, 1965

Dear Dr. Wolf,

It was good to see you looking so well, even better than the last time I saw you.

I have had Dr. Ed Ochsner of Ridgefield mail to you the Zimmermann report. After you have glanced at it you might mail it on to Dr. Leonard Bases of 359 East Main Street, Mount Kisco, N.Y. Dr. Bases is my Ear, Nose and Throat man and the report by Zimmermann really should go to him.

Sooner or later I wish to arrange with you to obtain more of the material which reduces hardening of the arteries. My blood pressure is low, my cholesterol is low and my weight is down 25 pounds from where it was a year ago. Therefore I do not feel in any [immediate] danger on this front. My cardiagrams [sic] have always been normal. Nevertheless, I have the greatest confidence in your suggestion. Sooner or later I wish to order through you a supply.

By the way I have been taking intravenously some calcium gluconate and intramuscularly heavy dosage[s] of Vitamine [sic] C and essential parts of the B complex twice a week.

I begin to believe that I am now getting stronger. The operations took more out of me than I anticipated.

By the way my left foot is puffy. I suppose that is natural. My mouth tends to overflow with saliva. The small of my back is weak for the first time in my life. I only notice it when I do push-ups. The small of the back gives out before the arms. This was not true last February. Then I could do 4 times as many push-ups as I can now.

Let me know when you think Niehans might help me. Frankly I am dubious about him.

Sincerely yours,
[signed]
Henry A. Wallace

Dr. Hadhanyi, mentioned below, had been experimenting with proteolytic enzymes.

Although ACS occasionally has been produced in the United States, it is extremely difficult to obtain. It is rumored that former New York City Mayor Fiorello Henry LaGuardia's wife desperately beseeched one importer to give ACS to her husband on the eve of his death from cancer. The importer, a timid man, procrastinated and LaGuardia died without having received the injections.

FARVUE FARM   SOUTH SALEM   NEW YORK

May 12, 1965

Dear Dr. Wolf,

I have your report and in conformity therewith will now increase my [dosage] of Wobe candy and will also take intramuscular Wobe twice a week.

I shall probably have to order more of the Suppositories in 6 weeks or so. The work of Dr. Hadhanyi at Un. of Valencia sounds most interesting.

I am glad my Wobe has doubled my proteolytic enzyme count but sorry that this is not enough.

Dr. Houston Merritt thinks it good for me to take twice a week high vitamin dosage intramuscularly. Think I shall take this in one thigh and the Wobe in the other thigh.

What is the full name of the ACS and the name and address of the man in Tennessee who makes it from goats? Where can I buy the ACS?

You have been most kind and thoughtful in every way. I appreciate it.

Cordially yours,
[signed]
Henry A. Wallace

Wallace's experience, as he observes in the following letter, was similar to that of many others of Wolf's patients, who report that the doctor always answers their questions at great length and in gratifying detail.

In the Haubold report that Ochsner received, the Munich physician reported glowingly on his patient's character and strength. "As I already mentioned in a letter to Dr. Wolf," wrote Haubold, "the patient is ruled by a great will to live and fortitude, and it is astonishing how he can take pain. These normal and biological qualities should be activated consciously in our communal struggle for the life of the patient, by his doctors as well as by his relatives." Yet, Haubold's prognosis was still dim: "A complete cure, unfortunately, seems impossible. But one should at least aim to slow down the disease."

FARVUE FARM   SOUTH SALEM   NEW YORK
                     May 19, 1965
Dear Dr. Wolf,
   You have gone to great pains, not only examining my blood and urine a number of times but also writing me most inter-esting letters in long hand. Your approach to me makes sense. The regular MD's have nothing to offer except physical therapy and perhaps injections of adenosine phosphate or heavy doses of vitamines [sic]. Wobe seems the only thing which offers hope . . .
   Your treatment has doubled the enzymes content of the blood. We have made a start due to you. My leg is not yet better but that could not be expected.
   After I use up the two doses of ACS or RAS [another form of ACS] can I get more? After I use up the Candies and the Suppos-itories, can I get more?
   Now please send me a monthly bill. If you do not I shall send in late June a substantial contribution to the Biological Research Inst.
   I have sponged off of you long enough.

                                   Sincerely yours,
                                   [signed]
                                   H. A. Wallace

   I shall speak to Ochsner about your technique of judging blood and see if I can get him to get from you the necessary instructions. I go to him twice a week for Wobe injections. We can make this into a scientific approach without the need for me to go through the very tiring trip to the City [New York].
   Ochsner is open minded. He is not a typical member of AMA. Completely the contrary. He speaks & reads German. I like Ochsner.
   Ochsner just received a report from Haubold which he will send you.
   I see Dr. Bases the Nose & Throat man this afternoon.

   The "great news from Czechoslovakia and Greece" in the next letter was a favorable report on the short-term effects of Wobe enzymes on multiple sclerosis and amyotrophic lateral sclerosis patients. Unknown to Wallace, however, there were only four ALS patients among the test group. Subsequent reports on the enzyme results for both MS and ALS patients showed that while the therapy achieved noticeable amelioration in many cases, it was not a cure.

FARVUE FARM   SOUTH SALEM   NEW YORK
May 25, 1965

Dear Dr. Wolf,

As soon as certain dividends come in in June I shall be glad to make a more substantial gift to the Biological Research Inst. than I did last time.

I have used the first of the ACS yesterday and will use the second one in late June. I appreciate your offer to send more of the ACS to me.

With regard to the candies and suppositories, I have enough to last me another two months. So there is no need to write Ransberger until late July. By the way I wrote him about three weeks ago but he did not reply. I wished to get back from him the report of the Mayo clinic, which I gave him in late February. I would suggest mailing Wobe in small packets. Perhaps with Haubold's name.

I am transmitting to Ochsner your willingness to give him instructions in determining the enzyme level. I assume it would be wise to wait until late July to make another test.

Heartiest congratulations to you and Karl on the great news from Czechoslovakia and Greece. Karl had told me something of this but I did not know it was so extremely good. I wonder how many of these cases had amyotrophic lateral sclerosis.

By the way Bases found I still had some infection when he washed out my left sinus. I am going back for another washing tomorrow. It was this sinus which Zimmermann found was so slow in clearing up.

In deep appreciation,

Best regards,
[signed]
H. A. Wallace

Gilles Lambert's enthusiastic account of cell therapy was probably the most persuasive factor in Wallace's decision to try it. After

studying Wallace's dossier, a neighboring Connecticut cell therapist wrote to Vevey asking whether the injections might help his
ALS patient.

Dr. Walter Michel, Niehans' assistant, replied to the request,
saying CT was definitely worth a try, even though CT is nowhere indicated for such a nerve condition in the CT literature.

FARVUE FARM   SOUTH SALEM   NEW YORK
May 26, 1965

Dear Dr. Wolf,

Dr. [X] who rides horseback with my very good friend [Y] has
loaned him a book by Gilles Lambert, translated from the French
entitled the Conquest of Age, the life of Dr. Paul Niehans. It was
first published in 1959.

[X] is very strong for the Niehans treatment. He claims to know
you and seems very proud of the acquaintance. Apparently you
were of some service to him at some time.

Glancing through the book I note the reference to the Abder-
halden test. Also Haubold is mentioned. Prof. Doctor Haubold.
(By the way he has sent a report to Ed Ochsner at Ridgefield. Shall
I have him mail it to you.).

[Y] will put great pressure on me to get in touch with [X] at
once. [Y] means well. I know nothing of [X] myself.

Sincerely yours,
[signed]
Henry A. Wallace

According to Max Wolf, Wobe enzymes react most favorably
when taken on a regular basis. Patients often seem to relapse when
they cease taking the enzymes, then gain upon resuming them.

The answer to Wallace's question below about Dr. Wolf's successor is that Karl Ransberger in Munich would probably handle
his laboratory research. It is doubtful whether any other physician
could substitute for him clinically, since Dr. Wolf's unique personality is so vital a part of attraction to patients.

By this time, Wallace was having trouble getting to sleep. He
woke up and read during the night, scorning any kind of sleeping
pill, including chloral-hydrate which a local physician said was
non-barbiturate and without side-effects.

FARVUE FARM   SOUTH SALEM   NEW YORK
June 2, 1965

Dear Dr. Wolf,

I stopped taking Wobe for a day or two and found it diminished my strength. The strength promptly came back when I resumed Wobe. As a result my faith in Wobe has increased.

Of the Wobe suppositories I have on hand about enough to last for two months. Of the Candies I would guess I have enough to last four or five months. And of the injections as given twice a week I would guess I have enough for a year. So it would seem I would soon have to begin thinking about getting more Supositories [sic], assuming that I shall run out in early August.

You may be sure that Wallace Genetic will make a nice contribution in late June.

Who will have charge of your Foundation if anything happens to you? Who will be the driving scientific force?

Most cordially yours,
[signed]
Henry A. Wallace

Wolf's Biological Research Institute is linked to his European laboratory in Grünwald, a Munich suburb, which employs some thirty-four technicians. The lab is chiefly concerned with Wobe experimentation, production of Wobe enzymes, oil-soluble vitamins, and ACS and cancer research.

Dr. X, in the end, decided to use Niehans Cellorgan lyophilized cells instead of the Heidelberg Siccacells. Cellorgan cells are produced near the Niehans clinic in Vevey.

Wallace's concern whether the Wobe proteolytic enzymes possibly were accelerating the demyelinization of the nerves was probably unfounded. Although Wolf currently includes lipolytic (fat-dissolving) enzymes in the Wobe group, he did not when Wallace was taking them. Since the myelin sheaths are fat and not protein, the proteolytic enzymes should not have affected them.

FARVUE FARM   SOUTH SALEM   NEW YORK
June, 8, 1965

Dear Dr. Wolf,

Enclosed a small contribution for the Biological Research Inst. Inc.

Do you think there is a chance that Wobe itself might demyelize nerves?

I checked with Ed Ochsner on the Haubold report. While he left the door open for virus as a cause he seemed [to] center on the possibility of insecticides being the cause . . .

The most notable characteristic of all the nerve people is that they are long on diagnosis but are completely in the dark as to cause and cure. All are just guessing and their suggested cures are purely empirical. Wobe seems to be the one exception.

I shall be glad to send another contribution to the Biological Res. Inst. as I learn more about it.

If it is not too much bother you might mail me a prescription for DORIDEN.

I wish an experiment with various types of cancer or leukosis of the Rausch Carcoma in chickens could be set up with the New Engl Inst. for Medical Res. at Ridgefield, CONN. Heller there has a fixation on an extract out of fresh shark's livers being a great source of strength to the Reticular Endithelial [sic] System. I have a hunch that Wobe might prove under experiment to be better than Heller's shark liver extract. Heller is trying to identify chemically just what it is in the shark liver. [X] worked with Heller at [one] time.

Best regards,
Cordially yours,
[signed]
Henry A. Wallace

Ransberger is a good man but I wish he would return my one page Mayo report.

In the letter following, the "surgical visit" may refer to a hernia operation Wolf had. The aging specialist also had a slight heart attack that year. The attack occurred during a period when Wolf had neglected his customary self-treatment against cardiovascular accidents with cells, ACS, and Wobe enzymes. Wallace mentions the Trujillo family. They had long been patients of Wolf's.

FARVUE FARM   SOUTH SALEM   NEW YORK
June 14, 1965

Dear Dr. Wolf,

I was deeply grieved to hear of your surgical visit to the hospital. Get well soon but please do not hurry to answer my letters.

At the moment I am trying some voltage electrical stimulation twice a week to the right thigh. It may be as good as physio-therapy but I wonder if it is any better. It seems to me that your proteolytic enzymes or the cellular treatment of Niehans is more fundamental.

I have decided that the sclerosis has affected the muscles of my tongue as well as my entire left leg and possibly the lower part of my back.

When I discontinued Wobe for a short time there seemed a temporary improvement and then deterioration which was remedied by resuming Wobe.

There is an interesting article about your old friend Trujillo by his daughter in this week's issue of Look magazine.

Sincerely,
signed]
H. A. Wallace

The classical progression of ALS from the legs to the arms is seen below.

Wallace's cell therapist advised strophantus and musk as a preliminary to CT, although most cell therapists would probably use it only where there was a suspected heart weakness.

FARVUE FARM   SOUTH SALEM   NEW YORK
June 15, 1965
Dear Dr. Wolf,

I trust you are feeling better.

[X] is an interesting chap, very much hipped on Strophantus and Musk as a preliminary to Niehans. Whether he will get anything from Niehans remains to be seen.

I stopped Wobe for 3 days and then resumed again. The Wobe makes me feel better.

I believe the trouble is very gradually spreading to my arms. Not serious at all but I cannot use my arms nearly as well as normally. How much of this is due to the back lash of the March and April operations I cannot say.

Recently I have been taking first thing in the morning a 10 mg. tablet of methyl testosterone [male hormone] under the tongue with the Wobe candy.

Beginning in 1957 under the prescription of Dr. Raffsky, the father I took methyl [testosterone] for a number of years (10 mg by way of mouth once a day). Belsky of the Danbury hospital wanted me to stop this. Subjectively I would say I feel better taking it and the combination of Wobe Candy with it seems to be good.

Raffsky the father I [believe] was almost next door to you. He died of cancer and his daughter carries on.

There is no need for you to answer if you are feeling under the weather.

Sincerely yours,
[signed]
Henry A. Wallace

Wallace was having trouble getting to sleep. Wolf proposed he try the simple "Schultz autohypnosis" method, which enables the would-be sleeper to empty the mind of all other matters by concentrating on something unmitigatedly trivial. Wolf personally concentrates on his right arm or left big toe to achieve this effect. The secret is to repeat over and over to oneself: "My right arm is getting heavier and warmer." While the right arm actually *does* become heavier and warmer (Wolf has tested this effect scientifically), the patient quickly drifts off to sleep. Usually, about a month is needed before the patient develops the requisite capacity for single-minded concentration, Wolf says.

Wallace's doctors still debate whether it was wise for him to undergo treatment that required extensive hospitalization while he was enduring the onslaught of ALS. It is thought by some that any surgery should have been postponed so that he could preserve his strength.

Below he speaks of his stay in hospitals as a debilitating factor.

FARVUE FARM   SOUTH SALEM   NEW YORK
June 21, 1965

Dear Dr. Wolf,

I find I have Wobe suppositories for 6 weeks. Of the candies and the injection material I have plenty for the time being, perhaps enough candies for 8 months and injections for a year (on a twice a week basis).

Therefore I would like 30 of the Wobe [suppository] packets at some convenient time.

I am very slowly getting over that part of the muscular weakness which the weeks in the hospital gave me. However, vis-à-vis the virus which has been destroying the nerve sheaths, I am not sure whether I am making progress or not. I am not sure whether it is

good for me to take Doriden. My best sleeping pill is to be tired
and to go to bed after 11 p.m.

Sincerely yours,
[unsigned]

In taking the candies I wish to ask,—Is it alright to swallow
them or is it better to let them dissolve slowly in the mouth. I
have been letting them dissolve slowly under my tongue. This
process seems to affect the character of my mouth and its ability
to taste. Not serious but I thought I would ask if it is o.k. to swallow without dissolving in the mouth slowly.

The Ransberger letter referred to in the next communication
shows that 50 percent of the ALS cases treated in Greece were
helped by the Wobe therapy. But the sample was probably too
small to be authoritative. There were eighty MS cases, but only
four ALS cases (of which two were helped). "Now," wrote Ransberger in his letter of July 3, "it is our problem to investigate how
long this form of improvement will hold and whether permanent
remissions will take place. I will report to you about the further
developments. I am sorry, that you did not show much or any improvement because of this therapy. Dr. Wolf wrote me about
it. . . ."

Although Wallace is pessimistic about his progress with Wobe
at this point, later on he reckons that it has helped him more than
any other treatment.

FARVUE FARM   SOUTH SALEM   NEW YORK
                   July 17, 1965
Dear Dr. Wolf,

I received a very nice letter from Karl Ransberger. Please give
him my best regards when you see him. He was most helpful to us.
I trust he did good business in Greece. He reports that Wobe
helped in about 50% of the amyotrophic lateral sclerosis cases
there.

In my case I seem to get steadily just a little worse. Now my left
arm is gradually getting weaker.

Yesterday the sicca cells arrived from Vevey and now [the cell
therapist] plans on beginning treatment about July 23. He has
been giving heavy doses of the achromycin. [sic] for [sic] 7 days
(6 a day). He hopes to stop the infection in my left sinus this

way. Dr. Zimmermann found this sinus much more infected than the right sinus. It has steadily showed continuing signs of infection. I have been washed out once every week or two. The organisms are harmless.

After [the cell therapist] gives the sicca cells treatment I was thinking of the live cell treatment. The Francis Cebrini Corp. is located at New Rochelle with Achilles Cebrini in charge. They are following the [Niehans] method with Lymph and heart extract and with Cerbatrol. I think this outfit has some connection with Niehans.

I am now beginning to type with my right hand only because the left becomes uncertain.

I trust you are well and that you [had] a rewarding time in Munich.

Sincerely yours,
[unsigned]

Wallace had begun to deteriorate fast. To stem the tide he was now taking all of the major "rejuvenation" treatments available in Europe: Wobe, Procaine H3, CT, ACS.

FARVUE FARM   SOUTH SALEM   NEW YORK
                      Sept. 18, 1965

Dear Dr. Wolf,

It was good of you to write. I trust you made progress in Munich.

My ALS is causing steady deterioration. On July 24 I took the injections of 11 different sicca cells. So far as I can tell to date,—no effect.

On Sept 12 I began on a three times a week basis the H3 or Procaine treatment as developed in Rumania, using the H3 direct from Rumania. I am supposed to take it 4 weeks and then 10 days without and then four weeks again. I have enough to last for five or six months.

I am still taking mild [doses] of Wobe by suppository and mouth. I stopped injections when I began the H3 injections.

The trouble has invaded the left arm so that I do not use the left hand much in typing. It becomes hard to use the electric razor. The right arm is beginning gradually to go. So far the right leg seems good.

I have the physio-therapist come three times a week. He is always encouraging. That is part of his trade.

What would you say is the prognosis? I understand that the disease usually results in death in two years. This would give me until next July. I shall do all I can to beat the average.

Sincerely and gratefully yours,
[signed]
Henry A. Wallace

In answering the last letter, Wolf pulled no punches. With the absolute candor that had marked their relationship since the beginning, Wolf told his patient that there was "woefully scant" information available on ALS and that everything he had read was "generally fatalistic" in prognosis. Wolf believed that such degenerative diseases could be checked only by an unrelenting battle against their characteristic chronic inflammation and virus infection as well as a general detoxication of the body. The detoxication, wrote Wolf, required a diet that would assist the detoxicative liver function and prevent toxic absorption from the colon.

By October, 1965, Wallace's condition required intensive care, and he was hospitalized at the National Institutes of Health clinic in Bethesda, where ALS was under study by a team of the nation's top nerve specialists.

As always, despite his suffering, Wallace impressed his doctors with his courage and desire to help them understand this mysterious affliction.

[from the hospital, undated]

Dear Dr. Wolf,

Just a short note to say that I am located at

Room 213   5E

Clinique

National Institute of Health

Bethesda, Maryland

On Oct. 6 I had a hole cut in my neck and a tube run down the Oesophagus. My throat & tongue and cheek muscles had become so weak I could no longer swallow even liquid food. I fear this cuts off putting the Wobe candies in the mouth.

This Institute has handled 300 cases of ALS.

I shall soon have a chance to talk to the top man and get their theories. This is a truly remarkable hospital I shall remain here several weeks.

The problem of taking care of mucous [sic] by suction machine has become exceedingly annoying and somewhat painful.

Fortunately ALS has not yet reached my right leg.

I am think [sic] about getting them here to try Dr. Aslan's H3. Hope you are well.

All the best,

Your friend
[signed]
Henry A. Wallace

A month before the next letter was written, Wallace had sent a touching note to his sixteen-year-old grandson, David Douglas, who had been vacationing in Colorado. It read in part: "I like your appreciation of the mountains. They are made for your nose and my nose, for your eyes and my eyes. There are so many new experiences in life. Life is a serious thing for some people, but it can also be joyous if lived with common sense." Even here there is hope. In the opening paragraph of the letter below it is interesting to note that Wallace, who had kept abreast of NIH research, has crossed out "other cases," and substituted "other human beings"—slightly more awkward, but probably reflecting a special esteem for the human situation that his tragedy had given him.

[NIH Hospital]
Oct. 21 [1965]

Dear Dr. Wolf,

At last the people here have a lead as to the cause. In 22 ALS cases they have found cells taken by biopsy and grown in vitro that there was an enzyme destroying the collagen. They did not find this in other human beings.

They are taking a biopsy on me tomorrow.

I wonder what the enzyme is?

Could you send me Wobe suppositories to H. A. Wallace, South Salem?

I do not take Candies because I now take everything by tube & do not use the throat.

My left arm is going. No muscles in cheek. Swallowing muscles mostly gone. Tongue muscles mostly gone.

I shall be home about Oct. 29.

Gratefully yours,
[signed]
Henry A. Wallace

Normally, three months are supposed to intervene between CT injections and the presumed benefits. By October, Wallace's three months were up, and he felt no improvement.

Certainly, if one believes the indications listed by cell therapists and procaine therapists for their respective remedies, procaine would hold the greater promise. Most reputable cell therapists are dubious in the extreme about CT's helpfulness in nervous system disorders.

[from the hospital, undated]

The dry Sicca cells did me no good.
Dear Dr. Wolf,

Thanks for your letters.

I continue to lose muscular control.

Through the tube in my neck they are giving me extracts from pancreas, liver and stomach.

I wonder if you could send me a fresh supply of Wobe suppositories.

I shall be home on Oct. 28 by ambulance.

Sincerely yours,
[signed]
H. A. Wallace

Haubold has some faith in the [Gerovital] of Aslan. No faith in Niehans for this purpose.

The "beautiful set-up at home" alluded to below refers to the transformation of the Wallace downstairs dining room into a hospital bedroom. Mrs. Wallace had installed an electric bed downstairs and built a new bathroom next to the dining room. The family feared these changes might upset Wallace by emphasizing his invalid status, but in the end he appreciated their convenience.

[Farvue]
Oct. 29, 1965

Dear Dr. Wolf,

Got home, by ambulance from Bethesda yesterday to find your letter and suppositories.

I found the NIH M.D.'s quite open-minded.

Their own approach at the moment is glandular extract.

So I am starting 4 suppositories daily.

By the way a letter from Haubold turns thumbs down on Niehans approach to ALS. But he is quite friendly to the [Gerovital] of Aslan. The NIH people were not friendly to [Gerovital].

NIH gives me atropine or belladonna to dry up excessive mucous [sic]. Produces very dry mouth.

I find from every hospital I come back weaker.

I have a beautiful set-up at home here for maximum comfort.

I trust all is well with you and Mrs. Wolf.

Sincerely yours,
[signed]
H. A. Wallace

Despite his tonsillectomy in Europe, Wallace never ceased having difficulty with his recurrent focal infection, as is seen in observations in the following letter.

[Farvue]
Nov. 9, 1965

Dear Dr. Wolf,

Again my deep appreciation.

The candies produce an excess of mucous [sic].

The injections I take three times a week.

Mrs. W. is reading to Dr. Ochsner both your letters over the phone.

By the way, Ochsner believes Wobe has done me more good than anything else.

Mucous [sic] causes me great discomfort. I like the idea of cutting out [Atropine] and increasing benedryl 50 per cent.

I have a suction machine at my bedside. The atropine and benedryl have cut down the need for the machine but now I get a varnished mouth and a type of mucous [sic] more difficult to handle.

My vital strength holds up but my muscular strength declines.

Again my deep thanks.
[signed]
Henry A. Wallace

One week later he wrote his last brave reflection on what it was like to see life slip from his passionate embrace. He died in peace at Farvue a day later.

In the weeks that followed, his widow wrote gracious thank-you letters to all of his doctors of last resort who had helped this strong man war against overwhelming odds. Despite his determined effort, despite the numerous therapies he undertook, Wallace failed to make his July target date for survival. It would at least have given him the average longevity expected of an ALS victim. But if it is true, as Ivan Popov suggests, that with great men one must calculate the mileage as well as the years, then Henry Wallace lived to be a very old man. And he had the satisfaction of going down fighting.

Very few terminal or incurable patients are able to fight such a battle. Most doctors are extremely loath to search for experimental remedies which offer only the barest hope of doing some good. They argue that they have their hands full treating patients who can be helped. It is also true, however, and quite relevant, that doctors today also have their hands full managing their lucrative investments and meeting their busy recreation schedules. The incurables, the very old, the terminally sick understand very well why they are not permitted more of their physicians' time.

An interesting Freudian explanation for this situation is given by Alex Comfort, the British gerontologist. He suggests that the incurable patient castrates the physician by shattering his "Great Healer" pose. Several recent studies have shown that many young men go into medicine precisely to overcome their abnormal fear of death. The confrontation with a dying patient may brutally remind the physician of his own mortality, a fact that can conveniently be ignored as long as he is regarded as the omnipotent healer.

Certainly, there are many people who have no wish to prolong their lives when confronted with the prospect of imminent death. But any man willing to fight for his life as hard as Henry Wallace fought for his deserves inspired, imaginative assistance. What stands to be advanced is not only the individual life, but human life itself.

CHAPTER NINE

Ivan Popov's True Confession

"I am not only a prostitute," said Ivan Popov, MD, former physician to King Peter II of Yugoslavia and versatile rejuvenationist, "but a pimp."

Crushing his Gauloise in a clay ashtray on the hand-hewn oak table in his Midi farmhouse, he added: "I am also, by the way, a hermaphrodite."

The remark startled me. He was a rugged Slav, on the under side of sixty, with tragicomic blue eyes, furrows on his cheeks and brow that bespoke an animated life, and a Byzantine basso that was growing huskier with each infusion of Pernod 45.

"A hermaphrodite?"

"Yes, because I look like a man—*mais je suis con.*"

I laughed at his little joke, immensely relieved at not being invited to contemplate some monstrous gonadal configuration.

Popov regrets not only having sold out, but especially having sold out so cheaply. *That's* why he is *con.* His revolutionary ideas on cosmetics, perfumes, hair preparations, and various rejuvenating agents have made millions for his clients, he says, yet he is still a poor man.

Popov farms a small area of his lawyer brother's 86 acres in the south of France, near the village of Opio. His home is an old mill he converted with his own hands. Dark, cool, and cavernous, it exudes a quiet, rustic simplicity that becomes strangely majestic with familiarity. The four-hundred-year-old millstone, large enough to support a wheel of chorines or a small circus act, is situated on the raised level of the salon, near the yawning fireplace. The floor is composed of tree sections, with the cracks filled with cement. The olive press still radiates a slightly acrid odor, even though it was permanently retired last season (or perhaps the season before). The furniture manifests the effort of Popov's back, his sinewy forearms, and calloused palms. Every line, every object, testifies to Popov's credo that nature must always carry the design.

If some doctors board the medical fringes uniquely for financial enrichment, that cannot be said of Popov. He is in the game for its high challenge and enjoyment. Life is to be lived *sans calcul*. Pleasures, like the best beefsteak, are to be taken raw. Beautiful women are created to be loved.

With this philosophy, money tends to disappear quickly. When it does, the fun stops, Popov shelves his latest inspiration, takes a deep breath—and looks for an "assignation." This is the hard, the hateful, part of living. Not that there is any dearth of buyers for his services. Cosmetics manufacturers are always eager to have him brew a new product, or produce an improvement on interesting new patents. "This," boasts Popov, "is easy work. I do this *after* ten o'clock in the morning. *Before* ten [he rises at four-thirty] when my mind is fresh, I do serious work. In the afternoon I do such nonsense as to talk with you."

Popov pioneered the introduction of placenta and embryo extracts into cosmetics, and of antiseptics into shampoos. His background covers the map of Europe. He got his first MD in Naples, another in Belgrade, studied in Germany and France, and has taught biology and chemistry. During World War II he fought alongside the Chetnik leader Draža Mihajlović, then emigrated to England and worked as a physician with POWs. He has experimented with any number of rejuvenation ideas (royal jelly, embryo extracts, cell therapy, biostimulants, hair restoration) but believes that the future of rejuvenation lies with aromatics.

It was Sevek—a soulful, cosmopolitan, shaggy-maned painter of cats that look like *gamines* and *gamines* that look like cats—who suggested I get in touch with Popov. Sevek, whose atelier is perched on top of the rocky prominence of Èze Village on the Grande Corniche, had been a patient of Popov's.

"If you want to meet the one man who knows everything there is to know about rejuvenation," said Sevek earnestly, "then you have got to see Popov."

Popov does know his subject. Perhaps not *all* there is to know, but he displays a staggering familiarity with the lore. Moreover, although he has kept a long, at times painful, silence on important matters, he wanted to talk. Not only about himself, but about his patients (always nameless) and his colleagues (always named, but who cannot be named here). He would say, for example: "Unfortunately I cannot give you the name of this patient . . . because if I could, all your doubts about regeneration would vanish. . . . You couldn't find a better-known name among the people who stay young."

Or: "The best of all in aromatics is Professor [X], the head of state research for [Country A]. He works on the side for private companies. If I am a prostitute, my God, he is the mother of all prostitutes! But he knows the problem and the possibilities."

Or: "If you go to [Country B], you must see Dr. [Y]. He's done very nice work. He is a different type of prostitute. I am a simple Belgrade prostitute. He is a *cocotte de luxe*."

While I was unable to see Professor X, I did see Dr. Y—and he was cast exactly as Popov had characterized him.

Popov first began experiments in rejuvenation after the war in Krefeld, Germany, on recently released Yugoslav POWs. Extensive double-blind studies (where neither doctor nor patient is aware of the identity of the injected material) with incubated eggs—chicks whose hatching has been interrupted—gave startling results. Emaciated POW's given incubated egg embryos recovered from their assorted miseries far more quickly than the controls; their memory loss (practically epidemic among POWs) was considerably less; they suffered fewer aftereffects of concentration-camp life, fewer diseases, and gained weight more rapidly.

Unhappily, Popov's results were leaked to the press, and regeneration-hungry Europeans everywhere began to eat incubated egg embryos (the egg yolks were separated from the whites and, while still warm, swallowed whole) for breakfast. There were good results, to be sure, but there were also casualties when the incubation failed (producing toxic embryo cadavers).

A ubiquitous German youth doctor, who has been in and out

of jail, and is doing a brisk business in Southern California, says that egg therapy originally was started by a postmenopausal Soviet woman doctor who boasted that her ill-timed pregnancy was due to incubated eggs. During the war the Germans worked with incubated eggs on the Rothschild estate just outside the Austrian city of Linz. Projekt Jot, as it was called, involved some three hundred patients (male and female) and was administered by fifty scientists brought from various European countries. Results were said to have been good, the patients experiencing renewed vigor and stamina. When the Nazis fled that part of Austria, the Russians took the entire research group back to the Soviet Union and continued the incubated egg experiments. The German youth doctor slipped by the Russians, escaped to the West where he hit upon the gimmick of adding young *human* testicle extracts to the chicken embryos. As revolting as the idea was scientifically, aesthetically, and morally, it turned what had been a fairly brisk business into a nonending gold mine for its author, who quickly purchased a Rolls-Royce for his palace calls.

Prospective rejuvenates listened breathlessly as the doctor described the subterfuges he had to use to procure the fresh, adolescent glands from monk initiates of a Riviera monastery. His $10-000 to $25,000 pricetag for these embryo-cum-human-testicle injections only made his mogul-clientele more enthusiastic than ever for the treatment.

Although Popov's more simple if less titillating incubated egg embryo experiments showed great promise, they did not impress British universities where he sought admission to conduct basic research into biomedical revitalization. Having become a British subject, he was then forced to return to France. Finding work there was never a problem. The egg therapy had become famous, and one Paris institute leaped at the chance to exploit it. Popov prospered, but the experience revolted him.

"I had to deal with old trouts who came because their titties had been hanging, and elderly gentlemen who had a new girl friend and wanted to take advantage of her. As soon as I saw a woman coming with a lot of feathers and flowers in her hair I ran away. I had prostituted myself. Still, I had dozens and dozens of cases I could treat."

Two years later, he chucked the Paris job and retreated to his

brother's spread in Opio. He began to farm chickens, English ban-
ties, and to build up his own practice. It was better than taking
patients potluck at the institute. Here he could take them or leave
them.

He kept careful records, matching his layers and patients. It
occurred to him that one group of chickens was giving infinitely
superior results. Curiously enough, these were chickens that had
been sick from coccidiosis (a barnyard disease)—so sick in many
cases that their embryos had died.

Until then, he had believed that the healing power in his eggs
came from what Alexis Carrel had called *"tréphones,"* or special
nutrients. It was a reading of the Russian ophthalmologist Vladi-
mir P. Filatov that convinced him otherwise. The ailing egg embryos more likely contained what Filatov had termed "biostimulants," certain ill-defined, ephemeral substances produced by a
suffering organism's cells to help promote survival.

"Have you ever noticed," says Popov, "that children, after
they've recovered from a sickness, grow much faster? Have you
ever noticed with a wound, a cut, a scar, that on the surrounding
tissues the hair grows faster and better?"

Any one of several infections presumably could create biostimulants, but Popov quickly found a much easier, safer, more efficient
method. He simply turned the incubating eggs upside down once
a day. This forced the tiny embryos to struggle against gravity,
and, in so doing, produce powerful biostimulants.

Popov began to think of pharmacological applications for these
egg biostimulants (he had studied with the Belgrade pharmacologist Professor Pavlovich). Why not put them into cosmetics?

Although the eventual commercial success of this idea was
broader than he ever dreamed, it did not work out exactly as he
had hoped. Almost immediately Popov got quite promising results
with placental tissue—theoretically a natural biostimulant factory
because of the mother's prolonged labor. Yet once one of Popov's
clients discovered that placenta from Caesarian deliveries could
be obtained much more cheaply than regular placenta, it was
used almost exclusively in hair preparations. But these results
were practically nil (since, according to Popov, the surgical inter-
vention deprived the placenta of any biostimulant production
caused by labor).

"Oh, my God," says Popov hotly, "when I think of the dirty, piggish nonsense that is being sold under the name of placenta!"

Always trying to infer medical principles from nature, Popov pioneered in the application of royal jelly to face preparations. This, too, became a worthless gimmick in commerce. Conceivably, surmises Popov, one might benefit from large amounts of royal jelly—"but you would have to feed a human being on the same scale that a queen bee is being fed, at least two to three grams [daily], and it would cost hundreds and hundreds of dollars."

"I was always prostituting myself . . . always trying to make something which could be sold. . . . My life was a constant fight with my bank. I had to make money."

Whenever he could steel himself to work full-time for a commercial client, he made money. But once his outstanding debts were paid and he had a small bank account, Popov would go back to youth doctoring on his own.

He once found himself tied to the multimillionaire hair king Lynn Akers, of the worldwide Akers hair clinics, for four long, turbulent years. Initially, he had gone to work for Akers merely to get out of the red. He had been hired as the medical director for the entire chain of hair clinics, supervising the research of fifty-two qualified physicians (most of whom Popov imported from East European universities, the rest of whom Akers personally had signed up in Italy). Popov viewed it as an unparalleled opportunity to review hundreds of thousands of hair-loss cases and follow them up with optimum research techniques. This it most certainly was. The fly in the ointment was Akers himself.

"Akers," says Popov, "is one of the most sympathetic and intelligent men I have met in my life. He is even the godfather of my son. Only, he is a crook."

During his tenure *chez* Akers, he often had reason to doubt the legitimacy of the operation. But whenever he voiced his suspicion to Akers, the mogul replied, "Ivan, if ever you notice anything that you consider not ethical, please tell me and the man will be sacked tomorrow."

While Akers at first fired several employees, eventually whenever Popov embarked on an inspection tour the manager seemed to expect him.

In most cases, baldness is the result of hormone imbalance,

hereditary inclination, or local infection. With Popov's biostimulants and aromatics, "unbelievable results" were sometimes
achieved—but only where hair loss was caused by hair follicle degeneration (the majority of cases). The business became morally
odious, says Popov, when Akers insisted on treating hormone-
caused baldness.

"He started growing titties on men, [creating] impotence and
effeminacy [by giving] estrogens, locally applied."

In theory, states Popov, Akers' so-called "trichologists" (hair
experts) would treat only patients screened and approved by competent medical practitioners. Usually, only those cases certain to
be approved—that is, curable by normal methods—were forwarded to his medical staff. The minimum tab was rarely less
than $300.

Other questionable dodges employed by Akers included:
treating women who had lost their hair following the birth of a
child (such hair returns normally); treating young patients suffering from simple infections that could have been relieved by an
antiseptic shampoo; diluting once-effective hair medicaments until they became little but colored water; and using heavy sales
pressure (pretty girls, "expert advice") to convince hopeless cases
they could be treated.

For his sins, Akers wound up with a seven-month jail sentence
in Brussels, and a two-year-and-nine-month sentence in Italy. In
Belgium, he jumped his heavy bail. In Italy, he was able to time
his prison entry to coincide with a Christmas amnesty so that he
was out almost as soon as he was in.* In the United States, his
clinics got into trouble with the Internal Revenue Service, but he
himself was never prosecuted.

Some of Akers' clients took the treatment knowing full well it
could do nothing for them.

One ambassador who traded on his distinguished shock of white
hair used to drop into a London clinic three times a week, will-

---

* A U.S. Embassy officer in Rome writes the following: "according to the Italian
National Police, Lynn Robert Akers, a U.S. citizen, was arrested in Milan, Italy, on
November 18, 1965, and charged with aggravated swindling, unauthorized medical
practice, unauthorized sale of medical products, setting up medical agencies without
authorization, and unauthorized medical advertisement. At that time Akers was operating the 'Akers Hair & Scalp Clinic' in Milan. According to the Italian National
Police Akers appealed his sentence of 2 years, 3 months and 10 days which is still
pending before the Pretura in Milan, Italy."

ingly handing over £2 for each treatment. Reluctant to tell him that the treatment was worthless, Popov simply said to him: "I'm very happy with the results you've had. But you don't need any more treatment."

Later on, in Brussels, however, the same fellow appeared again for therapy:

"For heaven's sake," said Popov, "two years ago I told you that you don't need any more treatment. Why in hell do you come here?"

"You mustn't tell anyone," said the diplomat. "But, you see . . . this beautiful white hair is my entire career. So you may be perfectly right. But as long as I can keep it, I don't mind coming to Akers three times a week."

The unsavory revelations of Akers' Rome trial convinced Popov of what he had long suspected: that the clinics were thorough-going frauds. Even though Akers was acquitted by one judge, Popov began making surprise inspections of the clinics himself.

"I found out that whatever was said in court was true: that he had accepted people who should not have been accepted, on whom you couldn't grow anything . . . and that they counseled useless treatments. . . ."

Popov pleaded with his friend to operate the clinics honestly. But his request fell on deaf ears, according to Popov.

Once the two men planned to engage in a gigantic, wholesale rejuvenation business (using Popov's savvy) for corporation ex-ecutives. For $5,000 per month per client, a business could ship its senescent directors to the Akers-Popov regeneration clinic— and hope to get a few more years out of them. It would have oper-ated similarly to a Maine Chance sort of enterprise—but using the best hard-core rejuvenation therapies.

Popov's eventual disenchantment with Akers put an end to the idea, however. When Popov resigned in 1962, he took with him his entire crew of Balkan medicos. Akers' Italian group, however, stayed with the hair magnate until the bitter end.

Could the rejuvenation farm really have worked?

Popov thinks so.

With proper selection of clients (weeding out the basically in-firm) so as to treat only the rejuvenable, Popov estimates that at least three-fourths could be made to feel years younger.

What can one do to protect one's hair, then—if Akers and his ilk are not the answer?

"Look, let's not start giving people psychoses. All you have to do is start thinking that you're going to lose your hair and you'll start losing it. If I start telling you anecdotes about bald people, you'll laugh your head off." Somewhat reluctantly, Popov offered the following advice for men with hair problems. It should be noted that many American dermatologists (such as Manhattan's Norman Orentreich) do not view the problem as Popov does.

"We lose our hair because we use bad shampoos," says Popov. "If every male before puberty were given a good shampoo you'd cut the number of bald people to about one in twenty or one in thirty.

"But . . . *every* shampoo on the market is a *bad* shampoo. They are all based on chemical detergents. Before, they were based on soap (catastrophic for the hair because you change a basically acid condition into an alkali). The answer is biological detergents. But they're expensive. If I told you what they were, [my clients] would drop me. The shampoo you buy doesn't cost more than ten cents to make. Before you leave, I'll give you a bottle of shampoo, which you cannot buy and which I cannot sell to you. I'll give it to you . . . to show that you *can* make a good shampoo. But it costs me a dollar to make it. I make it for my personal use, for my friends and for my children. [I used up the bottle he gave me. Though it was small (8 oz.) it lasted several months, and was unquestionably the best I've ever used. It kept dandruff away, and my hair was soft and shining.]

"It is made of biological detergents, three or four of them, which clean, which foam, and [are combined] with tensioactives and antiseptics which are not harmful.

"Egg shampoos are definitely good. But, unfortunately, they are usually associated with soaps or chemical detergents which kill the benefit of the egg.

"If you think there is any real difference between the stuff you normally wash your hair with and what you wash your car with, you're wrong. They're exactly the same except that the one is cheap and the other is expensive and has a little perfume and natural essences.

"A good dandruff shampoo would contain .20 percent of G11 and, let's say, .10 percent of G4. Put them into any shampoo and you will get good results. But [it's better] if you put them into a biological shampoo."

He counsels hair brushing.

"It's good," he said, "if you have the right brushes. The wrong brush is a split brush. You tell by using a magnifying glass. If the ends are not split, you can use the brush. For once I am for the synthetic product rather than the natural. Nylon brushes are excellent. Clean them with any detergent in tepid water."

Scalp massage is also good, he says.

"I strongly advise massage. But don't rub the hair. Just put your fingers down on the scalp and move the scalp around to circulate the blood."

With his third tumbler of Pernod, and the lighting of his fourteenth Gauloise, Popov began to talk about himself.

"I am a very old man, actually. With old men, as with cars, you don't ask about the year the car came out. You ask how many miles. And, my God, my life . . . the mileage has been terrific!"

During the war, Popov was parachuted into enemy territory eleven times. At forty-seven he suffered an infarctus. The wear and tear of battle and his weak heart have made deep inroads into his physique. Still, Popov lives a life that scrupulously omits none of its wear-and-tear pleasures.

"I smoke sixty cigarettes a day. I drink as much red wine and pastis as I wish. I'm doing everything that shouldn't be done in a cardiac condition—*because I know that I can keep my body regenerated.*"

When he undergoes his periodic special "cures," however, Popov avoids excess.

"I never go to bed later than ten. I have a regular siesta. I get up at four-thirty A.M. I always introduce a live element into my diet. I eat vegetables right from the garden . . . lots of oysters . . . radishes . . . I eat raw meat . . . I adore drinking blood. . . . . It's a very bad habit. I drink it like I would milk. I put a little salt and pepper on top of it. I did it regularly in Paris when I'd go out to collect fresh organs for my experiments. I make my children drink milk fresh from the cow."

Popov regards man's "natural" aging as premature and unnecessary.

"I think that man, as an animal, is getting old too soon . . . and for too long a time. Look at the animals in a natural state. The older they are, the stronger they are. Then they die. And we spend half of our lives senile, impotent. It's due to bad nutrition, an abnormal way of living, the stress under which we live.

"The animal eats living grass, or he kills and eats the live body of his victim. Even if he eats a putrid body—there is nothing more 'alive' than a cadaver, do you understand?"

It wasn't until I formed a mental picture of a deceased, maggoty animal that I understood what he was driving at. He laughed.

"We humans, though, are cooking, sterilizing, pasteurizing, disinfecting everything we come in contact with. You saw my two children. There is no mercurochrome or iodine in this house. I let them fall, become infected. It's a lesson for you Americans. In the hospital, where European patients would stay two or three days, Americans would stay ten times as long. Their bodies would worsen because they haven't been *used*."

In attempting to drum up a large rejuvenation clientele, most practitioners merely reveal the emptiness of their pretensions and the commercial nature of their enterprise, Popov says.

"I know all of my colleagues' work. *Nine-tenths is just bluff, bluff, bluff*. But [they] do get results. You cannot, however, concentrate on just one method. I once thought that the embryo would solve the problem. The embryo is not going to solve *any* problem."

Medicine, Popov feels, is necessarily an individual matter. A pair of twins suffering from the same disease have to be treated differently. Ultimately, he asserts, the culprits are the scientists who allow pharmaceutical firms to publish their work in its experimental stages.

"How much nonsense have I spoken and written in my life? I found out I didn't have the right to trust myself. All the books I read when I was studying medicine are now a laughing matter . . . nonsense called established truths . . . which change from day to day. I am sorry for every line I have written and published."

Nothing, he says, can replace the physician's carefully considered prescription for each patient.

"In the old days, when a child was sick, the doctor gave him the best medicine for what ailed him. Today they don't do it. They give him what is commercially available. . . . Something good for ten thousand people cannot be good for one man—except perhaps for antibiotics or aspirin. Nothing else."

In rejuvenation therapy, the physician is plagued by rich patients with superficial complaints—usually psychogenic.

"I don't want to be known as a rejuvenator. I don't want Rolls-Royces and Packards coming with a lot of impossible characters, because I know I'd lose my [temper]. In my forties I accepted them . . . I bound up the titties and cocks [by improving the general condition of the body through cell therapy] . . . but today I would kick them out."

Ideally, he believes, a rejuvenationist should handle no more than a half dozen senescent patients—rigorously checking up on each treatment. When wholesale rejuvenation begins, the youth doctor begins to cheat. Because of the lure of profit, he says, cell therapists, for instance, almost inevitably wind up compromising their integrity. "If you do it honestly . . . you go bankrupt," he says.

"I am honest. Perfectly dishonest in cosmetics. Because I accept publicity—although not in my name—and knowing perfectly well that it's false. I tell them the truth. They do what they want. But when it comes to medicine there is no money which could buy me. You could offer me a hundred thousand dollars to treat somebody, but if I knew I couldn't do anything for him, I wouldn't treat him."

Popov has been hindered in his research by a lack of funds. The small plowed patch of ground in front of his house, the handful of chickens and rabbits in homemade coops and hutches are his laboratory. Given the means, he would explore CT by trying to discover precisely which benefits the cells yield to their human recipients. This would entail correlating the data gathered by the reputable cell therapists (he thinks the French are the best —next to Niehans) and doing extensive double-blind control studies.

He would also check out sulfadiazine, which his colleague A. Ravina of Paris has boldly labeled "a veritable process of rejuvenation"—in no less an esteemed medical organ than the *Presse*

Médicale (June 19, 1965). Ravina claims to have significantly lengthened the lives of animals, and obtained amazingly good results on his human patients by giving them sulfadiazine in conjunction with B vitamins, calcium pantothenate, and magnesium ascorbate. In his eight years of experiments, Ravina has noted radical improvements in patients' hearing, vision, general activity, genital function, tissue condition, and circulation. He views sulfadiazine not only as a rejuvenating agent but as a prophylactic "in the prevention and retardation of aging."

As Popov began to speak of the possibilities of rejuvenation therapy, the *mea culpa* attitude disappeared. Suddenly he became positive and enthusiastic. He began to explain a new—and yet at the same time a very old—rejuvenation idea: regeneration through perfumes.

Perfumes?

"I consider that the future belongs to a combination of biological and aromatic [which are also biological] substances. Chemists analyze everything. They know exactly what perfumes consist of. But only in its *natural* form does it have an effect. With chemistry, the results are never constant, and highly doubtful. The trouble with natural products is that they are expensive and industry cannot make money on them."

If anything is going to revolutionize the field of rejuvenation in the next few years, says Popov, it's going to be aromatics (especially stimulant and tranquilizing aromatics). Alone, they have incredible properties. Used in conjunction with other treatments they often possess a powerful synergism, greatly accelerating and augmenting the regular beneficial effects. Moreover, their application is utterly simple. With aromatics, rejuvenation can be performed at home in the bathtub or bottled in an aftershave lotion. They are easily preserved, easily dispensed, and have a constant quality—unlike, say, cell therapy.

Aromatics are different essences extracted from flowers, plants, and animals. Some smell good; others smell bad. They were the backbone of Egyptian medicine, which had classified—albeit very capriciously—some seven hundred different substances. Basically, Popov has taken over where the 65-foot-long Therapeutic Papyrus of Thebes (1552 B.C.) leaves off, integrating and refining primitive speculation with his knowledge of modern biochemistry and testing methods. While conducting research for the French perfume magnate Antoine Chiris five years ago, Popov began to adumbrate a monumental chart of the properties of four hundred of the ten thousand common aromatics. Each substance is situated on a point within an eight-spoked wheel that looks something like this:

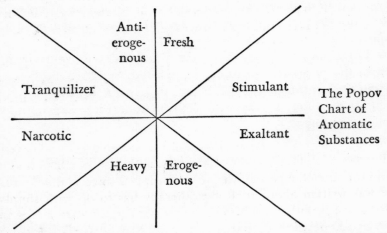

The spokes represent polar opposites in effect of aromatics upon the organism. The names of the particular substances are sprinkled all over the chart—each one tested on a minimum of one hundred patients in French hospitals, according to Popov. "We checked the experiments, made controls in hospitals, sent out questionnaires," he says. The controlled clinical trials have given him an estimation of proper dosages and a certain precision as to the effects of each aromatic, alone and in combination with other aromatics and with other rejuvenation therapies. Once he inspected a young female patient who had been given aromatotherapy in a Grasse hospital. She was obviously in bad shape.

"You have committed a major error," he told the attending physician.

"No, I haven't," insisted the doctor.

When the records were brought out, Popov was proved correct. The girl had been given ten times the aromatic substance prescribed for her.

"I could tell," says Popov, "because I saw the physiological effect that the perfume had had on her."

Popov rules out completely the possibility of synthesizing aromatics. "Don't talk to me about synthetics. I use them very often. But in biology there is one rule. Two and two make anything but four. Never try to compete with the good God. I found that out with my microscope. There is a point at which you have to stop. Each cell of our body is a laboratory a thousand times more clever and powerful than all the laboratories on earth created by human beings. This is fantastic knowledge. There is always the right response."

There are three basic ways of applying aromatic mixtures:

"The first is by direct absorption into the body. If you rub it into the body, the volatile elements get into the blood circulation and come into contact with the central nervous elements to produce a special effect.

"Another method is inhalation, and the same effect is achieved.

"The third method is reflexotherapy. It was much talked about during the interwar period. But it was dropped since so much nonsense was written about it. Reflexotherapy has to do with simply smelling the aromatics. Through action of certain extremities of the sympathetic nervous system they can have a direct effect on the brain. It is now being studied in the Paris Medical School. They are burning certain parts of the nasal mucosis and getting effects elsewhere in the body. But this is too brutal and not natural. They cured many illnesses, including certain cases of paralysis. They affected hormonal disturbances."

In testing reflexotherapy, researchers found that the same results could not have been accomplished by absorption of the aromatics into the bloodstream—the reaction occurred too quickly. It was decidedly a *nervous* impulse.

Popov bemoans the increasing American financial control of the French perfume industry, since synthetics are now being substituted wherever possible for natural essences. And while the fragrances give similar olfactory effects, the physiological effects are not the same.

Natural aromatics, believes Popov, could revolutionize sleep-induction techniques.

"I can put anybody to sleep without harmful effects, just using aromatics. I would use bergamot [an Italian citrus oil], for example; some neroli [an orange-blossom oil]; geraniol [an alcohol found in oils of flowers such as rose, geranium, sassafras, and lavender]; the whole group of roses. They can be given in a bath."

To overcome frigidity in a woman, Popov would give erogenous baths. Most of the erogens come from animal extracts. He would use sterax (an opium derivative), civet, musk, or jasmine.

"Roses and jasmine, they are fantastic! Jasmine is used in all modern perfumes. It is highly erogenous. Both the man and the woman who smell it are aroused by it."

While many of the aromatics have easily predictable properties, Popov emphasizes that each individual's needs differ from another's.

"I am now using aromatics on my heart. I make combinations. I know, for example, that *eau de citronnelle* [a fragrant Ceylon grass extract used as bug repellant] is good for me. But it would be bad for somebody else."

His eyes had grown heavy, and the lids began to blink more frequently, washing away the sting from his cigarette smoke. Remembering that I had robbed him of his afternoon siesta, I thanked him and began to wrap up my tape recorder and cameras.

"Don't forget, though," he said, "rejuvenation is still only an art. It is not yet a *métier* [trade]."

Popov constantly emphasizes the preeminent place of the sensitive physician in rejuvenation. It is he, the man, the doctor, who rejuvenates. No drug, no process, no known nostrum can do the job. It is the physician who, sensing the psychophysical needs of each individual patient, brings new youthfulness to the senescent, he says. An art, indeed. And until such time as science discovers a basic biochemical aging-reversing agent, the small progress that can presently be achieved in this area will depend greatly on the unorthodox work of such "perfectly dishonest"—but compellingly candid and apparently clinically scrupulous—artists as Ivan Popov.

CHAPTER TEN

Hurricane over Procaine

Next to Professor Niehan's diced sheep cells, a clear, transparent Rumanian-born liquid called Gerovital H3 (or just Gerovital or H3 alone) is the most coveted youthefier in Europe today.

The remarkable revitalization of Nikita S. Khrushchev midway during his chairmanship of the Soviet Communist Party's Central Committee was rumored by the press to be due to Gerovital injections.

Field Marshal Bernard Montgomery's enduring verve has been cited as a prime example of the shots' efficacy.

The late Henry Agard Wallace, former Vice-President of the United States, was given a Gerovital mutant called Impletol (containing procaine and caffeine) in a desperate, but vain, attempt to stem a mysterious wasting nerve disease.

In his old age the late Konrad Adenauer took both cell and Gerovital therapy—both of which, he was convinced, hugely revivified his senescent tissues.

Despite some rather exciting claims made for Gerovital by its creator, professor and doctor of medicine Ana Aslan, the FDA has outlawed its importation into the United States—except for a brief experimental fling in the late 1950's which, apparently, didn't pan out.

Gerovital, according to Dr. Aslan, chief of the Bucharest Geriatric Institute, has cured such varied complaints of senescence as arthritis, arteriosclerosis, eczema, wrinkled skin, baldness, gray hair, angina pectoris, asthenia, loss of appetite, heart disease, deafness, neuritis, neuralgia, Parkinson's Disease, a host of psychic disorders, and that classic embarrassment of the senile male—impotence.

A group of one hundred and eleven patients controlled by Madame Aslan over the past fifteen years has exceeded expected life-spans by about 30 percent—and with general good humor and optimism. The publicity accorded this and other rejuvenation experiments on twenty thousand patients throughout Rumania has attracted a steady stream of customers from both sides of the Iron Curtain.

Her usual geriatric course (for patients past sixty) consists of three injections weekly for four weeks, followed by a ten- or twelve-day hiatus, then repetition of the cycle. The prophylactic treatment (for healthy patients between thirty-five and sixty) is the same, except that the hiatus is usually two months.

Unlike CT, Gerovital therapy is no one- or two-shot affair. It is a lifetime romance with a syringe. "You can't," warns Madame Aslan, "stay away from it for one or two years without slipping backwards."

Gerovital began as simple procaine (pro—instead of; caine—short for cocaine), which is the generic term for the dentist's anesthetic, Novocain. But it has grown up since. She experimented with procaine for three years before deciding that it was an excellent drug which, at the very least, could do no harm.

She discovered the rejuvenation effect of procaine at the Imisoara Faculty of Medicine in Transylvania. On April 15, 1949, she inquired of the staff if it had a rheumatism patient who wouldn't mind trying a new treatment. A twenty-year-old medical student, bedridden for weeks, volunteered, told her to go ahead. His right leg was locked stiff at the knee, totally immobile.

She injected 10 cc of procaine into his right femoral artery. Almost immediately the youth burst into hysterical laughter. The pain had vanished. Moreover, he could bend his knee. Once, twice, three times. The injections continued and within days he left the hospital.

"I saw," says Aslan, "that the idea had further application."

She waited for her fiftieth successful procaine case before publishing her ideas. Even at that, it may have been too soon—or rather too *late*, depending on how you look at it. Since 1930, well over one hundred papers had been written on similar results of procaine therapy by oral, intramuscular, and intravenous application. She had read none of them. The authors, like Aslan, generally conceded that procaine, in small dosages, exerted a stimulating effect upon the central nervous system. Her embarrassment was great when her critics accused her of plagiarism.

When she read in a French medical journal that, in very rare cases, an alkaline procaine solution could cause complications, she immediately had a pharmacist make up a buffered (more acid) procaine solution. "And that," says Aslan, "is how Gerovital got its start."

With this new mixture, her purported results were better than anyone had ever seen with ordinary procaine. Many physicians staunchly refused to accept them as valid. Their negative reaction was buttressed by the complete inability of reputable researchers to duplicate her results. They, however, were using ordinary procaine for their experiments (since she had not revealed the formula). Was there a significant difference?

While Madame Aslan was not permitted to reveal the exact process for manufacturing Gerovital (it belonged officially to the state factory), she *had* revealed that it was a buffered solution between pH3.4 and pH4. Since that was all she had told her own pharmacist, she assumed that any clever chemist easily could put together a similar solution with those data.

It was *not* enough, however. To quell the gargantuan uproar against this "Faust in skirts," she finally revealed the exact contents of her Gerovital: procaine 2 percent; benzoic acid 0.12 percent; potassium metadisulphite 0.10 percent (an important element, since it allegedly "potentiates," or increases, the action of the procaine). Yet, even the formula, she later confessed, might not be enough to reproduce the Gerovital magic.

"It's also very important," she says, "what you do first and what you do after that." So the exact process to this day remains a factory secret.

Madame Aslan is remarkably casual in explaining the difference between her solution and procaine. She uses, in conversation, the terms Novocain, procaine, H3, and Gerovital interchangeably. She has even compared Gerovital's popularity to that of a best-selling brand of aspirin.

"Well," she said, "everybody asks for Bayer aspirin, don't they?"

"No," she was told, "not everybody. Only those who don't know that all aspirin are alike."

Yet, at times, she appears to contradict herself, saying, "I am convinced that one must use only this product."

The AMA, for one, adamantly insists that there is no real difference. In the AMA publication *Today's Health* author Ralph Lee Smith states in an article entitled "A Phony Fountain of Youth": "H-3 . . . is procaine, better known to the public as the universally-used local anesthetic, Novocain. H-3 is simply—Novocain."

This is not true. Experiments by independent researchers using Gerovital and American procaine have proven that there is a substantial difference, therapeutically as well as chemically, and that Gerovital is the better rejuvenating agent. Biochemists at the University of Chicago Medical School compared the two on a group of patients. The Rumanian elixir significantly improved lung and nerve function and boosted the patients' psychological and social dispositions. The regular procaine did little good.

Other studies have been less encouraging to Madame Aslan. The negative tests are constantly cited by the AMA and the BMA to prove that Gerovital is a hoax, no better than a sugar pill—and that Madame Aslan is a fraud. Of these experimental failures, Madame Aslan says tersely, "Treatment was not applied according to our method nor with our drug."

One reason for her much-acclaimed success in treating oldsters in the "Home" section of her Bucharest Geriatric Institute may be the fact that many of them, for the first time in their lives, are being cared for. Her critics suggest that perhaps the *care* alone, and *not* the Gerovital, is responsible for her glowing reports. Dr. A. N. G. Clark, consultant physician to the Geriatric Unit of Stoke-on-Trent Hospital, England, notes: "It is commonplace in geriatric practice to see the isolated or neglected patient improve greatly with hospital admission or day hospital attendance. This category of patient also becomes extremely susceptible to suggestion in response to interest in their progress and improvement."

A remarkable faculty of Madame Aslan's drug is its purported ability to return hair to its natural color. In 90 percent of her younger patients, and in 50 percent of her patients over sixty, she claims to have witnessed repigmentation take place. This is a bold claim for any rejuvenationist, since hair color is a visible, easily observed phenomenon. Either it's there or it isn't.

As she recounted her success in repigmentation one day in Vienna, I looked at her closely. She did seem far perkier, more active than her age—sixty-nine—would indicate. And she was far from unattractive. I looked at her brown curls. Well done. But not one white hair among them. Was this an example of Gerovital's wonder-working?

I was extremely skeptical.

"But *your* hair is colored by a chemical product, isn't it?" I asked.

The dry statistician suddenly became a coy woman.

"I don't talk about myself," she said evasively.

Herself, however, is the very crux of the matter. One has little more than her word to go on that procaine recolors hair or rejuvenates the body. If her reports are accurate, then she has produced a remarkable drug—certainly something that deserves serious exploration. If she is fibbing, she is just another youth-doctor-enthusiast-opportunist.

Madame Aslan has made little headway even in Rumania beyond institutions that she controls directly. Many Rumanian medical centers won't touch Gerovital, and despite her highly placed guardian angels, she frequently has come under fire from the Party for her "false theories." Several times her passport has been taken away from her, preventing her from attending international congresses overseas. In November, 1959, during a session of the Rumanian Academy of Medicine, a Professor Dr. Lupu ordered her to submit her formula to "Centrofarm" (Direction of Pharmacies) so that it could be mass-produced and tested against senescence by others. This she did. But when Lupu tried to mount a formal censure motion against her and Dr. Milcu, an Institute co-director, the Academy members rallied to her defense.

That same week things got worse. She was denounced by the Party for "sheltering reactionaries in the 'Home' section of the Geriatric Institute instead of letting them 'die in the streets.' " One doctor charged that she had mollycoddled landowners, former generals, and bourgeois parasites such as Miss Cantemir (former Lady of the Court to Queen Mary) and let them "live off the sweat of the working class."

So ferocious and so insistent were the attacks that she was compelled to confess her "errors." Henceforth, she promised, she would publicly reveal the names of all Institute patients. But when neither she nor Milcu showed up for work during the next few days, gossip in medical circles had it that both were finished.

Nonetheless, within a week or so, she was back at the old stand. In a few months her passport was returned, and ever since she has traveled widely abroad. Despite her bourgeois-cosmopolitan cultural tastes (German classical music, Van Gogh, Venice excursions, Paris junkets), she has told intimates that she lives in Bucharest because the spring is "more pleasant there than anywhere else." Her personal habits are fastidious. She smokes and drinks moderately; she avoids all sweets—which accelerate aging, she believes—but drinks large amounts of coffee. Although she is unmarried, her name has been linked romantically with a former diplomat, Duiliu Zamfirescu.

Some of her work sounds like sheer fantasy. Ironically, even before she has presented solidly documented double-blind control studies of Gerovital's effectiveness against aging, she has already embarked on rat studies to see if Gerovital-induced traits can be inherited by the next generation. "We are trying," she says, "to see if we can transmit this acquired resistance in the organism to descendants. You can talk about theory all day long. I want to see for myself if the descendants of those who take the treatment are going to live longer."

How Gerovital might influence the genes she neglects to explain.

One of her protectors within the political Establishment has been none other than Constantine I. Parhon, the now senile former President (1948-1952) of the Grand General Assembly of the Rumanian People's Republic. Had it not been for Parhon, the name Ana Aslan might never have echoed beyond the Carpathian Mountains. It was Parhon who commissioned her to direct aging research at his Endocrinological Institute.

Parhon himself was once regarded as a preeminent authority on several areas of medicine: biochemistry, general pathology, endocrinology, and geriatrics. Shortly after his presidential inauguration, he appointed Ana Aslan to head up Rumanian geriatrics at her present Institute.

At first she found it profoundly unpleasant. She was distressed by the stench of the unwashed, the hopelessly infirm, the wretched old people. She wondered why she had ever conducted a three-day hunger strike in her teens to force her family to let her study medicine.

But she knuckled down and worked hard. In a short time, the old people's home turned into something more akin to the scientific institute she had always dreamed of running. Today she has a gleaming laboratory, all the equipment she needs for research, generous funding for her projects. What turned out to be most important of all for her were the very oldsters that had so depressed her in the beginning. They have provided her with a great opportunity to test her nostrum on human patients over several years. Few youth doctors have had such an advantage.

Several visitors to the Institute agree that her patients are in remarkably good shape. In addition to the procaine treatment, she has given them regular exercise, careful diets, intellectual or manual labor wherever possible, and entertainment. It is hard to know to what degree procaine has kept them vigorous.

Her oldest patient was one hundred and six upon arrival at the Institute. According to the life expectancy tables, he could count on one more year. Yet, after taking Gerovital injections according to Aslan's scheme, he lived for another seven years.

Her most celebrated success was the "rejuvenation" of an Armenian docker named Parsch Margosian. He entered the Aslan clinic in what appeared to be a terminal stage of senility—mute, depressed, unable to fix his mind on anything, struck by a total incapacity to remember anything that had happened in the recent or distant past, and a hopeless cripple. After five years of procaine therapy, the old man appeared alert, vigorous, mobile, completely resuscitated.When a photograph of the rejuvenated Parsch appeared in a Soviet newspaper, his daughter recognized him, and brought Madame Aslan documents attesting to his age of one hundred and nine.

It was this case, widely publicized in the Eastern Bloc, that probably persuaded the USSR's ebullient then-Premier Nikita S. Khrushchev to have a whirl with procaine injections in 1959. It is not known, however, whether he continues the treatment today.

The procaine ampules are available in the Soviet Union, but, according to Soviet geriatricians, the therapy has not caught on generally with Russians.

A German physician, Fritz Wiedemann, of Ambach am Starnberger See, has treated over six hundred patients with KH3, an oral version of the Aslan formula. Of them some ninety have had no other therapy but the KH3. His results have been "stunning," he reports.

Wiedemann states that benefits from KH3 (which is potentiated with hematoporphyrin) sometimes occur with great rapidity. One sixty-seven-year-old female patient given to crying jags, suffering from arthritis and a total inability to work, was back on the job within one week of KH3 therapy. Within three months after beginning the treatment, her swollen hands became thin again and her arthritis pains disappeared. Two months later her hair regained its former color and began to grow in where it had fallen out. To top it all, in her sixty-eighth year, the woman's wisdom teeth appeared, "proving how extensive regeneration had occurred in her case," says Wiedemann.

The KH3 oral version of Gerovital seems to be a highly salable commodity in Europe, since it obviates the need for frequent, expensive visits to the doctor.

How Gerovital really works is a bit of a puzzle—even to Ana Aslan. "It all happens," she declares, "as though it were stimulating life in its vegetative form at the level of the cell vitality it stimulates."

Something in the product seems to react directly upon the central nervous system—before it breaks down into para-aminobenzoic acid (PABA), which is the precursor of folic acid (a B2 complex factor), and diethylaminoethanol (DEAE), a precursor of acetylcholine, which assists in the transmission of nerve impulses. When PABA and DEAE are injected separately into the organism, the rejuvenating effects of the whole procaine do not occur.

Parhon, her mentor, is of the opinion that a vitamin reaction is involved. It was he, in fact, who appended the H3 (for "Vitamin" H3) to Aslan's term Gerovital.

How firmly entrenched is Madame Aslan at her prestigious geriatric institute? The question is interesting because her influence upon the political hierarchy will greatly determine whether she will be able to continue her experiments on a longitudinal, or long-term, basis—and eventually convince the Western World that she actually wields a powerful weapon in the battle against old age, as she claims.

Personally, she is a delightful, charming, easygoing woman. This is always an asset. Another factor in her favor is the earning power of her Gerovital, which is sold all over the Eastern Bloc and which brings in hard currency through licensing agreements with West Germany, Belgium, Switzerland, and Mexico.

The de-Sovietization of Rumania conceivably could cause trouble for her. Immediately after World War II, rumors spread among Rumanians that the Soviet occupiers had pillaged Aslan's rejuvenation secrets, and it was thanks only to her craftiness that she was spared. These rumors, however, seem without foundation, for her prestige and power were highest during the reign of the avidly pro-Soviet Parhon.

When the membership of the National Academy of Medicine was recently reorganized, the name Ana Aslan failed to appear on the roster. This ouster is viewed by some as a sign of disfavor in high places.

The Aslan phenomenon has not gone unnoticed abroad. Scores of doctors appear to be only too happy to leave less stimulating (and less remunerative) practices for procaine therapy.

Not all of the foreign procaine practitioners use the *echt* Gerovital. At last count, there were over one hundred imitation procaine products being sold for rejuvenation purposes outside of Rumania.

Because of federal prohibition on importing Gerovital and the AMA's inevitable scowl whenever the subject is raised, there are few procaine therapists in the United States. A handful of doctors give injections to demanding patients—using drugs smuggled in from Switzerland or Mexico.

Curiously, many medical "outsiders" won't touch procaine. Old-time youth doctor Else K. LaRoe believes there may be *something* to procaine, but she doesn't know just what it is. Dr. Wolfgang Goetze-Claren thinks procaine may have some application for patients with "the jitters"—as a kind of shock treatment for the peripheral ganglia. But he by far prefers his own version of cell therapy plus RNA injections, which he calls genetic therapy.

There is at least one American-based MD who boasts openly of a procaine clientele. He is seventy-eight-year-old Albert C. J. Simard, a testy, loquacious expatriate Frenchman who commands the Free French fort on Manhattan Island with one hand, and carries the gospel according to Comrade Aslan with the other.

Simard has about fifty patients who receive Gerovital therapy regularly. He seems to enjoy inveighing against the oppressive reactionary record of orthodox medical groups, despite his membership in the AMA, the New York County Medical Society, the New York Academy of Sciences, the American Geriatrics Society, and the New York State Medical Association.

With solemn reverence, fingering his lapel rosette of the Légion d'Honneur, he speaks of those martyred by the Establishment (several of whom he worked with in Paris at the Institut Pasteur). They include: cell therapist Paul Niehans ("whom they drag in the mud"); polio vaccine creator Jonas Salk ("those Boston bastards held up the vaccine but . . . finally had to eat crow"); Raymond Gaston ("whose remarkable discovery of the antidiphtheria toxin was welcomed at Pasteur by an explosion of incredible rage by the head of the diphtheria service"); Felix d'Herelle ("discoverer of ultra-viruses, who was immediately dismissed from the Institut Pasteur); and Ana Aslan ("treated like a charlatan, a liar, a personal publicity seeker").

Has he himself ever been so scourged?

"Well," he says, "I've never met anybody who said to my face: 'Monsieur, you are a charlatan and a thief.' However, I'm sure it's not for lack of somebody's wanting to say it.

"When two astronomists," says Simard, "quibble over the location of a star of the nth magnitude, nobody gives a good goddam. But what's horrid in [the medical] profession is that when doctors argue over something which is good, they fill hospital beds and cemetery graves."

Simard was attracted to procaine, he says, partly out of chauvinism (since it was a Frenchman, René Leriche, who pioneered experiments in Western Europe), and partly because during a trip to Bucharest in 1956 he was "struck by Ana Aslan's honesty." Upon his return from Rumania, he applied to the FDA for authorization to import the genuine Gerovital H3. His request, he says, was granted "because of my titles." *

Fortunately, he says, he was able to hoard a vast supply of the drug—which he dips into for his senescent clientele.

Would he reveal how much he had brought into the country?

"No. I wasn't born yesterday."

Simard has been his own guinea pig, and, in his opinion, a successful one. He has taken Gerovital as prescribed by Aslan over the past ten years and offers the following testimonial:

"I don't think I look my age, and I'm sure I don't act like others my age. I fish. I hunt. I ski. I make love twice a week. I feel extremely well. I work a lot. The more I follow this technique, the more stupefied I am at the results—not only physically, but mentally and emotionally."

His approach, however, sometimes departs from Madame Aslan's usual *ordonnance*. "In some cases," he says, "I give patients three injections weekly—but without the customary pause after each series of twelve." He stops the treatments "only when I go salmon fishing during the summer."

His Gerovital treatment does not seem to help such conditions as disseminated arteriosclerosis or Parkinson's Disease. On the other hand, he claims to be able to cure some 80 percent of his schizoid patients, and he says he has "witnessed extraordinary modifications of character—with depressed patients, for example."

Simard once rid a shell-shocked Guadalcanal Marine veteran of both a buzzing in his ears and a scalp eczema that had made him bald. The leatherneck, says Simard, was prepared to commit suicide if he wasn't cured soon. He had practically abandoned all hope after vainly consulting several specialists. After Gerovital injections the buzzing and eczema disappeared simultaneously. The hair, unfortunately, never grew back—but the Marine was able to face life again.

Dr. Herman Goodman, of New York's Upper East Side, believes

* Which include: former chief of the Endocrinology Department and Director of the Metabolic Clinic, Columbus Hospital of New York City; former medical director of Air France; Medical Counsellor of the French Consulate-General in New York; Medical Editor of *France-Amérique* (a French newspaper in the United States); former chief laboratory associate at the Institut Pasteur; founder of France Forever, the U.S. Free French Movement; Secretary General of the Society for the Prevention of World War III; former president of the Society for the Defense of the Human Person, Commander of the French National Order of the Légion d'Honneur.

that, for some strange reason, Gerovital works well in Europe, but does not work so well in the United States. Goodman, who visited the "Home" section of Aslan's Institute several times over a period of five years, was very impressed with her treatment. The proof of its efficacy, he says, is the fact that a Gerovital-treated group suffered one-fifth the usual incidence of influenza during a Rumanian epidemic several years back.

Dr. Harry Benjamin, who has known many of the great youth doctors personally and tried out their therapies on his own patients, thinks that procaine may work synergistically with vitamins and hormones, possibly by producing a vasodilatory effect.

Unfortunately, even after twenty years of intensive research, there is little agreement—even among therapists—as to what this drug can do for the aging patient. Madame Aslan's research, as she describes it, has persuaded few Western geriatricians that Gerovital holds any promise whatsoever.

This, it should be said, is not a definitive evaluation, or even a fair one, by any means.

Professional medical associations are not tremendously different from a flock of sheep. Both tend to fear whatever is new, strange, loud, or moving. The scientific community frequently seems beset by prejudices, personal idiosyncrasies, and bias against novel clinical measures. In the wilderness of research into the aging problem, there are few compasses. Each researcher must feel a professional frustration at not being able to come to grips with the elusive essentials of this cosmic problem. All this tends to color judgment. Madame Aslan may be quite right—and her detractors may be quite wrong.

But Madame Aslan, unlike other workers in rejuvenation, has held office within her country's Establishment for two decades. She is comfortably fed and housed. Her work is generously subsidized by the state. If Gerovital is what she says it is, she is in a uniquely fortuitous position to let the world know about it. If she fails to communicate the message, she has only herself—or her pet drug— to blame.

CHAPTER ELEVEN

The Skinners

When one talks about insecurity today, we're talking about 100 per cent of the population. I've yet to see anybody, either in my profession, among my friends, or among my patients who does not have a sense of insecurity. So one cannot talk about insecurity.
DR. ALBERT BEST (*Los Angeles plastic surgeon*)

She was a pretty, sensitive, ambitious $75-a-week contract player with one of the big Hollywood studios—and getting nowhere fast. She was trying hard to make good. Too hard. She lacked self-confidence. She knew something was missing, but she couldn't put her finger on it.

Her awakening was a shattering experience. One night at a party, she overheard herself referred to as "a chinless wonder." She brooded for days. Finally, she told her troubles to a friend, who gave her the name of a dermatologist, who, in turn, recommended her to one of Hollywood's top plastic surgeons.

"I know I'm no actress," she told the specialist. "And with this chin of mine the star gets the good lighting. If the camera starts to catch me in profile, I forget the three words they told me to say."

The plastic surgeon was sympathetic. He told her that her micrognathic mandible could be corrected with a simple fifteen-minute operation involving the insertion of a small piece of bone under her chin. The scar would be barely noticeable. She agreed to the procedure.

"I don't want anybody to know about this until I get a good picture under my belt," she cautioned the surgeon. "They could cancel my contract."

The operation went smoothly, and the actress, an unknown who had adopted the name Marilyn Monroe, had herself a brand-new chin.

Five days later, a top Hollywood director called to see if she would try out for a picture. Quaking, Miss Monroe told him she couldn't make it right away—since she'd fallen and "cut her chin."

A week later, however, her surgeon gave her the green light to take the test. Fortunately, the part was still up for grabs. The whole studio, from the producer to the cameramen, turned out for her test. With the confidence her new chin gave her, she performed smoothly and walked away with the part.

After the test, the producer leaned toward Miss Monroe, chucked her under the chin, and observed knowingly: "Honey, you should have cut your chin two years ago."

The picture turned out to be a box-office smash, and Marilyn Monroe overnight achieved deification as America's reigning sex goddess, joining Bara, Harlow, and Garbo as the popular culture's ideal of female perfection.

Similar success stories glut the files of Hollywood and New York cosmetic rejuvenators. Their role in helping otherwise talented performers to overcome physical eccentricities and the assaults of time should not be underestimated.

"Practically all of the aging stars who look so good have had rejuvenation work done," a Hollywood plastic surgeon who has done more than his share of it confided to me recently. "Many of them lost work for a long time, finally decided to have plastic surgery, and then made a roaring comeback. But we don't dare mention their names."

I mentioned the name of a much-married actress whose silky-smooth face and coquettish, sexy allure have made her the darling of café society, top-rated nightclubs, and an occasional Hollywood film.

"She's had some work done, shall I put it that way?" replied one doctor. "She said she didn't, but she did."

The name of another much-suffering, silent-picture sex queen was brought up.

"She once began a lawsuit over a public mention of a facial change she had done years and years ago. There was a big spread in the newspapers about it. So everybody thought that she didn't have it done. But she *did*. Of course, there's nothing to prevent her from filing a suit."

How could he be so sure?

"Look," blurted the practitioner, embarrassed, "I can't . . . well, yes she *did* . . . but if you saw her early pictures and saw her now you'd know damn well. . . . She insists that she didn't have it done. I'll put it this way: I know her pretty well."

Quite often, celebrities who have gone in for one kind of rejuvenation eventually wind up trying them all. One of the most avid rejuvenates of all time has had her face lifted ten times, according to a prominent dermatologist. Such correctives are commonly regarded as "rejuvenation" treatments. To become more beautiful is to look younger. To look younger is to become more beautiful. The two concepts go together.

I approached this area of cosmetic improvement with a greater wariness than I had the other aspects of rejuvenation, but also with some hope. I began with little knowledge of the methods of rehabilitating leathery skin, which makes a person look and feel every day of his advancing age. My own mother's dermabrasion treatments fifteen years ago were a turning point in her life. Even she, I think, failed to realize how her long-standing acne scars had depressed her, causing her chronic melancholy and timidity. The moment she could look into a mirror and no longer see the shadowy scars she rejoined society. Today, confident and extroverted as she has never been before, she is constantly complimented on her lovely face—not greatly different from the face that first captivated her husband-to-be many years ago.

Unfortunately, not all stories of attempted aesthetic and cosmetic rejuvenation end so happily. Even the simplest revision of one's natural features by fully qualified practitioners entails the gravest risks. The professional societies are no guide to quality work but merely first-step referral services. A prospective patient would do well to do some shopping. Mistakes can be difficult, or impossible, to rectify. Nothing less than the best available work is good enough in this most delicate province of rejuvenation.

It is a seller's market, and fees are high. These youth doctors customarily reject one half of their applicants as poor psychological risks. The usual failing of the rejectee is expecting too much from a procedure that might only deepen his neuroses.

Rejecting poor risks is quite literally a life-and-death matter. A bad guess haunts the doctor afterward. Flesh excision and reworking the anatomy are secondary to managing the brutal anguish and psychosis that lurk at every step of the attempted rejuvenation. The most brilliant technical work, the most eminently satisfactory results, often fail to quell the disappointment of the mental misfit who believes that a $2,000 or $3,000 investment should yield nothing less than eternal life-of-the-party popularity and sovereign charm.

Even veteran plastic surgeons of the highest caliber who turn down a high percentage of applicants sometimes fail to spot the potential troublemaker. One such was a thirty-four-year-old New York chauffeur, Eleodore Moreno, who underwent a novel hair transplant operation by plastic surgeon Louis Feit three years ago. Although the transplant seemed successful by any dispassionate reckoning, Moreno was bent on do-it-yourself touches to "improve" his own appearance, such as making his own bandages. His insecurity brought him back time and again to his youth doctor's office, where he frequently arrived unannounced—and uninvited—for reassurance.

Eventually, when his marital problems became more than he could bear, Moreno decided that his coiffure was to blame.

At precisely 6:45 P.M. on March 26, 1968, the 240-pound patient stormed into Dr. Feit's office in a rage, seized a scalpel, and began to wreak what he probably considered poetic revenge on his imagined tormentor by slashing Feit twenty-five times across the face and neck. The incident's poetic justice in fact lay not with this insane "retribution," but in the deft reconstructive work that Feit's former pupils at Polyclinic Hospital performed to save him from permanent disfigurement.

Charity in plastic surgery is not unknown, but the fancy petit-point aesthetic work is considered a luxury and is never given away. While only the well-heeled can pay the fee without smarting, it is surprising how many middle- and low-income patients are willing to forego six months' salary for a morning or afternoon with a plastic surgeon.

"If I am doing a socialite or somebody who comes in with diamonds and emeralds or a movie star, I charge them more for several reasons," explained one Hollywood youth doctor. "For one thing, you're on the spot a lot more. It's more responsibility if you're going to do a top-ranking star than Mrs. Joe Doaks down the street. The star is going to be much more demanding. Another thing is that your reputation is on the line when you do one of them. And, people wouldn't come to you if you didn't charge them. They don't appreciate it."

Yet, the price tag is low if one considers that a good job can be an invaluable asset to the patient. On the other hand, a bad job, at any price, spells bankruptcy—emotional, professional, and financial. Most practitioners protect themselves by demanding advance payment and the patient's signature on a very tight legal release from responsibility should the work not pan out. This is usually termed a "consent to surgery."

The classical options for rejuvenating and beautifying the face, skin, and figure include: cosmetic products—makeup, the face-lift, dermabrasion (or surgical planing), chemosurgery, varieties of reconstructive surgery, and transplants (especially hair).

Often, rejuvenation-minded patients ignore the simplest—and, in many respects, the most effective—means of doing the job: sufficient sleep, regular exercise, fresh air, a little sunshine (with the accent on little), proper diet, cleanliness (avoidance of too many and the wrong kind of cosmetics is essential), and an optimistic attitude toward life.

It is appalling to see a woman muck up a naturally beautiful face. Yet American women especially fall victim to cosmetic advertising come-ons, and ceaselessly paint their way to facial homeliness. My conversations with dermatologists have reinforced my basic prejudice against cosmetics in the main—though I believe that women *do* need cold cream and emollients to keep their skin soft and smooth as they grow older.

Yet, if there is one single, valid notion within the rejuvenation mystique, it is probably that nature is the best healer. Whatever fights, sidesteps, or masks nature is probably not the best answer to an aging or cosmetic problem.

Fundamentally, cosmetics are a distinctly unnatural solution. Benefits from the finest cosmetics are fleeting and dubious at best. Yet their increasing popularity is nothing less than sensational. In 1964, total cosmetics sales in the United States reached a grand total of $2,551,900,000. The next year, volume was up to $2,898,-500,000, and by 1966 it registered $3,103,100,000. The 1967 figure promises to be higher by several hundred million dollars.

Cosmetics fads have been with us since the beginning of time. A Slav youth doctor recently created a frenzy when he gave one of Manhattan's *grandes dames* (who immediately became his protectress) a facial with Bulgarian rose petals. He quickly became the main topic of luncheon gossip at 21 and the Colony. When Polly Bergen recently put turtle oil into a cosmetic line, enthusiastic women from Seattle to Dubuque frantically searched for stores selling products containing this "latest" youthefying agent. The idea, presumably, comes from the turtle's renowned longevity— but, actually, the fad is as old as the oldest turtle around. In M. C. Phillips' 1934 exposé of cosmetics titled *Skin Deep,* the author spoke of turtle oil creams as having been "at the height of their popularity several years ago."

Placenta (see Chapter Nine) and hormone creams show some promise in propping up and smoothing out flabby, wrinkled faces— but it's too early to know precisely what they do. Beneficial results do not appear to outlast the evening of application, and doctors tend to denigrate legal over-the-counter hormone creams as too weak (restricted to 10,000 units of estrogens and 5 milligrams of progesterone per ounce of cream or lotion) to accomplish anything substantial. (However, Drs. Emile Klarmann and Samuel Peck of New York's Mount Sinai Hospital, among others, have shown that regular application of hormone creams on the face definitely fattens out tissues and smooths out wrinkles. It is known that women's skins deteriorate rapidly with the onset of the climacteric and its estrogenic dropoff.)

In addition, women have claimed to have experienced every conceivable benefit in a gamut of dubious powders, creams, liquids, soaps, astringents, masks, luminations, packs, salves, and lotions containing every alleged rejuvenating agent—animal gland extracts, carbons, oils, paints, greases, cornmeal, acids, muds, waters, perfumes, salts, gases, alcohols, glycerines, sulfurs, hexachlorophene, beeswax, lanolin, dyes, borax, lecithin, cholesterin, petrolatum, jellies, pollens, juices, seaweed, royal jelly, and what not.

Deftly, sparingly applied, cosmetics can enhance natural features. But just as the insensitive cook abuses her spice cabinet to compensate for indelicate food preparation, many women apply their makeup with ruinous abandon.

A handicap to the cosmetic chemist is the fact that he doesn't know with any certainty why skin ages. As a famous dermatologist once told a seminar on aging skin:

"We all know that an ancient person has paper-thin, shriveled, cracked, lifeless, spotted, yellowish, hairless, hanging skin—but we don't know how it got that way."

One guess as to how it got that way comes from Dr. John M. Knox of Baylor University's College of Medicine. At the 110th Annual Meeting of the AMA in New York, in 1961, Knox fingered sunshine as the culprit and backed up his hypothesis with a test he did on twenty-eight persons of mixed ages and races. He theorized that if time alone were responsible for "aging skin," then it should produce changes all over the body. Yet, in all of his cases, the skin on the buttocks was youthful, while the facial and arm skin of those who were regularly exposed to heavy amounts of sunshine looked old. He also found that Negroes had about eight times the natural protection of Caucasians thanks to their melanin pigmentation (which filters out the sun's rays)—which is why they so often appear more youthful than their Caucasian contemporaries.

Knox's ingenious theory was challenged by many of his colleagues. Their main objection was that it sounded too simple. Unfortunately, as is true of all areas of dermatology, rigorous, dispassionate research is in dreadfully short supply. Most of the available data (much of it contradictory) has been provided by the spare-time labor of busy practitioners.

With the great dearth of popular guidance in the purchase of cosmetics, the public grasps at any straw. Usually so-called "beauty counselors" do no more than help a customer decide which of *their own products* they ought to buy.

One such is Erno Laszlo ("the Svengali of the skin"), who has a concession at the Saks Fifth Avenue department stores. After one day's "intensive" training by a Laszlo assistant, the Saks salesgirl is able to tell—by analysis of a brief questionnaire—which of Laszlo's products ought to go into the "skin-saving kit' (cost: $58 to $79) for a particular client. From the answers the client gives in this questionnaire, the salesgirl determines whether she has "plus" (oily) or "minus" (dry) or "balanced" (normal) skin. A "balanced" skin, presumably the ideal, does not exempt a customer from the need to "save her skin" with at least $58 worth of cosmetics. Nor does chronological youth. Laszlo advises mothers to start their seven-year-old daughters on a cosmetic program.

The Laszlo pitch is that while he personally can afford to treat only the likes of the Duchess of Windsor, Greta Garbo, Baroness Philippe de Rothschild, Anita Colby, Gloria Vanderbilt Cooper, Dina Merrill, the Countess Mona von Bismarck, Jennifer Jones Selznick, Jacqueline Kennedy, Princess Lee Radziwill, and Doris Duke—any washerwoman with $58 in spending money can avail herself of Laszloesque advice. Laszlo himself is not seen by his Saks customers. The cosmetics mogul maintains that an "invisible consultation," a longer questionnaire that his New York "Institute" goes over, is sometimes more effective than a personal interview because "women are apt to lie when they talk to me personally, but on paper they tell the truth. So I am better able to help them."

The giant of the cosmetics business is Avon Products, Inc., which does an annual business in excess of $400,000,000 in door-to-door sales. But the runner-up, Revlon, strives to exude an image with more pizazz, more chic. To bolster this image of irresistible femininity, Revlon has set up an overdecorated, overmannered high-priced beauty salon called the House of Revlon. Celebrities such as Joan Crawford, Bess Myerson, Connie Francis, and Phyllis Diller grace its confines from time to time—although some of them occasionally are serviced by Revlon in the privacy of their homes.

For the extra dollars (an average day with the hair stylist and cosmetician runs from $50 to $100), the customer is catered to amid antiqued cream walls, Louis XIV and XV commodes, gilded ceilings, walls, and mirrors. Pink-smocked habituées loll about the foyer, gossiping, pinching the kangaroo and lizard bags, trying on

jewelry and wigs and (for the conscience-stricken) buying $20
ties.

Madame X enters. She is tall. She has something on her mind.
She is troubled. She casts her bulk on the ottoman. Her eyes search
for one who is not present. She fumes while a spindle-legged eu-
nuch fetches a runty, thick-calved woman with hair the brilliance of
bursting napalm. She obviously knows what she's about, and steams
directly toward her mark:

"Ohhhh! Ohhhhh! What eez wrrrong, *ma chérie?*"

Madame X is in an anguished prerejuvenation condition, in
conspicuous need of a tint—among other things. She recounts her
woes. Her confidante is sympathetic.

"Ohhhh! Oooooo!"

Madame X smiles, for the first time. Madame X has rediscovered
her sense of humor. She is laughing. The House of Revlon's magic
has worked again.

The salon directress emerges and leads me into her office. She is
another make, a younger year, slender, businesslike, sharp. Could I
follow a woman through the famous Revlon "Day of Beauty," recording its rejuvenatory magic?

Revlon, I am told, allows nothing to appear in print about its operation that it does not control. There have been mishaps when
Revlon was not allowed to censor copy. If I would submit copy for
approval beforehand, then I would be given carte blanche. But only
on that condition.

I told her I could not accept those rules.

"On the Susskind show," she explained, "they took one of our
boys and made a circus out of it. He in no way represented the
House of Revlon or Revlon or the hairstyling industry—or profession as we prefer to regard it. . . . It was terrible. It was offensive
. . . to other people in this industry . . . to clients."

She is handed a telephone and confers with an associate.

"The woman was in tears. That wig. She was wearing it last
night. Went out with her husband and a business associate. Well
. . . it just assumed a life of its own. She'd worn it three times the
previous week. She was absolutely hysterical. You've *got* to do something." Turning to me, "We really don't mean to give you a hard
time."

202 THE YOUTH DOCTORS

A chummy, affable PR type enters. He is aware of my request. He interrupts, "But this is not a hard time compared to the hard time that *we* would get."

Heads would roll?

"No . . . but . . . our flesh is stripped off. Want to see rejuvenation? *We* are examples of rejuvenation. Flesh really grows back without scars.'

Turning to me, the directress adds: "We've got to be terribly sure that we're presented in the light that we've got to be presented in."

She assures me that censorship is *de rigueur* with nonbeauty magazines (they are trusted because "their aims are the same as ours . . . to lend an aura of whatever you want to call it . . ."). The *Saturday Evening Post*, she says, acquiesced to their request in an article that appeared in that magazine a while back. She recalls only too vividly having a Slenderella ("as aboveboard as you could get") salon shot out from under her by a book (*The Lonely Woman*) that was serialized in the New York *Post*. When clients "began to sort of question . . . they just didn't like being associated any more." Slenderella then went bankrupt.

The sensitivity of the cosmetics industry to press comment was illustrated by the demise of Revlon's placenta extract cream Wonderlift, following the appearance in the New York *Times* of an item about a competitor's similar product (Helene Curtis' Magic Secret). According to the directress, the article simply questioned whether the cream should be classified as a cosmetic or a drug. Immediately, *all* placenta creams, which hitherto had sold well, failed to move from the counters.

"We pulled it off the market . . . not that there was anything wrong with it . . . but when we have a product that's a bomb, we take it out of our line. I personally have kept here a hundred little jars of it because it's such a marvelous, marvelous product."

According to the directress, the facial skin (especially on women with bags or lines under the eyes) lifts and smooths down when Wonderlift is applied over a woman's cosmetics.

"What happens when you wipe it off?"

"You go back to what you were before. It lasts maybe six hours. If you're out for eight hours, you can just take a little water on your fingers and kind of pat it, it'll give it back its pull."

The only other product that could be considered "regenerative," she said, was Eterna 27, which "opens the doors of the skin and enables the moisture to come in."

"It's a night cream. It's not a permanent corrective . . . nothing is. It's like vitamins. I was never a confirmed cream user. Last year we went away for vacation, I didn't take anything along with me. I noticed after about a week I was looking tired. And then I saw the little lines . . . you know . . . the little crinkles around the eyes. . . . They weren't there before. I bought a jar, and started using it. In about three days they were gone again. . . . What this does is enable the underlying tissues to retain . . . moisture . . . because that's what causes wrinkling: The cell structure under the skin as you get old begins to lose moisture and the skin begins to deflate."

For millions, a mite of powder and rouge during the day and a little grease at night are not enough to conceal the litter of seesaw living over the years. These people are faced with a momentous decision, one that will affect the whole course of their lives: should they undergo plastic surgery?

If this is your problem, think hard on it. Plastic surgery can be an expensive one-way ticket to destinations completely unforeseen. Whatever improvements may be etched into your skin, you're going to need a lot of heart as well to better your lot socially and professionally. The doctor, at best, can give you only a chance to help yourself.

Let's suppose you're a man or woman over fifty, and your face has unhappily come to resemble the palm of your hand. You're undergoing a *crise de conscience*. Your spouse has taken an interest in other partners. You fear that he or she may be ready to cash in the whole idea of togetherness. At the office, it's clearly Deadendsville. You, the workhorse, suddenly find yourself Mr. or Mrs. Leftout. The big assignments are going to younger people. Are you on the way out?

It may all boil down to the fact that you (overnight, it seems) have begun to look old. What should you do about it? Indeed, what *can* you do about it?

Well, there's quite a bit you can have done. But for any single condition, you're liable to find several differing opinions from experts on what should be done. One doctor will tell you you need a planing. Another will urge you to have a peel. Still another tells

204 THE YOUTH DOCTORS

you there's nothing to equal an old-fashioned face-lift for results. Some will simply follow your judgment of what you think you need —to avoid "rocking the boat"—as one dermatologist put it to me. You need a specialist in whom you have confidence.

You won't get away cheaply. That's for sure. And your treatment, whatever it turns out to be, may be only the first of a series that will go on for months or years.

There is no such thing in plastic surgery as a "standard fee." Many variables determine the individual practitioner's rates. The following are no more than approximations of what is charged in Hollywood and New York:

For hair transplants, calculate $1 per hair—or about $2,000 for the average case of male pattern baldness. This assumes you've got hair to spare from the lower, nether scalp regions that can be planted front and center.

Eyelids have been done for as low as $100, but they usually cost about $750.

A complete face-lift ranges from $1,000 to $5,000.

A dermabrasion can cost as little as $500 and as much as about $1,000. If many planings are required, some plastic surgeons give the patient a considerable discount. Some will do the face and neck together for $1,000.

Pulling back droopy jowls alone means a minimum expenditure of about $1,000.

Nose jobs are performed for a minimum of about $500, but $1,500 tabs are quite common. At least one top plastic surgeon will throw in a new chin for another $50 if done with the nose. If done separately, it would cost $250.

Skin color was once thought improved by an elaborate "blood-washing" routine established by rejuvenationist Dr. Else K. La Roe. The price was $50 per wash, or $1,000 for the series, which was part of a general detoxification program. But Dr. LaRoe eventually gave up all rejuvenation therapy as hopeless. (There seemed some doubt in her mind that oxidizing and purifying the blood was any better than taking several good gulps of fresh air.)

Breast prostheses (silicone implants) cost $175 per pair from the manufacturer, plus a surgeon's fee of from $500 to $1,000.

Artificial testicles, also made of silicone, are a far better bargain.

Price: $19 per pair. Again, the surgeon's fee is supplementary.

Unfortunately, many plastic surgeons are notoriously poor artists. This is easily documented. The knowledgeable can spot most rhinoplasty (nose trims) operations as the work of a particular surgeon. The new nose conforms to the plastic surgeon's notion of what an ideal nose should be—and is not necessarily what best suits the patient. The best nose job I ever saw was one performed by a veteran plastic surgeon on his son. After excising a cartilaginous hump from his son's nose, this craftsman purposely left a minor crook. The result: the patient's character was not only preserved, but enhanced. Only the son's intimate friends are aware that he has had his nose fixed.

The unartistic renderings of most plastic surgeons have been severely criticized by Dr. Mario Gonzalez- Ulloa of Mexico City.

"The contemporary plastic surgeon," says Gonzalez-Ulloa, "even if he is well-trained with reference to the technique and way of resolving properly his technical problems, still lacks an appreciation of beauty. . . . Properly executed, the reconstruction should reflect in the patient's eyes his or her new identity as a normal human personality."

Plastic surgeons' curricula do not include courses in aesthetics, says Gonzalez-Ulloa. Distressed by this serious shortcoming, he began to wade through art bibliographies to find a workable standard against which the specialist could measure his diagnosis and results. The precepts of Da Vinci and Dürer he found interesting but too obtuse to be useful. It was the Dutch anatomist Pieter Camper's diagrammatic renderings of the evolution of the human profile that gave Gonzalez-Ulloa his cue for a workable principle. In their detailed drawings, Camper and an associate showed, by comparative skulls and fleshed-out profiles, that man becomes more animal-like as the line from the forehead to the upper lip becomes less perpendicular and more nearly horizontal. Eventually, Gonzalez-Ulloa settled upon the so-called Frankfort line, which consists of a pair of crossed lines that provide a norm against which deviations (and corrections) may be measured with great precision. The Frankfort line extends from the ear to the lower ridge of the eye socket. A near perpendicular (from 85 to 92 degrees) can then be drawn above and below the nasion (a point between the nose and forehead). With these two lines (using life-size X rays and photos), reconstruction of the chin, nose, forehead, jaw, and teeth can be plotted to the maximum aesthetic advantage.

Although human bones are still widely used in corrective surgery, silicone prostheses (artificial implants) are increasing in popularity. Silicones come in liquid and standard preshaped (hopefully permanent) forms. At this writing, the liquid is still in a highly experimental (and unproven) stage. No more than five plastic surgeons were originally allowed to work with it, and the FDA withdrew even those permits in 1964, after unscrupulous practitioners began filling out skinny go-go dancers and strippers with injected silicones.

The advantage of silicones lies in their chemical inertness. Ivory was once (but is no longer) popular for the same reason. The liquid silicones are devilish, however, for the ominous reason that they have a great wanderlust and often wind up far from the site of the injection. They also cause infection, look like cancer on X-ray prints, and may actually be responsible for cancer. Tales of liquid silicone catastrophes are legion among the trade.

A Manhattan skin specialist recently expressed his fear of liquid silicone injections:

"A lot of the stuff was disappearing. You didn't know where it was going. It was very insidious. We found that a lot of patients were urinating it. It always travels . . . [except] where you have scar tissue and it locks itself in. There you can use it as upholstery to bring up the epidermal lining."

A West Coast plastic surgeon told me of a colleague who wound up with several "telephone number" lawsuits resulting from silicones that refused to stay put in their recipients. The practitioner neglected to tell one patient, a fading Hollywood hero, that he had plumped out his wrinkles with silicones. One night, however, on a TV panel program, the surgeon described his "experimental work" with silicones on animals. He noted in passing that using liquid silicones on human patients was unlawful. The actor, whose face had begun to droop disastrously because of the injections, happened to watch the show, put two and two together, and became apoplectic.

"The surgeon used them on him just two weeks before," explained my informant. "And the patient—a very spastic individual

—rushed out and got an attorney and photographer, and everything else. So they're really in a pickle on that."

W. John Pangman II, MD, a prominent Beverly Hills plastic surgeon, warns that silicone injections often cause "horrible damage."

"I've had girls [treated by other doctors] in here to see me with breasts with nodules on them as big as a golf ball. Two or three of them are just going to lose their breasts."

One middle-aged woman had her plastic surgeon fill out her frown line with liquid silicones. The effect was pleasing for a while. But then, one morning, she woke up to find her nose stretching all the way across her eyelids and wider by an inch at the bottom. The condition was eventually corrected, but only after three operations on her eyelids and one on her nose to get rid of the runaway silicone.

A well-known movie actress was advised by her doctor that silicone injections might beautify her legs. She had the shots and gloried in her more shapely legs, until the silicones plummeted from the calves down to her toes.

"God damn it," says the doctor to whom she came for corrective help, "it just drives me nuts! Where she had neat little ankles before, now her legs just come straight down. Her ankles are four inches across."

Silicone sponges, however, show far more promise than the liquid, and are constantly being improved. While they once had a tendency to shrink, the best of the new ones appear not to. Breast and testicle sponges come in a variety of sizes, weigh and feel approximately the same as the genuine article and, if expertly inserted, have been known to fool even experienced plastic surgeons.

Twiggyism notwithstanding, women with stubby, wizened, or absent (due to surgery) mammaries tend to be subject to nightmarish depressions and fits of insecurity. On occasion it's the husband, not the wife, who is anxious about his spouse's modest bosom —and sets up the appointment with the plastic surgeon.

I asked one doctor who specializes in solid breast implants if he would dissuade an attractive woman with small breasts from having a silicone implant operation.

"It has nothing to do with what I think of it," he replied. "This has to do with the type of society we live in. I have an opinion on it, but that's a private opinion. The curious part about it is that several of these married women with children who come to the office to increase their bosoms subsequently have told me—or my secretary—that for the first time in their lives they feel like women. Now they feel they can expose themselves and compete with their fellow sisters on the beach, or in the bar . . . or wherever."

Nose plastic surgery is ticklish. Not because of any technical complexity but because of serious psychiatric considerations. Women tend to be better risks than men. Male candidates, according to a study by Dr. Wayne E. Jacobson of the University of California at Los Angeles, reflect a high degree of psychiatric disorder in their motivations for cosmetic changes.

In a study of one hundred and twenty patients at Baltimore's Johns Hopkins Hospital, the psychiatrist found that both male and female rhinoplasty applicants frequently had troubles with their mothers. Women rejected their mother's femininity, and often mentioned that their noses "would look better on a man's face." Men (in whom the "incidence of severe psychopathology was high") frequently felt an "unmastered, unconscious rage toward the mother" and often were deprived of their fathers in their youth.

Less than half of the men were accepted for surgery, and even of those accepted, many had a tendency to "put all their eggs in one basket" emotionally, disliked their results, and blamed their doctors. It should be said that these psychic problems often occur in patients who have their ears trimmed, need new chins, and undergo facial renovation of one kind or another.

Bold, brash, energetic, in his mid-forties, Norman Orentreich, MD, has made a great deal of money in a short time. In the recent *McCall's* article on "How the Rich Stay Young and Beautiful," his clients were reported to include Frank Sinatra and Hugh Downs. He is, without doubt, one of the most fascinating rejuvenationists (although he would probably reject the nomenclature) around. His plasmapheresis work is merely the latest of his daring medical innovations. What he is most famous for, however, is the auto hair transplant for the unhappy victim of male pattern baldness (MPB). MPB is characterized by a receding front hairline, with growing baldness on the top and rear of the scalp. Orentreich wears many hats (none to cover baldness, by the way). He holds open house every Friday morning for the trade to watch his dermabrasions, of which he usually does several in rapid-fire order—each patient occupying a small room in his clinic on Fifth Avenue. He is sensitive to the dichotomy between research and doctoring.

"You're talking to a very hard researcher. I can sell anything to a patient and make him feel better. But . . . the facts . . . back in here I don't lie to myself. I'll give an individual who comes to me hope, even though I know they are hopeless and helpless, because I think it's cruel not to give them hope."

This said, Orentreich lives as though time literally *were* money. For him, it is.

"My time," he said to me pointedly, "costs approximately three hundred dollars an hour. That's what I charge a company for my time. Minimum. I may charge them as much as a thousand dollars a morning. My overhead is two thousand a day. So when I sit here this morning, we don't take in a thousand bucks, I lose money."

Closest to his heart are his plasmapheresis experiments and aging parameter studies (of nail growth and wound-healing), all of which are strictly red-ink pastimes. He wondered why it took him twenty years to get interested in aging research. I suggested it might be because it takes a great deal of courage to depart from a comfortable sinecure and suddenly risk being known as a medical outsider.

"True," he answered, "[yet] I suppose I'm established enough as a physician, my ego is such, and the demands for my services both from patients and from medical schools and from other people to go on lectures is such that I really don't think that I could be hurt. Besides, I think I'm financially immune to any of these things— which is another important consideration. . . . If I *really* wanted to cash in, I'd continue working on my hair research, which, each time I do something, always brings in more income."

For MPB, there are two surgical remedies: the auto hair transplant pioneered by Orentreich and the still experimental, but quite promising, "bi-lobe flap" (in which a hair patch from near the nape of the neck is brought to the bare front and center portion), invented by Dr. Louis Feit.

The latter technique appears to have several advantages over the Orentreich plugs. First of all, it actually expands the visible hair-growth area on the scalp (by pulling tight the loose skin folds in back). Second, the hair loss is minimal compared with that involved in the plug transplant. The bi-lobe flap, while providing a natural front hairline, also permits use of a toupee to cover the very top.

The disadvantages of the Orentreich method are its "buckshot" pattern on donor areas and "honeycomb scarring" pattern in the receptor areas and the high loss of transplanted hairs.

"With the plug method," says Feit, "you're fortunate if fifty percent of the hairs survive."

Feit, nonetheless, uses the plug transplants himself on occasion. Usually to cover scars.

The hair plug transplant which Orentreich has developed is based on the principle that hair follicles (or "roots") will behave anywhere else on the scalp just the way they did in their original location. Even the baldest of MPB victims usually have a ring of hair at the back of the head which can be transplanted onto forward areas. Each follicle appears to obey an inexorable timetable for degeneration (at which time the hair falls out permanently). Therefore, the surgeon must carefully choose his grafts from areas not scheduled for early drop-out.

An indication of transplanting's popularity is the great number of doctors who have had it done on themselves. Forty-nine of one plastic surgeon's first fifty hair transplant patients were physicians.

It's a simple operation, requiring the assistance of a nurse, and takes approximately an hour from the moment the Novocain needle pricks the patient's pate until he walks out the door with a bandage over his head.

After the anesthetic is applied to donor and receptor sites, the grafting begins. A small punch, modified by Orentreich (exactly 5/32 of an inch in diameter), is used to bore out denuded skin plugs from the front areas where the hair is desired. These plugs are thrown away. Fifteen plugs per session are average; twenty-five are the maximum.

Then the donor hair is clipped short, and the same punch removes the hair plugs, each with from eight to twenty individual hairs. They are trimmed for fat and cut to the desired length. With a small forceps, they are then carefully inserted into the receptor holes. Congealing blood holds them in place, and the patient presses a bandage over the grafts for a quarter of an hour to permit the blood to clot and secure the grafts.

Within a week or two, a scab forms over the graft area and falls off. By the third week, the new hairs fall out. Then, within two or three months, brand-new hair growth can be seen. Usually the natural foliage in the donor areas is thick enough to cover the missing plugs.

Orentreich believes that his research has put the lie to quirk theories about MPB being caused by tight hatbands, assorted germs, a genius mentality, and so on. Without question, hormones play an important part. Eunuchs, for example, cease to bald from the moment of their castration. Knowledge of this fact sometimes prompts male psychotics to request specialists to save their hair by this highly effective, if bizarre, method. They are almost always turned down.

The attrition of the transplanted hairs can be considerable. Dr. Albert Best admits that he performs the transplants with great reservations: "I consider it a poor operation because while each plug may have from ten to fifteen hairs within its diameter to begin with, when transplanted and in the process of healing the transplant may lose half that amount. I therefore tell the patient beforehand that it is a tedious procedure, very costly, and the end results are not always satisfactory."

I could not help but agree with Best as I scanned the sparse new hair on a middle-aged lawyer in a skin specialist's office. Yet the patient was delighted to have something up front to comb. He had begun the transplants principally to please his wife, but ultimately became convinced that his more youthful appearance will help him professionally, too.

Some patients have begun to complain that the grafted tufts, sparse enough after the initial attrition, fall out entirely in four or five years. I noticed recently that TV personality Hugh Downs had begun to comb his top hair forward in bangs, toddler fashion. This bizarre coiffure did nothing to enhance his insouciant charm and smooth good looks.

I wondered about it until, a few days later, a knowledgeable Manhattan youth doctor told me that the performer's plug transplants had started to fall out. Although he makes no secret of his grafts—he had them done on TV—Downs is, like most men, sensitive about a rapidly receding hairline. In all likelihood he will have to demothball and dry-clean the old toupee.

If one could get along with only a few, the transplants would be cheap enough at $5 or $10 per grafted plug. But some two hundred are needed to rehabilitate the average case of MPB. The would-be rejuvenate must decide for himself whether a $2,000-plus outlay is worth the highly suspect benefits of an iffy technique involving periodic quarantine (from those who are to be fooled, at any rate), possible scarring, and the risk of transplant loss within a few short years.

As the Roman epigrammatist Martial said several centuries ago: "There is nothing more contemptible than a bald man who pretends to have hair."

Of course, the reason the hairless feign hairiness stems from society's obsession with this secondary (and rather indeterminate) sexual characteristic. Dr. William Montagna, a dermatological researcher, once said: "Interest in hair today has grown to the proportion of a fetish. Think of the many loving ways in which advertisements refer to scalp hair—satiny, glowing, shimmering, breathing, living. Living indeed! It is as dead as rope."

"A person is always startled when he hears himself seriously called old for the first time," Oliver Wendell Holmes once remarked. If he's especially susceptible, it's not long afterward that he begins to contemplate remedial action. More than anything else, it is the skin that solemnly, contemptibly discloses to others that we are getting along in years.

Sooner or later, we all begin to crinkle and loosen about the face. If we are the blond, blue-eyed, fair-skinned progeny of Scottish or Irish parents, we tend to look older before our contemporaries because of greater skin sensitivity to the elements.

While the precise cause of "aging skin" is unknown, we are now fairly aware of what's going on. In old age, less blood (ergo, less nourishment) reaches the skin. The vessels have trouble contracting and dilating; the papillae shrink; the epidermis is thinner; and there are fewer of our precious glomus units (blood flow and temperature regulators between small arteries and veins) around. The skin becomes rigid—possibly because of collagen fiber cross-linkage and a curious inhibition of enzyme action to break down such ties. The horny skin layer is also thinner. With less sebum and fat to lubricate it, the skin starts to scale. Scars from small physical insults and shocks that once were automatically sloughed off hang on as unwelcome guests.

On top of all this, the skin becomes increasingly susceptible to pigmentation, freckles, liver spots, and mysterious bouts of itching.

The face itself ages progressively. At about thirty, "personality lines" begin to appear; at thirty-five or so, muscle lines about the eyes show up (earlier in those troubled by poor eyesight); then, in order, skin lines, wrinkles, neck lines, folds and pouches, and a general relaxation of all tissues develop. One of the few advantages a fat person has over a thin person is that his skin doesn't seem to "age" as fast.

It all sounds hopeless; but it's not—quite. At any stage of this progression, there are surgical techniques that can be applied to make you look younger. Men and women today begin to seek rejuvenation treatments in their forties, whereas previous initiates were at least fifty.

The most widely accepted method for removing wrinkling and pouching is the face-lift. Sometimes all that's needed is work on the upper and lower eyelids. Often, however, both the eyelids and a general face and neck skin tightening are in order. Formerly, this meant simply cutting off excess skin, and tucking the peripheral skin flaps under (usually behind or even inside) the ears. But now surgeons are emphasizing work on the underlying muscular bed as the key to a good face-lift.

In this connection, Dr. Feit points out that the results of a simple skin excision are not long-lasting. A truly expert face-lift, on the other hand, should last a decade: "You have to know which muscle action to eliminate. You want to eliminate the frown muscle if you can," Feit says "You have to do enough undercutting of the skin. That's where the greatest pitfall is. Some doctors don't expose enough of the skin, undermine it adequately, separate it from the muscles. They also run into problems in reapproximating the skin. It has to be suspended in the proper directions."

In all lifting techniques (chin, lips, eyelids, face), the skin is eventually drawn into natural folds, where it will be least conspicuous. This holds true even for the thigh-lift, where the skin is pulled up on both legs and tucked into a crease around the groin in the middle of the thigh. (Cost of a thigh-lift is approximately $1,000.)

Improvements in cosmetic surgery have been unconscionably slow in developing. Both the medical profession and the aesthetic rejuvenators themselves are to blame. One root of the trouble is that even today facial rejuvenation is regarded as a luxury treatment. Doctors and patients alike are quietly scorned by many of the powers that be in medicine.

Feit described the cradle days of cosmetic rejuvenation: "This whole field just sort of grew. The tragedy was that most cosmetic surgery was done behind locked doors in the clinic, downstairs. Plastic surgeons doing cosmetic work weren't accepted upstairs. It was 'beauty surgery.' You weren't 'dealing with the sick.' They simply thought this was not the duty of a doctor. You were just supposed to take care of the 'sick.' They never realized that you were dealing with mentally disturbed people at times, and with people whose personalities were not completely adequate."

Today, the professional societies continue to be rent by dissension, jealousy, and interspecialty rivalries. The rhinoplasty specialist feels that only he is competent to correct nasal irregularities and assails the plastic surgeon generalist for intruding on a domain he claims as his alone. Another camp feels that only basic reconstructive surgery (for cancer or accident victims, for example) is legitimate activity. Excessive candor and forthright promotion of new ideas are often rewarded by ostracism, resulting in coteries of "insiders" and the "outsider" opposition. Only within the past fifteen years have plastic surgeons begun to describe their precious techniques in detail in the medical journals. Yet many of the best petitpoint cosmetic surgeons still conceal their secrets from their colleagues. Practitioners of one specialty unhesitatingly malign and impugn the integrity of other groups.

Dermabrasion created a violent stir when some of its enthusiastic pioneers boasted that its advent would make face-lifting obsolete. This it has not managed to do, although its popularity has grown tremendously in the post-World War II years. One reason it hasn't supplanted face-lifting is that its effects are limited to the outer skin layer. To correct changes in muscular activity, a face-lift is a must. And while even the most die-hard dermabrader admits that his high-speed (15,000 rpm) rotary brush or serrated burr can remove only light wrinkles and acne scars, there is considerable debate as to the permanency of the wrinkle demolition. Many experts advise a combination of face-lifting, dermabrasion, and chemical peel for maximum effectiveness.

Even Dr. Adolph Brown, who eventually became loyal to the peel, previously found the effects of dermabrasion quite impressive. Brown cited the case of a brilliant thirty-eight-year-old scientist suffering from premature senile facial rhitidosis (wrinkling) who had shied away from teaching because of his appearance. After a deep dermabrasion, with excellent cosmetic results, Brown reported, "The improvement in the morale of the patient is striking. . . . With his rejuvenated appearance, he has not hesitated to take a position as professor, and speaks before audiences now with complete confidence."

Although most plastic surgeons use an ethyl chloride spray, which freezes and anesthetizes the skin, an intravenous general anesthetic permits the doctor to make a more meticulous calibration of the dermabrader's penetration. If the abrasion is too deep, the skin can become shiny and glazed.

The most frequent use of dermabrasion is in whipping away acne pits. The brush is drawn over an area marked out with dye, in overlapping strokes from the outside toward the middle (to prevent bleeding from obscuring the next operating area). After it is cleaned and bandaged, the face begins to weep a plasmalike fluid, which congeals and eventually forms a crust. The crust falls off in six to eight days.

One advantage of dermabrasion is that it can be done in the doctor's office. Only the most daring or foolhardy surgeon would perform a face-lift without hospital safeguards and facilities. A disadvantage it shares with the chemical peel is the omnipresent danger of delving too deep—producing a terrible scar-burn-contracture which can turn into keloid scar tissue. (A description of the skin peel is included in the next chapter.)

The latest kink in the commercial tangle of cosmetic rejuvenation is the American debut of a bright, attractive Rumanian aesthetician named Christine Valmy. In the few years that she has been in this country (previously she worked in France, Greece, and Rumania) she has tried both to usurp the heretofore unchallenged prerogatives of beautician-cosmetologists (doing facials), and to do the dirty work left undone by dermatologists (cleaning out acne sores pustule by pustule). No small-time operator, Mrs. Valmy has brought from Europe an array of twenty-nine expensive beauty machines which, she maintains, will do exquisite things to female American faces never before accomplished (such as cleaning them). As well as operating her own school for aestheticians (it translates badly from the French *esthéticienne,* but there is no alternative, the idea being to avoid confusion with *beautician,* a term she contends is a euphemism for hairdresser), she has opened her face-and-skin salons in a number of Eastern department stores such as Bamberger's, Macy's, and Bloomingdale's. Her gripe with the "beauticians" is that, in their standard thousand-hour course of study, only forty-two hours are devoted to skin care per se. The American woman, she says, deserves better. If her lobbying with the New York legislature bears fruit, the law will demand a minimum requirement of seven hundred hours of skin care for an aesthetician's license. Thus, the beauticians will be out of the skin business, and the aestheticians will be in. But *very* in.

Strangely, perhaps because she is capable of talking the dermatologists' own language and keeps up with the literature, she has had no trouble from organized medicine so far. In fact, she estimates that over half of her clients are doctors' wives.

"By now I know every time a woman comes in here, and says she wants a peeling and . . . says 'Do you mind if my husband comes in,' I know he is a doctor. I can swear it. So I say, 'Of course, I don't mind,' and he comes in. By now I don't even talk with the woman, I explain to him."

Dermatologists are a bit nonplussed by Mrs. Valmy, whose gadgetry and methods most have never encountered before. Whether her Vapozone machine actually results in true skin "penetration," or her Nemectron (galvanotherapy machine) in point of fact does firm up muscles by sending a current through them—is anyone's guess, they say.

Basically, she is concerned only with the outer layer of *healthy* skins. The diseased patient she leaves to the dermatologists.

"You should see a woman who, for twenty years, has never *really* cleaned her face—how she looks after the first treatment," says Mrs. Valmy.

The treatment consists of allowing the "skin to breathe" by

cleaning the face with lotions, a "disincrustation" of blackheads, another cleaning (by suction cups), an opening of the pores with the Vapozone, an antigravity massage, a hydrating mask, and the Nemectron. The cost is $20.

A complete facial muscle firming treatment, consisting of twenty-five sessions, costs $195.

A de-wrinkling treatment (a tedious pinpoint electro-coagulation of skin albumin) is $20 or $25 per session. Duration of the de-wrinkling: about four months.

A five-day crash program (with home skin-care lessons) runs $100.

A "light" chemical peel with resorcinol and diactin costs $30.

A "medium" peel is $154 ("Every woman over thirty needs a peeling once a year").

She hews to a flock of standard European rejuvenation ideas. Niehans' lyophilized cells, when applied locally with massage, are wonderful, she maintains, for tightening floppy breasts. Carrel's chick embryo "biostimulants" allegedly boost skin metabolism. Even Popov's aromatics (such as orange blossoms, roses, willow) find a place in a Valmy salon as hydrating agents. "The senile skin is one that lacks water. It would appear, as far as skin is concerned, that hydration of the skin [is essential to] having young-looking skin. Paraffin masks are also employed to "maintain hydration."

Valmy's acceptance by American women has been qualified. When she mentions "breast rejuvenation," she often finds herself talking to a stone wall.

"In France it is very important. In this country it's unheard of. When you talk of it, people think you are out of your mind. Don't forget, America is still very puritan." Her belief in the efficacy of tissular extracts for breast rejuvenation stems in part from the fact that she has tried it—and successfully—on her own bosom.

Like most youth doctors who are not practicing endocrinologists she is dead set against hormones. "Endocrinology today is completely unknown; it's in an infancy stage. Everything that is done is on the basis of: Let's try it and see if it works."

An article in the *Saturday Evening Post* on hormones induced her to try estrogens "because when [anything comes out] I want to try it."

"I went right to my doctor and said I want to try this. I don't know if it did anything to me . . . but I started to be so nervous and so unhappy. I was in such a state with this tiny pill. I wasn't myself at all."

With some of her clients, she is part doctor of last resort and part child psychologist ("You don't know *how* much").

One woman who came to her recently was happily married—but on the verge of suicide because of disfiguring pimples. She had spent a fortune on doctors over five years trying to get rid of them, but to no avail.

"I would give anything to have a skin that wouldn't need makeup," she told Mrs. Valmy through her tears.

The aesthetician told her that she'd seen far worse conditions, and she'd have a go at getting rid of the pimples. She succeeded, and the woman effusively told her: "Mrs. Valmy, I love you."

A few months later, she called her—again desperate, again talking of taking her life. This time she had acne on her neck because of an internal condition.

It was too much for Mrs. Valmy. "Do you remember how you were crying for a nice skin and how much you would give to get it? Did you get it? Yes," she said sternly. "So now you have something on your neck. Just look in a mirror at your *face*. And for God's sake, put a scarf around your neck!"

While Christine Valmy and her new aestheticians may solve some of the minor skin problems that confront women, the major work still must be done by the plastic surgeon, who continues to be regarded as an *enfant terrible* and "scavenger specialist" by many of his professional brethren. Bit by bit, however, he has come into his own. The medical profession seems at last to have acknowledged his truly therapeutic function. By normalizing his patient's *soma*, he often helps heal his *psyche*.

Unquestionably, good looks have become for many a genuine social and economic necessity. As scarring and wasting diseases become rarities, as the latest fashions and styles quickly appear on department store bargain counters, we are becoming a nation where "the beautiful people" are no longer mainly rich people but almost anyone and everyone.

The cosmetic surgeons have brilliantly argued their brief that their work can be as noble an endeavor as setting a fracture or excising a neoplasm. We are convinced. Even the hidebound medical conservatives have grudgingly conceded this point. The one group that remains notably cynical, curiously, are the plastic surgeons themselves.

While some will reconstruct a cheek eaten away by cancer on a charity basis, virtually none will shave the excess from a bus driver's gargantuan schnozzola for less than the going rate. This is still regarded as "beauty surgery" by none other than the practitioner himself, who for years has been asking us to consider his labor basic, essential, and a "necessity."

Why should this be?

The doctors themselves have an answer that makes a great deal of sense.

An older plastic surgeon who, until seven years ago, spent about 40 percent of his time on charity work—but considerably less since then—told me: "We went into medicine as dedicated men in my day. But how can you be dedicated when the doctor-patient relationship is no longer marked by mutual confidence? I have patients who, just before I'm about to perform surgery, will tell me: 'If this doesn't come out all right, Doc, I'll sue you for everything you're worth.' "

American doctors carry an extraordinary medicolegal responsibility in their practice—far greater than any other nation's. While most doctors will warily run the risk of malpractice lawsuits with patients who are paying their regular fees, they are extremely reluctant to do so with a charity patient.

If there was a way of obviating the lawsuit menace, some plastic surgeons say they would be willing to treat poor people on a sliding scale—or even free. The release that the patient signs before undergoing treatment is far from ironclad, and only additional legislation, it seems, can relieve plastic surgeons of their reluctance to rehabilitate the poor. Not the least important benefit which would derive from such legislation, it seems to me, would be the moral rehabilitation of the American plastic surgeon.

CHAPTER TWELVE

The $3,000 Bargain Bottled Baby Face

To inflame tempestuous male passion in the grand manner, a baby face is absolutely indispensable. The blank, innocent, even inane, look is always at a premium—no matter what men may tell the women they've contracted to adore or what women wish to believe about the male nature. Maturity? Certainly. Many impecunious or fragile men have had to settle for mature women. It may well be that not all of these men are wretched, frustrated creatures, but it has yet to be proven conclusively.

The trouble is that few baby faces outlast their owners' teens. As a woman grows older, her need for the attentions of the opposite sex increases. What is she to do to compete with her saucy, unscrupulous juniors?

Cosmetics are a poor, blatant deceit. Although some camouflage the wounds of time, they are at best a mask, and both the wearer and the beholder know it.

What are the alternatives?

There are the classical surgical face-lift and dermabrasion, which for many women are excellent defenses against the inroads of time.

There is, however, another answer—one that has lain virtually dormant since it was discovered about a half century ago. It is known as a "facial rejuvenation" or "the deep face peel" or the "phenol peel." As a solution to the aesthetic problems of millions of women, it does things none of the other processes can do. Yet the public has been deprived of this bottled baby face by a rather bizarre chain of circumstances.

The tragic story of the woman who pioneered in providing fresh new baby faces to women who had long outgrown their originals is a tangled and sordid affair.

Cora Galenti is a solemn, humorless, mystical, slow-moving and slow-thinking little lady who never quite managed to shake off the bumbling ways of her native Mezzogiorno. Born on August 6, 1898 ("I'm a Leo. I roar in a quiet way.") in the Sicilian village of Valguanera Caropepe, near Catania, she was, from the age of eight, brought up in Brooklyn, where her father ran a saloon, complete with billiard tables and a boccie court. She was quickly taken out of public school ("because I was backwards") and placed in a "special" boarding school. Later she went into her mother's fashion business.

Despite her intellectual shortcomings—a gummy memory for everything, poor articulation, spotty education—Cora eventually parlayed a facial rejuvenation "secret" into what her lawyers estimated to be a $10,000,000 fortune. The money was hers ever so momentarily, for she got caught up in an excruciatingly costly game of tag with the American Medical Association, the Federal Bureau of Investigation, the Federal Food and Drug Administration, several county medical associations, the Better Business Bureaus of several cities, the Department of Justice, the U. S. Post Office, and a posse of law enforcement agencies of California and Nevada. Cora was always "it." When the game was over, she found herself an involuntary expatriate, practically penniless, ruined professionally, and a fugitive from a jail sentence that hangs over her head to this day.

As imposing as her opposition might seem, the case against her was not as clear-cut as the authorities pretended. The evidence strongly suggests that wonder-worker Cora Galenti was put out of business for reasons that had little if anything to do with her skill or lack of skill as a youth doctor.

She possessed the ability to manufacture a mysterious clear liquid which, she claimed, could wipe away from five to forty years from the aging or ugly human face. She maintains that the formula was handed down to her by her grandmother, Josephina

Consoli, "of the House of Savoy." While he does not reject his mother's story outright, Cora's son, Anthony Palma, believes the formula probably came from a former French rejuvenationist colleague.

Cora Galenti promised a near miracle, a process apparently far superior to face-lifting or dermabrasion. For $3,000—give or take $500—she could burn away the marks that age had etched and battered into a face, including wrinkles, splotches, furrows, lines, blemishes, bags, bulges, and pouches. There were no difficult parts, she said, such as the nose or eyelids (which dermabrasion misses). Almost every ugly formation either vanished or was markedly improved.

Her method is elementary, but it must be done painstakingly by an expert. For some clients it is very painful, so sedatives are usually administered. A three-week sojourn *chez* Galenti is customary.

The first step is to apply the formula (containing a buffered phenol base) with cotton swabs. "I brush it up into their faces. If they're nervous, I stop and wait a day or two before finishing. If they're not, I finish the whole face in one session."

When enough solution has been applied, the skin turns white. Within a quarter of an hour, it turns red. Some feel a burning, others an icy, and still others a throbbing sensation. Toward the end, the face begins to itch.

Then, to prevent the natural liquid exudate from escaping, the face is covered with waterproof tape in small (1/4-inch to 3-inch) lengths. "This," she says, "is where my designing skill has helped me. All the doctors I work with have a rough time learning how to apply the tapes. I stick the tape directly onto the treated skin, starting at the bottom and always working upwards. The secret is uplift. I pick up even the nose—which drops with age—sometimes as high as a half inch. I also shrink ear lobes that grow heavy from wearing big earrings."

A bandana is applied over the tapes and kept there for a day or two. When the tape becomes loose because of the accumulating moisture underneath, she removes the tape.

"The more liquid the facial pores produce," she says, "the 'younger' the face gets."

While the face is still wet, she applies a powder that thickens into a crust. Six days later, this crust is loosened with oils, topped with an astringent cream containing zinc oxide, and removed. At this point the face is at its most beautiful—slightly puffed and glowing. In two months the skin returns to normal, minus wrinkles and blemishes.

Miss Galenti provides a straw-fed, low-calorie liquid diet throughout the entire period—since mastication would be agonizing exercise.

Her clientele was a Hollywood *Who's Who,* including a welter of nobility, a handful of wives of heads of state, scores of doctors' wives, at least two clergymen, and many colleagues in the cosmetic and rejuvenation business. A clear plurality of the celebrated grandmother-age movie star rejuvenates are Galenti women, she says.

The late cosmetics queen Elizabeth Arden, whose Maine Chance beauty farms were models for Cora Galenti's own emporia and who dedicated her life to glamorizing the lackluster housewife, is said by Cora to have offered her a fortune for her formula.

Cora claims that her process is more effective than any ordinary peeling formula because of one secret chemical agent that probes more deeply into the fatty tissues, produces greater suppuration— and far greater rejuvenation. Gloria Gasque, the Woolworth heiress, says Cora, became so entranced with the Galenti personality that she offered her $100,000 a year to abandon rejuvenation and accompany her on her travels. The beauty expert's son, Anthony Palma, recalls seeing Ginger Rogers, Jean Parker, Loretta Young, George Raft, James Dunn, Gertrude Caldwell, Jessie Royce Landis, Bea Baron and stripteaser René André in his mother's immense Hollywood home.

Cora Galenti's conversation is a halting, twisting cryptogram —a concatenation of wishful thinking, half-truths, and serial contradictions. She greeted me with a wordless smile, motioning me to a sofa in her Tijuana apartment. *Grande dame manquée.* Ever so slowly, she had to be enticed, cajoled to a semblance of clarity. I was never sure whether her final declaration was the whole truth —or merely something she had conveniently chosen to remember.

Ruthe Deskin, a sympathizer who publicized her method and, later, one of her trials for the Las Vegas *Sun,* was constantly exasperated by her manipulations of the truth:

I caught her in a couple of little fibs. . . . She doesn't realize that newspaper people check everything. So anyway I said: "Cora, there's one thing that I will not have. If I ever catch you in a lie, you've had it with me. I'll never spend time listening to you. I'll never write another line. Never think I won't know when you're lying. Don't ever tell me that St. George [Utah] is [an airport] you bought for your husband and that's why you go up there. Are you doing any work in St. George?" [A court order had forbidden her to do faces at the time.]

She said: "I'd tell you if I were, you know I would." I said: "Look, I'm *asking* you if you are. You say you'd *tell* me if you were. What kind of answer is *that?*" So she finally admitted that she had been doing some people up there.

Anthony Palma views his mother's confusion of the truth somewhat more sympathetically: "Being essentially a creative and artistic person, she does not really understand anything except her dreams and her work. When she talks to you, she is talking out of her dreams and aspirations as if the kingdom of heaven had already arrived and you are a resident there."

Boldly, blatantly, Cora advertised in the women's pages and magazines ("Permanent Rejuvenation Without Surgery . . . the only method of its kind authorized by The Women's Federation of America"). One of her brochures tempted prospective customers with "three weeks of gracious living in a fabulous Italian villa, perched on three acres of isolated hill overlooking Hollywood . . . privacy is complete . . . no unwanted visitors . . . no intruders."

The three-story, twenty-three-room villa had been purchased from a Coca-Cola vice-president and, overnight, transformed (thanks to rejuvenation money) into a glittering, rococo *palazzo* befitting the Fountain of Youth's carriage trade. Doors, entire ceilings, and walls were shipped from the old country to Hollywood. Two opulent apartments were built over the old bowling alley. The luxurious library, greenhouse, gardens, fish pond, and swimming pool were left pretty much as they had been.

For herself, Cora chose a quiet little back room—without a view. She said she was happier that way.

While the facial rejuvenation did not come cheap, she convinced many of her affluent customers that "many a vacation has cost more and has been enjoyed less." As a bonus extra, there was a special diet to round out the treatment which would produce "new figures to match . . . new faces."

A few people have played major roles in the Galenti saga. One was a mysterious Frenchwoman named Antoinette la Gasse. "Antoinette," as Hollywood knew her, probably gave Cora Galenti her facial rejuvenation formula.

AMA files show that Antoinette was arrested and charged with unauthorized medical practice in California on April 21, 1939. Despite some legal troubles after World War II, Antoinette never left her Hollywood salon for long, clandestinely rejuvenating the faces of fading movie people. By the late 1940's, she had taken on an apprentice named Cora Galenti. The two women lived *en famille* in a large colonial house on Hollywood Boulevard, where the rejuvenation was performed. Cora's energy complemented Antoinette's *politesse*. Together they made a lot of money.

Then, reports Cora, in 1952 or thereabouts, Antoinette died of cancer, willing everything she had, from house to secret rejuvenation formula, to Cora. Unmentioned in the legacy, but carried over from the Antoinette period was one of the Frenchwoman's compatriots, M. Adelaide Giroux, who became husband number two for Cora Galenti. As accurately as I can calculate it, Cora Galenti has been married six times. The first time to Charles Palma, who, she allows, was "a very fine man, a very bad husband . . . a playboy." Of Giroux, she says, "He was a Frenchman [who] used to own fishing boats in Hollywood." The third, fourth and fifth times were to Robert Smith, a private detective (she thinks but is not sure). "I would divorce him and then my lawyers would say that I cannot do that, because it would give me bad publicity. And then I would find myself married to him again." The sixth time, she says, was to Antonio Saras Hernandez, who is on the staff of the University of Mexico—"He's the man they pay the fees to."

Cora, confident of her ability, tried to get legal sanction for her work from the state. After much buck-passing among bureaus, she was refused a license—but was not directly forbidden to do her rejuvenation treatment.

Another principal in the Galenti saga is petite, blond Miriam Maschek, another facial rejuvenator. Not only did Mrs. Maschek ply the same trade, she also followed the Galenti tactic of advertising a "secret" formula that had been willed to her by none other than Antoinette. Mrs. Maschek found her own champion in Chicago *Tribune* writer Norma Lee Browning. Miss Browning had undertaken an assignment, "in cooperation with the AMA," to "expose her as a fraud."

"My specialty," Miss Browning told me, "is exposing medical quacks, for which I have won some renown and prizes. . . . Anyhow, I can smell a quack a mile away and MM wasn't one and of course the AMA screamed to high heaven about my series and tried to put her out of business."

After visiting Francis and Miriam Maschek at their posh North Miami Beach "wrinkle farm," Miss Browning syndicated a highly laudatory fourteen-part series in twenty-odd newspapers on the $2,500 rejuvenation of a Chicago housewife, Anne White. Day after day, as the peeling process was suspensefully described, readers were left hanging . . . wondering what would happen next. Finally, Mrs. White's "dried-up, weather-beaten skin" vanished, and the rejuvenate emerged "like a butterfly from its cocoon with the pink, glowing skin of a newborn babe."

One year after the treatment, the *Tribune* ran a photograph of Mrs. White with the caption: "Here's Anne today. She's 41. 'Look at my eyes,' she says. 'Aren't they stunning?'" In point of fact, her eyes were the least attractive part of her. Under mascara-beaded lashes, the wrinkled eyelids (apparently unrejuvenated) contrasted forlornly with the rest of the face, which did appear more youthful.

Not only did the series attract a land-office business to the Maschek wrinkle farm, but the rejuvenator couple had it reprinted in quantity and distributed for advertising and publicity purposes.

The state of Florida permits "facial rejuvenation," and the Mascheks operate quite openly under a state license obtained in 1957 by their attorney, Robert Riddle.

According to Cora Galenti, Mrs. Maschek—with the aid of a female detective—stole her rejuvenating formula during treatment by her to remove pigmentation caused by overexposure to the sun. At that time, says Miss Galenti, the two women discussed the possibility of Mrs. Maschek's starting a Florida franchise of

the Galenti process. Nothing came of their conversation, and Cora
lost track of Miriam Maschek until she began reading press accounts of her successful Florida operation.

With Cora under fire from California authorities, Mrs. Maschek
did not hesitate to fire off salvos (such as this press statement) at
her West Coast competition: "I've had to patch up several of
Cora's botched jobs. That's why these people get into trouble with
the medical profession—they use things like phenol and turpen-
tine which can be very injurious to a woman's face."

In point of fact, the Mascheks were using a *phenol derivative*
called resorcin, or resorcinol, whose action is similar to phenol.
Chicago *Sun-Times* reporter Gabriel Favoino, assigned to scotch
the *Trib* reports, had been secretly informed of the Maschek formula by Dr. Veronica Conley of the AMA Cosmetics Committee.
The Mascheks, when approached by the *Sun-Times* man, apparently thought they had been betrayed by the *Trib*'s Miss Browning. (Chicago's competitive paper-eat-paper journalism, however,
would have made such collaboration between the two dailies unthinkable).

> *Sun-Times*: Is it true that your formula is based on resorcin and
> salicylic acid?
>
> *Mrs. Maschek*: Yes, it's true. But I don't feel you should print it if
> you are fair. I told about this formula in strictest confidence [to a
> reporter for another publication]. I'm not giving you permission
> to print it. I'm not going to give you the formula or the propor-
> tions.

In its series, the *Sun-Times* shattered the Florida rejuvenator's
holier-than-Cora pose and, effectively, the *Trib*'s snow-white portrait of the Mascheks. Favoino published evidence revealing that
five Miami area doctors had treated ten patients for scars resulting from lay face peels—all performed by Miriam Maschek.

One woman was purported to have suffered keloid neck scars,
which look like hunks of bubble gum stretched across the skin.
She told Dr. Hollis F. Garrard, Jr., of Miami that her ordeal was
"agony, a very painful process." Other victims had acquired an
unnatural pigmentation following treatment. Still others had lost
what pigmentation they possessed. Several suffered ectropion, a
rolling outward of the eyelid, which causes intense distress. One

of these was a silent-film queen who, at seventy-two, according to Dr. Leo H. Wilson, "was trying to reclaim some of the old glamour and got pathetically trapped." Plastic surgeon George W. Robertson, who repaired her condition, said that the former actress had developed chronic conjunctivitis, which caused her pain because the eyeball was constantly exposed to wind, cold, and foreign matter in the air.

Finally, the *Sun-Times* managed to document with its tape recorder that the Mascheks had "paid off" an unhappy customer to avoid suit. This sort of thing plagues most rejuvenationists operating in fringe areas, but is generally hushed up:

> Q. Is it true that you paid Mrs. Dorothy Pickett $5000 not to sue you when she emerged from your treatment scarred and disfigured?
>
> A. Yes, it is. . . . Now that you've brought that up, I want to show you something. . . . She was going to sue us. . . . We don't want no beefs so we paid the $5000. Here's a photostat of the release she signed for us and the cancelled checks. The reason there were two payments is that we didn't have all the cash.

Despite the claim by Tony Palma that his mother's "secret" had been pirated by the Mascheks, and the subsequent *Sun-Times'* disclosure of ingredients of the Maschek formula, Palma insists that the entire secret is still unknown to medical science.

Both Cora Galenti and Miriam Maschek were getting fantastic results, by and large. Authorities trying to prosecute Cora literally refused to believe their own eyes. Confident of her abilities, she attempted to persuade the Los Angeles Better Business Bureau to look over some of her work, thinking that an actual demonstration would end the alleged "harassment." On December 20, 1957, the Bureau, in the person of E. B. Beeley, accepted her invitation. Accompanying him was a man identified only as Mr. Hooper.

When the men entered, the masked and powdered denizens of Cora's salon shouted giddy testimonials to her prowess. One, a physician's wife, told the BBB agent that she not only had been facially rejuvenated, but relieved of a partial facial paralysis and a disfigurement, thanks to Cora Galenti. "Bless you, Cora, you will never know what your work has meant to me!" she said. A young man and several other women added their own laurels.

When the two men were walking out the door, Cora Galenti looked squarely at Beeley and asked him if the mysterious Mr. Hooper was from "the Medical Association." Beeley admitted that he was. At this point, Hooper, a special investigator from the Board of Medical Examiners, muttered, "I see the results, but I'm from Missouri. I don't believe them."

For years, the public has speculated on how one veteran movie actress with sultry, sexy beauty has maintained her standing as a romantic lead and avoided slipping into grandmother roles. The answer is Cora Galenti, who has given her two peels and would have given her a third had it not been for her trouble with California and federal authorities.

It seems probable that Cora is in great part responsible for having rejuvenated a face which, by the mid-1940s was showing definite traces of the actress' hectic life. Soon after the first treatment, the star, whose fading career seemed all but on the rocks, got a small role that catapulted an otherwise ordinary picture into a box-office smash. She's been on top of the pile ever since. Unfortunately, this rejuvenate did not testify in Miss Galenti's behalf when the federal government began to accuse her of perpetrating an "unworkable" treatment.

One actress who did go on the line for her was Jean Parker. In a signed Las Vegas *Sun* article, Miss Parker compared her former face, marked by "long years of suffering . . . and failure," and her pretty new face. "Who have I got to thank for it?" she wrote. "Cora Galenti, and her facial rejuvenation process. And I want to say it . . . Thank you, Cora! My gratitude is too much to keep buried."

Women often seek a facial redo to keep a husband from philandering or from getting a divorce in order to marry an attractive young secretary. The treatment, however, sometimes produces far more than the expected degree of self-confidence. Recently, a West Coast newsman unceremoniously dumped his wife in favor of a lovely young Lolita. The wife appeared on the verge of suicide. A relative implored Cora Galenti to rejuvenate her face. "I know," she told Cora, "if you do her face, her husband will come back."

The woman was not a good business prospect. She was penniless and a mass of nerves. After considerable hesitation, Miss Galenti finally consented to give her a $6,000 face, neck, and shoulders job. The woman was allowed to work in return for the treatment. Once she found how attractive the rejuvenation had made her, she promptly divorced her husband and ran off with a wealthy MD.

Several rejuvenated female septuagenarians actually snared husbands in their twenties (probably not the most *normal* twenty-year-olds available, but twenty-year-olds nonetheless).

Palma tells the following anecdote: "I was about thirty at the time. I saw a doll when I came [into the salon] who didn't look a day over twenty, twenty-one, to me. Her body was trim. Her hair beautifully done. She was a doll, that's really the word for it. I made a couple of passes at her till I saw that the hands were old. Only later I discovered that she was seventy years old. Her name was Gertrude Caldwell."

Gertrude Caldwell's rejuvenation, incidentally, was marked by an incident which, if true, means that medical science probably does *not* yet know the precise Galenti formula. "Her own doctor . . . was asking her a question," recalls Miss Galenti, "while I was applying the mixture to her face. Gertrude turned her head quickly and the entire swab got into her eye. She got excited. The doctor got excited. 'Don't be frightened,' I said. 'Nothing can happen. Nothing can hurt her unless I *brush* the formula. Without friction . . . nothing can happen.' Her tears washed the eye. What I'm trying to say is that *it doesn't burn*."

That a phenol or phenol relative could land in the eye without ruining vision permanently strikes medical men as impossible. Hollywood plastic surgeon John Pangman's reaction to the above episode was typical: "Horse manure! You spill some phenol on yourself and you've got the worst darn burn you've ever imagined—unless you put alcohol on it immediately. But either one in the eye would give a horrible ulceration, inflammation. I had a nurse anesthetist who was just cleaning the arm to put the needle in and she slipped . . . and a little bit of it went into the patient's eye and . . . God . . . I called in an eye specialist and it was two weeks before he knew whether he was going to save the eye or not. And that was just *alcohol,* not phenol. Phenol is highly corrosive."

What really catapulted the little lay practitioner into the big time (and big-time trouble, as well) was a *Confidential* cover story (November, 1956) which she had reprinted and mailed out to prospective clients, along with publicity brochures. The magazine ballyhooed:

NEW FACES FOR OLD—WITHOUT SURGERY . . . THE MIRACLE THE MEDICOS CAN'T EXPLAIN

What happens to the tired faces that vanish through the doors of the quiet house on Sunset Boulevard? The answer baffles the doctors, worries plastic surgeons, but delights some of Hollywood's most remarkable grandmothers.

The piece, written by Cora's publicity man, was, for the most part, a factual account of the process—except that the treatment was not, as claimed, "without burning," or "without peeling" (save in the technical sense that there was no fire and no visible peel). Otherwise, as dermatologists have testified, the Galenti method involves a second-degree burn and a peel, the latter coming off invisibly under the mask. The before-after photographs were those of the PR man's own mother. Before it got to *Confidential,* every other editor who had seen it had rejected the article because of the incredible before-and-after pictures.

The *Confidential* publicity was electrifying. It took four secretaries to handle the fan mail. No longer did the rejuvenationist have to seek out business. She was inundated with reservations and $1,000 check deposits.

The article attracted not only hundreds of prospective customers, it also attracted prospective troublemakers: con men, government investigators, medical society undercover men, and "rejuvenation scar victims." The flies had found the honey pot.

With surprising swiftness, the medical profession, which had so long ignored her, began to flock to her. Physicians, dermatologists, plastic surgeons crowded into her salon to watch her perform. Some MDs, fearful of being embarrassed, sent associates or detectives in their stead.

Unquestionably, Cora Galenti's celebrity figured prominently in the development of facial rejuvenation. But what few doctors realized at the time was that the deep peel originated not with Cora Galenti, nor even with Antoinette, but from within orthodox medicine at least forty years previously. Superficial skin-peeling goes back to the Egyptians, Assyrians, and Babylonians, who used pumice for an aesthetic effect. Chemical exfoliation began some time after Joseph Lister popularized phenol (or carbolic acid) as a disinfectant—probably at the close of the nineteenth century.

By the 1920's, dermatologists and plastic surgeons were aware of the gamut of chemicals now used by facial rejuvenators, including regular and buffered phenol, salicylic acid, acetone resorcinol, solution of formaldehyde, beta-naphthol, glacial acetic acid, mercurial salts, sulfur, and solid carbon dioxide. The peel had been tried on enough patients to give doctors an idea of its advantages and risks. Even face creams that produce a slight exfoliation and shrinking effect (such as the expensive, but excellent, Cora Galenti line) were described in a paper published in the late 1930's by Dr. Joseph J. Eller and Shirley Wolff.

Some doctors, however, found the peel less reliable than skin planing or dermabrasion.

"I began to use it to remove birthmarks," says Dr. Eller. "I tried phenol on a birthmark first, then on larger areas. But I gave it up for one simple reason—the results were lousy. You don't think doctors would have given it up if it hadn't been a phony process to begin with, do you?"

Perhaps. But another possible explanation is that the peel, under the best of circumstances, requires a high level of artistry on the part of the operator. (The actual chemistry of the peel is easily grasped by any intelligent layman.) But digital dexterity and sensitivity are things you're either born with or not.

A plastic surgeon who did not hesitate to criticize his colleagues for their non- or anti-aesthetic performance was Dr. Adolph Brown, who, with his wife Marthe, began to resurrect long-abandoned phenol research work—and to conduct tests of their own. What they found convinced them that the peel was not only a useful tool, but that it was, as Cora Galenti's results had demonstrated, far superior in some respects to anything accomplished by dermabrading or plastic surgery. The Browns, Leo Kaplan, and

Samuel Ayres III—all of Los Angeles—spearheaded a campaign to endorse chemical exfoliation (or "chemosurgery," as they called it) within the profession, teach doctors how to use it, and put the lay operators out of business.

They failed to convince many of their colleagues of the peel's worth, although several respectable medical journals finally (and reluctantly, it seemed) published their papers. What they succeeded in doing was ruining Cora Galenti.

The face peel, which for so many years had been regarded as an unwanted, penniless orphan of dubious legitimacy, suddenly began to look like a charming child with a multimillion-dollar inheritance. A bitter, no-holds-barred custody fight began to rage.

The moment Cora Galenti set up a cosmetics concession at a major West Coast department store, Establishment forces moved in for the kill. A local plastic surgeon complained to the county medical society about permitting "such quackery," and requested the society to pressure the store into canceling her concession. In a letter to the society, the plastic surgeon alluded to "some deaths" in the area caused by the peeling process (although inquiries by the author to the plastic surgeon, as well as to legal and medical authorities, have failed to uncover a single such fatality).

One carefully raised eyebrow from the society did the trick. A representation was made to the store from the local Better Business Bureau—and the Galenti face cream line was dropped and her salesman expelled. The medical profession sought nothing less than full custody. And Cora Galenti, the foster mother who had nursed the child to health and prominence, was not to be allowed even an occasional visitation.

In denigrating their lay competitors' methods, plastic surgeons had the support of the powerful AMA. Dr. Conley, who had exposed Mrs. Maschek's "secret formula," said this about skin exfoliation: "Nothing we now know of can cause the aging process to regress. It's just a matter of time before the wrinkles will return. The irritation caused by the acid process causes the skin to balloon out and look younger, but when the irritation subsides the skin becomes loose again and the wrinkles reappear."

Other medical investigators, however, arrived at different conclusions. Several doctors began to work with Cora Galenti, some on a royalty basis—paying her a specific sum for instruction in her method and small quantities of her formula. In Los Angeles Dr. Robert A. Leader, Jr., used Galenti stationery in recommending her process to a Boston colleague. Dr. Arden Hedge's wife Helen, also on Galenti notepaper, wrote a chummy letter to Morris Yakowitz of the FDA, requesting him to have samples run for the correct Food and Drug regulations and specifications to obtain clearance. The letter declared that Gordon Woods, former FDA head, had checked Cora out a year previously but that she had no written clearance from the government.

Other dermatologists, shying away from personal association, began independent research. Dr. Thomas J. Baker and Dr. Howard L. Gordon explored peels together at the University of Miami. At the University of Southern California School of Medicine, Associate Clinical Professor of Dermatology Dr. Samuel Ayres III found that "phenol application [shows results] . . . in some cases superior to those from surgical planing."

On April 7, 1959, the suave, mustachioed Dr. Brown (now deceased) filed a successful patent claim for a phenol face-peeling formula. Cora's son subsequently charged that the Brown formula had been based on his mother's, and that it had been obtained through undercover investigators. True or not, the question arises: why had Cora Galenti herself not patented her formula?

The answer is that she had thought of it, but her lawyers had advised against it. Even if the formula *could* have been protected (and her lawyers were skeptical about this), it could easily have been copied, then slightly varied by some hotshot researcher, and she would have been out in the cold. No, they counseled, better to preserve formula, mystery, and mystique than to risk exposure.

Even getting the Brown formula patented was no easy business. The Patent Office at first rejected it as neither new or unique and too similar to germicidal soap and beauty-shop clay mask formulas. Attorney Herman Hersh, of the Chicago law firm of Ooms, McDougall, Williams & Hersh, argued successfully that the Brown formula had nothing in common with anything previously patented: "In germicidal soaps, the quantity of phenolic component is usually relatively small and . . . soaps . . . are not intended to produce changes in the deep layers of the skin."

As for the beauty masks, the lawyer contended that they were even more dissimilar: ". . . the phenol-camphor or phenol-sulphur form a part of the mask composition as distinguished from a fluid which is applied to the surface of the skin . . . which is thereafter covered with a mask having low vapor transmission characteristics."

Finally, on July 30, 1959, a patent was issued to Dr. Brown for a "Skin Treating Method and Composition." Clearly, Brown's motive was not personal gain. All rights to the formula and application process were turned over to Mount Sinai Hospital.

Versions of Brown's process began to appear in various publications. He published a "typical" formula in a paper on "Phenol-induced Histological Skin Changes: Hazards, Technique and Uses," in the July, 1960, issue of the *British Journal of Plastic Surgery*:

(All measurements by volume)

Phenol *	60-95 %
Saponated solution of cresol	0.3 %
Olive oil or sesame oil	0.25 %
Distilled water	q.s.**
	100 %

Was this, then, the famous Galenti secret formula?

It was not, said Cora Galenti.

Palma, however, attacked Dr. Brown for "crediting himself for [the formula's] origination regardless of the twenty-odd years that my mother's [preceded] his claims."

Was this or wasn't this an admission that Brown had successfully copied the Galenti formula?

Brown, for one, was convinced that he at last had exposed Cora Galenti's "secret."

In identical letters to Dr. Frances W. Lynch, in St. Paul, and Walter Alvarez, editor of *Modern Medicine,* in Chicago, Dr. Brown wrote:

The reason that we are sending [the paper] on to you is that the *Chicago Tribune* has been publishing a series of articles on Deep

---

* Paradoxically, the weaker the phenol solution, the more penetrating and dangerous it is to work with. Concentrated solutions cause formation of a protein precipitate which bars further penetration. Ignorant practitioners can ravage skin by timidly "going easy on the phenol."

**q.s. means "to add as much as may be needed."

Face Peels, extolling the work of lay operators. Regardless of the claims of the operators quoted who claim a "secret formula," I am quite convinced, from an extensive investigation, that the lay operators are using carbolic acid (phenol), and there is no "secret" formula. Phenol, we hold, is a very old and very dependable chemical in the hands of the physician. It is too dangerous, we feel, to be used by lay operators.

Two years ago there was a phenol death here during a "face peel" by a lay operator. Another notorious lay operator has just been convicted of practising medicine without a license after many victims complained of ectropion and keloidal scars after her ministrations with phenol. (She, too, denied that she used phenol.)*

Since there is such a public curiosity, the physician, certainly the plastic surgeon and the dermatologist, should be informed about this investigation. . . .

The public should know that there are *medical* channels through which they may safely benefit from this procedure and not be led to charlatans to be exploited. Further, physicians, certainly dermatologists, should know how to perform the work. . . .

There was one rather obvious reason for the fierce—but behind-the-scenes—professional opposition. In effect, Dr. Brown was saying that Cora Galenti's claims were not exaggerated, that the deep face peel removed wrinkles, as dermabrasion and face-lifting could not; that it rejuvenated the entire face, including nose and eyelids, with a single treatment; that it not only smoothed out the skin, but actually shrank and condensed skin volume; and that, most important of all, all of these changes were permanent and irreversible.

Interestingly, although Dr. Brown favored restricting face-peeling to the medical profession, he was fully aware that *any practitioner, no matter how highly qualified,* ran risks in using it. Number one in his eleven-step face-peeling process reads: "For such a controversial procedure a clear agreement in writing between doctor and patient is necessary. It should underline the hazards and specifically obtain release unequivocally stating the absence of warranty or guarantee."

* Brown erred in accusing a lay operator of causing a "phenol death." The Los Angeles death he likely was referring to later was determined to have been caused by heart attack. I have been unable to trace *any* death to the facial application of phenol by a lay operator. There have, on the other hand, been recorded instances of phenol-induced deaths by MDs trying to remove baby blemishes and scarification.

Nor could the physician avoid causing a degree of discomfort in applying the liquid. Demerol or morphine is indicated throughout the treatment.

While one might sympathize with Cora Galenti for developing the peel to a high, relatively safe, and extremely effective art, the public is indebted to Dr. Brown for having purged the process of its mysterious, "secret," expensive-parlor-game aura by bringing it back into the more disciplined domain of medical science. Yet his contribution has not been recognized by the whole profession. Outdated methods are still used where chemical exfoliation would be more effective.

Brown also found out *why* and *how* the peel worked. The phenol, he said, acts as an irritant, coagulating or cooking the skin's horny layer (keratin)—thus causing the skin to flake off. Large molecules are formed by combining phenol and the denatured keratin, preventing further penetration of the dermal skin layers by phenol toxins. He found that soap reduces skin surface tension, allowing greater penetration. Olive oil, on the other hand, "buffers" the solution, increasing skin tension and reducing penetration. The result of the peel is a permanent alteration of the gelatinlike collagen and albuminoid elastin pattern of the dermis. Microscopic photographs of eyelids treated fifteen years previously with phenol were used by Dr. Brown to show a new, permanent smoothness resulting from the flattening out and compacting of the skin's collagenous fibers.

Dr. Brown's process strongly resembled the Galenti method. He however, naturally emphasized certain medical safeguards—a few of which Miss Galenti adopted only after having been admonished by a court to do so in 1950. Since that year, she has always worked in the company of a physician, either the client's doctor or her own.

Dr. Brown warned that any phenol solution strong enough to remove wrinkles could also produce scarring—and that weaker solutions would not do the job.

He advised certain precautions, such as a skin patch test, a complete medical history with special attention to possible kidney malfunction, a check of pulse, respiration, and temperature every two hours during the peel, and tests to determine the pres-

ence of phenol in the urine and blood three hours after beginning the treatment.

Instead of Cora's cumbersome tapes, Dr. Brown proposed a
rubber mask (fitted exactly to the patient's features from a plas-
ter cast). The mask supposedly prevented the liquid exudate
from drying in the air and weakening the solution's activity upon
the skin.

Another Brown novelty was a five-fold facial division—(1) left
cheek and lower eyelid, (2) right cheek and lower eyelid, (3) chin
and under-chin, (4) nose and upper lip, (5) forehead and upper
eyelids—for administering the phenol, instead of the Galenti three-
fold operation, based about an imaginary "T" across the eyes,
down the nose to the collarbone.

With a deep-peel formula now published in the literature, organized medicine concentrated on putting Cora Galenti out of
business and behind bars. Suddenly, previous clients began to
sue her for alleged disfigurements. Many of the charges were obviously groundless, and Miss Galenti showed that several of the scar
victims clearly had failed to heed the normal precautions observed following chemosurgery.

After her brief period of success it suddenly seemed as though
the whole world had turned against her. Government and former
clients alike took her to court and began a ceaseless barrage of
charges that eventually put her out of business.

No sooner was the lay operator accused of mail fraud in perpetrating an "unworkable method of facial rejuvenation," than
all of her celebrated rejuvenates somehow vanished into thin
air. Several women did sign affidavits concerning her treatments'
effectiveness, and others did appear in court for her, but by and
large she was abandoned by the very luminaries who could have
done her the most good. Implied in the youth doctor-client relationship is the rejuvenate's inalienable right to deny on a stack
of Bibles that he has ever so much as *met* the doctor.

Even the most highly qualified plastic surgeons admit they run
a risk in performing the peel. And while Miss Galenti's work
seemed, for the most part, satisfactory, there were several cases
of disfigurement. West Coast courts made a number of awards to
what the press and federal government referred to as her "vic-

tims." Among these were Dorothy C. Nollau, $288.44; Louis and
Margaret P. Tangredi, $75,000; Ethel Watson, $35,000; Antonette
Martello Carter, $10,000 against each of six disfigurements; Della
R. Baum, $10,000 against each of six disfigurements; Mary M.
Sullivan, $37,500 against each of two disfigurements; Josephine
Kimball, $17,500 and costs. Actual payments by Miss Galenti were
made in only a few cases.

In the course of one proceeding in which both Cora Galenti and
an MD associate who had spent one year with her, were being
sued, plastic surgeons testified that facial rejuvenation was dangerous in anyone's hands, professional or lay. In examination-
before-trial, the plaintiff's expert medical witness was questioned
by the Galenti attorney as follows. (The defense was trying to establish that doctors protected themselves against damage suits
with "releases," while Cora Galenti laid herself wide open to such
suits by not taking this precaution.)

Q   You carry in your file one of your forms?
A   Yes.
Q   In which you have them warned that things may not go well?
A   Yes.
Q   That is a standard procedure among all plastic surgeons, de-
    signed by the Society to keep you from getting sued for mal-
    practice, is that right?
A   Actually not for malpractice. It is actually for assault and bat-
    tery.
Q   Then it is a question of self-protection?
A   It is primarily self-protection and also written evidence of
    again, self-protection by written consent of the patient that he
    can do such-and-such a procedure.
Q   That is looking out for number one?
A   I am sure everyone is concerned about number one.
Q   It is fair to state, is it not, that you do not warn a patient of
    all of the grave complications that could possibly result from
    plastic surgery?
A   This is true. I think in my previous statement I try to warn my
    patients of what I would say would be the common possible
    complications. In other words, the patient is warned of com-
    plications such as black eyes, if I do a rhino-plastic the pos-
    sibility of a nosebleed, of excessive swelling, the possibility of

many things all of which takes a considerable length of
time . . .
Q You don't warn them of death, do you?
A No.
Q That is an ever-present hazard, no matter how skilled the sur-
geon is?
A Absolutely correct.

The defense counsel then attacked statements that had appeared in ostensibly responsible professional journals, by ostensibly responsible authors, attributing deaths to lay facial rejuvenators and, by implication, to Cora Galenti:

A I did not say that. I had no preconceived idea as to who was
guilty or who was not guilty except that this patient had had
this particular effect from, apparently, a phenol application.
I had knowledge of a certain Cora Galenti in Los Angeles
area . . . who had been doing these procedures. I had knowledge of a number of people who had been rather horribly
scarred. Some died by these procedures. For this reason I felt
this was not conducive to good medical practice in the State of
California, and therefore I decided I would go along with this
particular patient and testify as to what she had in her defect
and what I would consider normal and ethical practice.
Q Doctor, aren't you overstating yourself and going overboard to
help out by saying that you know that some of these patients
died? That just is not true, is it, Doctor?
A On the contrary, it is true.
Q You know about this yourself?
A Except by hearsay.
Q All you are doing is repeating somebody's gossip, aren't you?
A Not gossip. Medical journals I consider not gossip.
Q Will you tell me which medical journals?
A The British Journal of Plastic Surgery in July 1960 [*i.e.*, the
Brown and Kaplan article previously referred to].
Q Somebody died of Cora Galenti's treatment?
A I did not say Cora Galenti's treatment. By these treatments.
Q You were talking about Cora Galenti's treatments?
A I talked about her because she applied the treatments.
Q You talked about several of her patients died and that is not
a correct statement?
A I did not say several of her patients died.

Cora's defense then cross-examined a physician witness called by the plaintiff:

> Q Have there not been many cases where a skin-planing [derma-brasion] resulted in infections and keloid scars?
> A Yes.

Even witnesses called by the prosecution admitted that they had consulted Cora Galenti because they had seen examples of her work that had deeply impressed them. Several physicians testified in her behalf as well, including Dr. Maurice Rosenberg, who had worked with her. In cross-examination, the plaintiff's counsel asked Rosenberg:

> Q Doctor, you say that 90 per cent of them were satisfied. Does that mean the other ten per cent were dissatisfied? . . .
> A The other ten per cent did not have any bad effects but the results were not sufficient to compensate them for the money they spent.
> Q You mentioned a [Mrs. X]. What happened to her?
> A . . . [Mrs. X] had a small scar on her chin. And the question of suing Mrs. Galenti came up and [Mrs. X] said she was herself responsible for the scarring, that she was extremely nervous and kept picking at the skin with her fingernails, so she never did take any action against Mrs. Galenti. . . .

Within three years of the appearance of the *Confidential* article, Cora Galenti was convicted in California of violating the medical practices act. On February 5, 1960, she was sentenced to summary probation for three years and a 180-day suspended jail sentence on condition that she pay a $1,800 fine. Until then, the debate as to whether face-peeling was properly a cosmetic or medical procedure had raged without conclusion. But Judge Harold Sheppard did not mince words:

"You are instructed that the treatment or removal of any ailment, blemish, deformity, disfigurement, disorder by surgical means constitutes the practice of medicine. I further charge you that the use of chemical means to produce the same end results constitutes the practice of medicine."

Judge Sheppard's ruling did not cripple Cora entirely. She was permitted to teach her technique to doctors, and to manufacture and sell her rejuvenation and face cream formulas. But the edict was tantamount to telling Rembrandt that, while he wouldn't be allowed to paint pictures any more, he could still whitewash fenceposts. She couldn't endure it.

In advertising Cora's face creams, the Galenti office casually sent out a reprint of the *Confidential* article—her most valuable publicity to date. Then one day the mail stopped coming to the Galenti rejuvenation factory.

"We discovered to our horror," says Palma, "that the Post Office was returning all the mail to senders, each envelope individually marked with a glaring red stamp which read: FRAUDULENT."

Something like a death wish seems to have directed Cora's behavior during each of her crises. Everything she did to protect herself turned out to be the worst possible alternative. Her silly prevarications damaged her case and alienated those who might have helped her. When, in December, 1960, she failed to appear at a pretrial conference for a hearing on a fraud order restricting her advertising through the mails, her business days as a facial rejuvenator in the United States were numbered.

Newspapers and magazines suddenly turned down her advertising. In one such instance, the Los Angeles Better Business Bureau went over the head of *Harper's Bazaar*'s West Coast advertising chief Philip Slater to censor Galenti ads. Bristling with contempt, the irate Slater fired off a complaint to the BBB's Helen Zellner: "One man . . . who has conducted an extensive investigation on Miss Galenti concurred in the opinion of others—that [she] is an honest woman being persecuted. *Harper's Bazaar* is no longer accepting Cora Galenti advertising. I look forward to the day when we shall. . . . In the meantime, I would suggest that you, Mrs. Zellner, practice some of those 'holier than thou' ethics your little sheet [the BBB house organ] screams so loudly of. . . ." Slater left his job shortly afterwards.

When California became too uncomfortable for Cora, she moved into Nevada. She raised $60,000 in seed money and then promptly launched a new corporation to operate The Fountain of Youth Ranch on a thoroughfare named Tomiyasu Lane ("Tomiyasu" in Greek means something on the order of "Drink to your health") two miles southwest of the Las Vegas Strip. The

ranch was a conscious copy of Elizabeth Arden's Maine Chance,
but somehow the Galenti version never measured up to the original's elegance (" 'Gauche' is the word for it," said one visitor).
Nonetheless, the attraction was the fountain of youth, and she
quickly filled its five bedrooms with patients—two to a room.

Still, her situation was precarious. Not only was she deeply in
debt, but her 1960 California conviction for practicing medicine
without a license dissuaded what, in other circumstances, might
have been natural customers. Deposits that had been paid up to a
year in advance had to be refunded. A valuable Boucher painting
(a present from a grateful English client) and several thousand
dollars in personal property were forfeited to Bekin's when she
was unable to raise a $900 storage fee. Her multiple real es-
tate holdings were tenuous affairs, and when the banks foreclosed
she lost practically everything.

Despite her financial difficulties, however, according to Charles
A. Miller, director of the Fraud and Mailability Division of the
U. S. Post Office, she was often seen in the casinos wagering "up-
wards of one thousand dollars per night."

At 3 P.M. on September 22, 1961, the last of Cora's dreams—
her beauty ranch—abruptly ended. Barging into a flock of screaming, half-dressed women, Clark County sheriff's deputies raided
her ranch, turning it inside out, confiscating the contents of her
laboratory, her address file—anything that looked as though it
might be of use in court. The slender charge: operating a business without a license. (She had applied for one, but had been
denied it.)

Galenti lawyers alleged that the raid was merely a cover-up
for an unwarranted higher-level federal investigation. The license
rap, as they predicted, *was* dropped, in fact. And the federal government *did* step in, prosecuting her for "mail fraud," largely on
the basis of an ad that promised "no burning, no peeling, no pain,
and very little discomfort in the Galenti process of facial rejuvenation that completely erases 20, 30 and sometimes 40 years of sags
and wrinkles."

According to the Chief Postal Inspector H. B. Montague, the
Postal Inspection Service interviewed about one hundred of her
former clients, subpoenaing twenty to testify, of which nine were
alleged scarring victims.

The prosecution probably established that the Galenti method was not painless—but little else. One witness's testimony that the formula felt "like liquid fire" made headlines across the country. Yet the prosecution failed to demonstrate that Cora Galenti had been solely responsible for the few scarring cases (of the three thousand she had treated) that the government had been able to muster.

In the single instance of severe disfigurement, that of restaurant owner Peggy Tangredi, affidavits were brought forth to show that the rejuvenate looked much improved immediately after her treatment—but might have suffered keloids by returning to her steam kitchen too soon (against Cora's routine instructions to avoid all heat).

The examination-before-trial of another disfigurement victim by the Galenti attorney is illuminating.

Q   Well, you considered that part of what you expected to receive was a face-lifting?

A   No. I had scars here and I still have the scars and she say [sic] that she would remove the scars completely.

Q   You had a scar on your face when you went in there?

A   Right there [indicating], yes.

Q   Where did you have this scar?

A   It is right there. You can see it, and it is larger now than it was before.

Q   Just a minute.

A   In fact, there are two now instead of one.

Q   This scar that you had on your face when you went in there, will you point on your face just where the scar was?

A   I have to have a mirror. It is right there some place. [Indicates]

Q   You were indicating . . .

A   . . . some place in here . . . [indicating]

Q   Right in the area of a little spot you have on your face?

A   There are two spots there I think.

Q   It looks like it might be a very small mole.

[The plaintiff's attorney]: Well, Counsel, I object to any characterization whatsoever. She is pointing with her finger to an area on the high point of her right cheek bone.

A   I have to have a mirror.

Q   I would say it is below the cheek bone.

A I have a little mirror here, excuse me. You see, right there, there is a scar, a mark there. [Indicating] . . .

Q What caused that little mark, if you know?

A I don't know. It was right there. It came by itself . . . It is not a mole. That is not a mole.

Q That scar that you have described, was that quite pronounced? You were conscious of it being there?

A Well, yes.

Q You could see it very plainly.

A I could see it very plainly.

Q That is why you went in there, to have that scar removed?

A Well, yes, the principal thing; and to have the face rejuvenated a little.

Q What else did you want in the way of blemishes taken off your face other than this scar you have identified?

A Nothing. What do you mean about . . .

Q What else did you want removed from your face?

A A few wrinkles, a few wrinkles.

Q Where did you have the wrinkles?

A I had it right here [indicating]. Very, very—they were almost invisible.

Q Could you see them plainly?

A You could see them, but they were not pronounced at all . . .

Q You wanted to get rid of them?

A Well I like to get rid of it . . .

Several others subsequently dropped their damage suits. Stripper René André wrote a formal retraction of her claim. One woman signed a sworn statement retracting her claim, and then wrote a letter of formal apology to Cora, stating that, at the instigation of a government official, she had seen an attorney who had several lawsuits against the rejuvenator.

Cora Galenti's dreadful memory probably influenced the jury against her as much as any other factor. On the witness stand, she consistently confused names, faces, dates, incidents. The jury was convinced that she was lying. Jurywoman Emma N. Sala afterward observed to reporter Ruthe Deskin, "She did misrepresent her treatment in my mind. She didn't do the things she said she did. This was proven to me . . . [Although] this woman was 64 and under a lot of strain. She could have made an honest mistake [in confusing identities]."

Cora's defense never seemed to get up steam. For one thing, her strongest witnesses were never examined before trial. Ruthe Deskin says, "I never went to [the lawyer's office] to discuss the testimony or anything. The first time I saw him was when I went to court." Even local physicians who had worked with her and were willing to testify for her were never called to the stand. A Tucson, Arizona, priest whose deep acne pits had been removed by her rejuvenation process was allegedly refused permission to testify by his bishop. On top of this, her lawyer's go-for-broke strategy of answering the jury's doubts by having her actually perform a facial rejuvenation before the court was demolished when the judge vetoed the idea. The crowning blow was the state's confiscation of her address file containing all of her celebrity clients' names, which Cora, typically, had forgotten.

Post Office Investigator Miller, who looked through the three or four hundred names in her file, said the only celebrity whose name he came across was James Dunn's. "If she had treated any of those [other celebrities] she would have trumpeted it in her literature," declares Miller.

Moving desperately against time and dwindling finances, her son, Tony, a Hollywood actor-playwright, attempted to salvage his mother's case. He tried to convince the U. S. Justice Department that a mysterious, highly placed government official had been taking bribes and blackmail money from Cora for years. After her husband, Robert Smith, had forced her to stop the extortion payments, the official sought to destroy her, said Palma. Although Palma informed editors, senators, congressmen, and Justice Department officials of his suspicions, no one followed up his charges with an investigation.

The bizarre character of the trial was compounded by a number of curious coincidences:

During the trial, a hysterical woman ran up the courthouse steps shouting: "We want our money! Your mother gave us a bad check!" (The incident, caused by the recent attachment of her Las Vegas bank account by authorities, was witnessed by a number of jurors.)

Between her conviction and sentencing, another lay operator was implicated in a suspicious motel-room death. Jurors read headlines such as: WOMAN DIES UNDERGOING FACIAL REJUVENATION.

(Two and a half years later—too late to do Cora Galenti any good —the "phenol-death" was proved to have been no such thing and the lay operator was acquitted of manslaughter. The actual manner of death, however, was never cleared up.)

A star prosecution witness admitted to *Sun* reporter Ruthe Deskin that she had perjured herself on the stand. Meanwhile, Miss Deskin was being pestered by anonymous phone calls warning her not to get involved.

First one wheel, then, a few days later, the other wheel, of Cora Galenti's *new* Oldsmobile dropped off while she was driving a nephew around mountain curves.

Few people in Las Vegas expected her to receive a jail sentence from Judge Roger Foley, although a guilty verdict seemed probable. Cora had been rather popular in Las Vegas, especially after a *Sun* series on her rejuvenation process (which she had performed on herself for the benefit of the press).

After the spectators had quieted down in the Las Vegas District Court room, Judge Foley announced in a stentorian voice:

"It is adjudged that the defendant is hereby committed to the custody of the attorney general or his authorized representative for imprisonment for a term of five years . . . and a period of probation to be consecutive to the term of imprisonment imposed on the following conditions . . . that she not teach, instruct, practice or in any manner engage in, or associate with the practice of facial or skin rejuvenation, in any manner, directly or indirectly, and she shall not permit her name to be used in connection with any such practice."

The hearing on her appeal in San Francisco's Appellate Court was a total disaster. The Galenti attorneys directed their appeal to suppress evidence seized in the Las Vegas raid, particularly a vial of liquid which was identified as composed of 48 percent carbolic acid, 50 percent water and 2 percent impurities. The state contended that this was her facial formula. Cora retorted that it was her callus-remover lotion.

As for the affidavit upon which the warrant for the search was made, the United States Court of Appeals for the Ninth Circuit ruled: "Unquestionably, the affidavit is poorly drawn. Nonetheless, in our judgment it meets federal standards for the issuance of a warrant."

The court's refusal to allow her to perform her treatment upon a witness was justified, ruled the judge, since "it might have required up to four months before any satisfactory appraisal could be made . . . [presenting] the court with undue delay and confusion on the one hand and inconclusive results on the other."

The appeal was rejected.

After failing to raise fees for a further appeal to the U. S. Supreme Court, the softly-smiling little lady packed up her three white poodles and strolled across the border to Mexico, forfeiting her bail and rights as a U. S. citizen.

She makes a melancholy Mexican, plying her facial rejuvenation trade in obscurity, hoping to return to California one day. Few customers—new prospects or veterans in need of a retread—know of her whereabouts thanks to a Post Office arrangement with Mexican authorities that returns her mail to senders. Her principal entertainments are the dog and horse races in Tijuana. And television.

The crackdown on lay practitioners proceeded apace. It looked like the end of facial rejuvenation à la Galenti. Florida operators were arrested for unauthorized medical practice. The AMA formally condemned so-called wrinkle clinics. The operators of a Connecticut facial rejuvenation center were put out of business and fined.

Anthony Palma's chief obsession these days is to secure his mother's rehabilitation and enable her to work again, perhaps in Florida, where chemosurgery by nonmedical practitioners is legal and back in full swing. There are others, too, who rather anxiously await her return: the bond company whose money went down the drain; unpaid former clients who had won disfigurement awards; the government.

Palma complained to me that the government was conspiring to get her back to the United States, perhaps by seizing her if she steps foot in a U. S. legation in Mexico to collect her social security money (which she apparently needs). I asked Charles Miller if this was true.

"No comment," he answered.

It is difficult to see tragedy in a destiny that has been marked by such staggering ineptitude and half-baked cupidity. A good deal of Cora Galenti's grief was brought upon herself. Yet—undeniably—

there is pathos in all this. Much of the woman's peculiar, self-defeating deviousness must be considered as pathological malfunction.

It is believable, even likely, that 40 percent of her clientele over the years were treated gratis. They include scarred war veterans, indigent clergymen, acned youngsters, and wretched old people. One is dismayed to think of Cora's cold-shouldering by other rejuvenates who, with but a word of acknowledgment of her artistry that saved *their* careers, might have saved *hers*. Even those who were treated free when they were down on their luck, and whose profitable latter-day youthfulness was pieced together, tape by tape, by Cora Galenti's sensitive fingers, resorted to the "I don't want to get involved" escape clause when asked to appear in court.

Organized medicine contends that the phenol face peel properly belongs to qualified MDs. But ownership of so valuable a tool carries with it an obligation to use it. So far the profession has not taken the trouble to learn about it or practice it.

The crying need for an effective, safe, inexpensive means of facial rejuvenation is apparent. Obviously, people would prefer to be treated by qualified plastic surgeons. But most professionals have charily avoided learning anything about the deep face peel. It seems the summit of hypocrisy, then, for them to feign shock or outrage when desperate patients seek out doctors of last resort like Cora Galenti.

CHAPTER THIRTEEN

All in the Mind

Yura left the room and told Egorovna to send in a nurse. "What's come over me?" he thought. "I'm becoming a regular quack—muttering incantations, laying on the hands. . . ."

DR. ZHIVAGO *by Boris Pasternak*

If there is one trait all youth doctors have in common, it is contagious optimism, a glorious psychic dynamism. Often, this alone is sufficient to "turn on" a patient—to restore his vim and make him feel younger. In traditional medicine this mystical healing agent is known as the placebo factor. It is also called the power of suggestion. It probably plays a vital role in most rejuvenation treatments.

Yet the youth doctors themselves are loath to credit the placebo. The reason is obvious. If the nostrum won't work for another doctor as well as it does for its inventor—then the critical healing element is probably not contained in the pill or ampule or serum or whatever—but in the rejuvenator himself.

Why is it, for instance, that Niehans can work therapeutic wonders that few of his associates can match? They treat the same ailments, kill the same sheep, insert the same needles, employ the same method of diagnosis. What's the difference?

The difference probably lies in the use, conscious or unconscious, of the placebo factor, or the power of suggestion. Niehans has a charisma few men possess.

There is one branch of youth doctoring that uses the placebo alone to effect healing. It includes faith healers, priests, psychiatrists, warlocks, witches, gurus, mystics, yogis, and so forth. Their therapeutic agent is one of the most powerful and one of the least understood of all. It appears to be a kind of kinetic relationship between two human souls.

As is true of other youth doctors, these spiritual physicians also strive to add life to years and years to life. The precise nature of their power unfortunately has not been subjected to conclusive testing, and the evidence is largely empirical. Yet their results can sometimes be so startling as to leave no doubt whatever that some of them possess extraordinary prowess.

Recently the fad of chemically induced psychedelia has caused a serious division in their ranks. One faction favors drug use, another regards it as sinful and/or self-defeating. Without question, the consciousness-expansion craze has attracted hordes of educated people to active contemplation of the psyche-soma liaison. One reason may be simply that the hypercivilized mentality finds a "high" attained by means of a tangible, visible chemical medium such as a pill more acceptable than a yogic trance.

Alan W. Watts, a Timothy Leary apostle, analyzes the new chemical supplement to classical mysticism in this way: "The traditional roads to spiritual experience seldom appeal to persons of scientific or skeptical temperament, for the vehicles that ply them are rickety and piled with excess baggage. There is thus little opportunity for the alert and critical thinker to share at first hand in the modes of consciousness that seers and mystics are trying to express—often in archaic and awkward symbolism. If the pharmacologist can be of help in exploring this unknown world, he may be doing us the extraordinary service of rescuing religious experience from the obscurantists."

In a sense, both the druggist and nondruggist healers are preaching the same gospel: that we deepen and sharpen our consciousness by transcending the limitations of habit and appetite; that we rediscover the glorious beauty of naked, unaffected existence.

The power of positive thinking has become a cliché, but few doubt its effectiveness. How positive thinking—physiologically or biochemically—rejuvenates and reinvigorates us, however, is still unknown to science. Instinctively, we regard nonmedical healers as beyond the pale. Their bizarre terminology is enough to outrage any scientific intellect. In fact, there is only one really good reason for not ignoring them altogether. They undeniably achieve fantastic results in circumstances where orthodox medical practitioners have given up. Unfortunately, the healer's methods appear to be distinctly personal. To know *what* he does is not always enough to be able to repeat his success.

All of us have experienced the phenomenon of psychic energy. We feel it within ourselves; we sense it in others. It is readily communicable. Certain people coming into the room instantly recharge us; others will drain us dry.

The late social psychologist Kurt Lewin's theory of psychic energy (as interpreted by Klaus F. Riegel in the *Handbook of Aging and the Individual,* James F. Birren, ed.) seems a good point of departure for speculating on the anatomy of faith healing. Lewin holds that the individual's many psychic needs create specific, corresponding tensions. Tensions are discharged by relating one psychic region to another, in the same way that current flows from one pole to another in an electrical battery. Psychic energy flows until the two regions balance, and an equilibrium results.

An older person evokes creative tensions with more difficulty for two reasons: one is the progressive loss of body energy; the second is the increasing rigidity of the barriers that separate one psychic region from another, making the buildup and release of useful tension more difficult to command. Old age's characteristic frustration and irritation may well stem in part from its loss of control over psychic energy.

Lewin sees old people as akin to run-down car batteries. Chemical deposits accumulate and impair efficiency; wires fray; the sum total of energy decreases until the machine stops dead in its tracks. The healer, then, clips a jump cable from his own to the patient's exhausted battery.

The psyche surely plays an important role in aging, just as it will surely play an important role in the eventual conquest of aging. The healers, however, are appallingly poor explainers. As Watts says, they carry "excess baggage." These are the Okies of the rejuvenation therapy trade—barefoot itinerants with oddball personal ef-

fects bursting through chicken wire harnesses, soup cartons, ruck-
sacks, laundry baskets, and flour bags. They seem just "too far out"
to be believed.

Nor are they made any more respectable by the company they
keep and their telltale portfolio of so-called (though not always
fairly) lunatic fringe causes and credos. They usually are hotly,
angrily, against communism, the FDA, most government, vaccina-
tion, insecticides, atheism, fluoridation, and happenstance theories
of events. On the other hand, they believe deeply in flying saucers,
God, health foods, individual freedom, a kind of ecumenism,
krebiozen, and conspiracy theories of events.

I had not intended to investigate the healers when I began this
book. They seemed too extreme to merit serious study. I definitely
wanted to stay as far as possible from the crackpot element in the
youth doctor field and concentrate on areas that showed serious
promise of real rejuvenation.

Several friends, however, argued persuasively in their behalf.
Dick Heinz, a Paris film producer, spent half a morning telling me
of his cell therapy-induced miseries (anaphylactic shock, fever, inflammation) at the hands of a Paris doctor. The other half was spent
in praising his _guérisseur_ (healer), who had cured him of his ailments and left him feeling like a new man.

The two faith healers I interviewed were quite different in their
approaches. Johnnie Lee Macfadden (publisher-naturist Bernarr's
third wife) sells earthy, affectionate counsel to Mr. and Mrs. Infe-
riority Complex and runs a cosmetic business on the side. Herbert
Herschel Blackschleger, a hard-core faith healer, takes himself and
life in general with anguished seriousness, using esoteric (Hindu,
Arab, alchemical, Greek, Latin) terminology to explain the mystical ways of the universe. The techniques of both are ostensibly
outlandish—but no more so than those of any religious person
would seem were his dogmas to be dispassionately probed.

When seventy-five-year-old Bernarr Macfadden married forty-
four-year-old Johnnie Lee, she was already a successful, and very
pretty, businesswoman, specializing in Cosmo-Dynamics, a blend of
love, personal magnetism, and rejuvenation. She looks back on her
late husband as a persuasive example of rejuvenated vitality in old
age ("Even at eighty-nine he could just talk to it and it would respond. He spoiled me for many others.")

Charging a $25 "love offering" per session ($5 if a client is "really poor"), she simply *talks* to the dispirited, the angry, the lovelorn— as though she were their guardian angel. Still blond, voluptuous, and interested, Johnnie Lee is a kind of doctoress of last resort for patients the usual doctors can't or don't want to bother with. Obvious oddballs and creeps she forwards to a psychiatrist friend.

Her attitude seems to be: "Tell me what's bothering you, honey . . . and I bet we can lick this thing together." Enthusiasm and common sense save her just when her lack of precision seems to be dragging her under.

She is strong on autosuggestive "gimmicks." For example, she recommends repeating this dictum over and over to oneself: "I absolutely refuse to allow anything or anybody that touches my life to take away my poise, inner tranquillity, and peace of mind. I truly realize that life will bring challenges—but I refuse to give anything power over me."

She also recommends a nocturnal between-the-sheets review of the day's activity ("even if you're with someone"). "At first it'll be annoying," she warns. "But analyze the day. If you find that most of the time you've had negative thoughts—and you've *got* to admit it—the next day you'll make a positive effort to watch every thought, word, and deed."

The results begin to show dramatically after one month, she claims. "You start feeling young again. You start showing it on the puss. You start giving life to every one of those cells—every tissue and sinew and the bloodstream."

She proposes a kind of "mental medicine" to combat anxiety. ("Worry kills the cells in the body—kills them, honey. *Absolutely* kills them. It's that simple.") As for surface rejuvenation, she feels that "a woman ought to have done whatever she thinks she needs done."

She told me of a middle-aged woman whose TV-personality husband was in love with his secretary. "She walked in here with her face down to the floor. She had neglected her personal appearance." After a general physical "rejuvenation" program, including a nose bob, regular exercise, cosmetic and fashion pointers, Johnnie Lee went right into "mental medicine."

"The first thing I taught her," she says, "was not to nag her husband. No whining and bickering. I told her every time a nagging thought came into her mind she had to learn to prune it off and mentally press that button of love." As for the other woman—Johnnie Lee's advice was to forget her. "If he finds a cute little thing, let him *have* a little bit of it."

The next step was reeducating her client in sex. "I bought her a lot of sex books and said: 'Read up on the subject.'"

Armed with new knowledge and a body that looked fifteen years younger, she got her husband back.

Hal Parets, producer of "The Joe Pyne Show," told me of a healer-rejuvenator who had appeared on the program and cured none other than the skeptical Parets of a nose polyp. From his Laurel Canyon home in Hollywood, he gave me the following account over the telephone:

> Herb Blackschleger is consultant to the Naval Ballistic Missile Weaponry Corps or whatever the hell they call it. [The Naval Ordnance Test Station, China Lake, California, is what they call it.] And he's got a whole lot of credits that are anomalies. It's a paradox. He's a wild-eyed man with such ridiculous thoughts.
>
> I had a polyp in my nose and I was supposed to go in on a Monday morning into the hospital and have it removed. I had to tape a show that night. Coincidentally, Herb Blackschleger was on. He wrote a book called *Hide*. If you can make any sense out of it, baby, like then you're much better than I.
>
> So I called the doctor on Friday, and I said: "I can get through the weekend with this goddam thing. It's a minor operation but I would bleed. Suppose we do it Tuesday instead." He said fine.
>
> So, Monday night I'm doing the show and Blackschleger is there. All of a sudden, Joe Pyne says, "You know, my producer Hal Parets has got a polyp in his nose. Could you remove it?"
>
> He says: "I will try." With a laying on of the hands, right? He put his hand about a quarter of an inch away from my sinuses, and the other he raised to the heavens, as though he were transmitting some special divine powers, right? And I don't know whether to even say this to you because *I still don't believe it.*
>
> But . . . as he did it, I felt the goddam thing draining. And I couldn't even breathe through that . . . nose for about a month. I knew that I had a polyp, and I was hoping that it would dissipate itself—which they are known to do. As he did that I suddenly realized that I could breathe. At the end of the program, the polyp had disappeared. I could feel it. It had shrunk.

The Master Storyteller, Somerset Maugham, found in CT a radical solution to his writing block.

Somerset Maugham's secretary, Alan Searle, was given CT as a Christmas present by his employer.

The list of celebrities who have been treated by Cell Therapy is a glittering one. In this picture, taken in 1963, West German Chancellor Konrad Adenauer *(right)* looks the picture of health and vitality.

United Press International Photo

Gloria Swanson, sixty-nine, whose beauty secrets are the envy of all women.

United Press International Photo

Polly Bergen, who recommends turtle oil as an effective facial rejuvenator, appears to practice what she preaches.

United Press International Photo

One of Paul Niehans' patients, Bernard Baruch, celebrating his ninety-first birthday in New York.

←

A lovely, youthful Dorothy Gish (*left*) returned briefly to Hollywood in the 1940's where she appeared in *Centennial Summer* with Jeanne Crain. Here they look over one of Dorothy's many scrapbooks.

United Press International Photo

Patrick McGrady J.

Rejuvenation continues to make giant strides toward the twenty-first century. Here attending the Cell Therapy Congress held in Bad Homburg in 1966, are three youth doctors *extraordinaire,* Franklin Bircher, Siegmund Schmidt and Wolfgang Goetze Claren.

I went to the doctor the following morning, called him up and said, "Cancel the bed and the surgery. Here's what happened. You wouldn't believe it, but I'm coming over and I want you to take a look."

I went to the doctor and he says: "Well, I'll be a son-of-a-bitch." And he put one of those scopes up my nose and said: "It's shrunk . . . Let's see what happens in the next couple of days." In the next couple of days the damned thing disappeared completely.

Two days after posting a letter to Blackschleger, I got a call from him, suggesting we meet at a restaurant in a northeast outskirt of Los Angeles. We had lunch together and recorded our conversation on tape. My wife, Colleen, was with us.

Herb Blackschleger looks like Mephistopheles. His top hair is sparse, reminding me of transplanted hair plugs. Rejuvenated hair it is, he admits, but regrown on a previously near-bald pate by his own willpower. Blackschleger looked younger than the forty-eight he gave himself. He is a powerfully built man who speaks in a down-to-earth manner that struck me as curiously mundane for our otherworldly discussion of interplanetary invasions, men from Mars, resurrecting people from the dead, rejuvenating by faith healing, and so forth.

He immediately volunteered that he had been dubbed "king of the quacks" by his critics (whom he calls "zombies"). "I'm an *unusual* quack," he continued, qualifying his title, "in that I've been to college . . . and a top honor student all the way through."

Checking him out, I found he had indeed been dean's list at the University of Cincinnati, where he was given a bachelor of science degree in electrical engineering; that he did have assorted honor credits from MIT, in ultrahigh frequency techniques; from Harvard, in electronics and cathode ray tubes; and from UCLA, in revolutionary guerrilla warfare. He also paraded such titles as an S.T.D. (Doctor of Sacred Theology) from a suburban Paris institution, a D.N.S. (Doctor of Natural Sciences) from a now-defunct Kansas City Institute of Naturopaths, and a perplexing T.A.N.O. (Thinking Agent of the Nameless One).

Despite his technical background—one of his papers written for the Navy is entitled "Ex Post Facto Reliability Considerations"—he nonetheless has managed to get acquainted with the flying saucer folk he calls *logi* or angels. They watch out for his friends' welfare and safety. He sees himself as "publicity agent for God . . . not one that shouts from the rooftops, but one that does express himself within limits to circles of people that will appreciate what we have to offer."

Financial exploitation of his psychic power is perfectly permissible, and he earns about $20,000 annually, he says, of which his "parapsychological income" is minimal: "Let's face it, most of the people who need help are broke."

The bulk of his income, however, comes from stints as corporation consultant. "I'm employed by some plants in the area," he explains, "to solve problems which their computers could not solve."

With such an abundance of manipulable psychic energy, one logical outlet would seem to be a gambling casino. Alas, pit men quickly spot him, he claims, and promptly upset psychic polarity by having a shill nudge him or offer him a drink, causing him to lose. What Las Vegas withholds from him, the stock market yields. He calls in his buy-and-sell orders with amazing precision, prophesying highs and lows within fractions of a point.

Some of his original open-order confirmations from the Los Angeles brokerage firm of Dempsey-Tegeler & Co. bear him out:

On April 27, 1967, for example, he sold 25 shares of Control Data at 85. The price promptly inched to a high of 85 1/4 and then plummeted.

On May 1, 1967, he issued a purchase order for 30 shares of the same stock at 75 5/8 ("I was going to order at eighty," notes Blackschleger. "While writing the order, a 'spirit' took over control of my hand, and made me write '75 5/8' . . ."). The "spirit" proved remarkably accurate. The stock dropped to not lower than 75 3/8 and, by the time of his writing, had soared well over 100.

On April 24, 1967, he bought 30 shares of Bunker Hill at 30 1/2 —its rock-bottom price—and the stock quickly leaped about 10 points.

On June 28, 1967, Blackschleger rid himself of 100 shares of Fresnillo Co. at 38. The price rose a mere 1/4 point, and then dropped rapidly.

On July 6, 1967, he entered a purchase order for 100 shares of Pacific Petroleum at 15. The very next day it hit 15 and then began to rise swiftly.

The Reverend Herbert Herschel Blackschleger has learned to

act cautiously. The theme of *Hide,* published in 1958, is that "persons who are far in advance of our society really should play dumb to stay out of trouble."

In his younger days, he says, he was less discriminating in elevating certain people "to the status of gods." He learned better when often "their first thought was to destroy me and become very powerful."

Blackschleger's innate psychic energy is, he says, at least partly biochemically generated. He claims that his blood sugar level ranges from 280 to 480, which would normally qualify him for a hospital bed or regular insulin injections as a diabetic. Yet, the higher it climbs, the more potent he feels. When the level is running near normal, at 120, he feels "lousy." As a gag, he carries a diabetic's card in his wallet, informing the reader that, if found unconscious or misbehaving, he is not intoxicated—but a diabetic.

He has, he avers, the right to appeal to "other sources," such as flying saucers, for extra power. "Primal creative rays" travel through his hands to and from his clients' bodies. Negative rays are extracted with one hand; healing rays are imparted with the other.

"Any lasting rejuvenation," he states, "must be based upon these primal creative rays."

His rejuvenation activity occasionally provokes "harassment" from government and professional policing groups that take a dim view of his "creative rays," primal or otherwise. To deter these groups, "Satguru Herb" (as he signs friendly letters) has tried to tuck such work under the protective wing of The Church of Rejuvenation, which he recently founded. Aiming toward a goal of peaceful, happy living for a thousand years, Blackschleger advises his coreligionists first to rejuvenate themselves, then their friends, then "this God-forsaken nation," and finally "this entire planet."

Because his income from healing and rejuvenation is erratic Blackschleger tries to limit such activities to a circle of friends or friends of friends. He believes that demonstrations of "so-called miracles" are important to establish credibility in his other pronouncements which are not so readily verifiable.

He prides himself on being a scientist, insisting that his feats can be repeated again and again—and even by others "with the proper preparation."

"My depth of analysis of reliability for some of our existing missiles has been so far beyond the comprehension of the average scientist, that it has taken as long as a year for some of the top scientists to understand my presentations. When scientists don't understand me on reliability and simple things, then I don't expect them to understand me on the more complex things."

Steering clear of the perilous shoals of unauthorized medical practice, Blackschleger simply refers to his clients as "friends" or "cousins." His services are compensated by "donations." While Blackschleger makes no bones about his need for a comfortable income, the primary purpose of the "donation" is to evaluate people, he says. "If I cure a person of multiple sclerosis, let's say, who visited six doctors and was given up as hopeless, and he gives me two dollars for letting him walk out of the room when he was carried in, then he's essentially hung himself as far as future help is concerned. So I don't try to set myself up as a judge, but I reserve the right to feel that these people are not expressing adequate appreciation. Not only toward me, but toward the people I work with. . . ."

Aging, to Blackschleger, is an accumulation of poisons in the body and increasing disuse of the mind. "The mind can actually rejuvenate the body by itself. Ten years ago I had diabetes. Two years ago I was bald. My hair's coming back. This is new hair." When I later asked him for before-after pictures of his hair growth, he wrote: "Prefer to wait until lots more hair appears, and the difference will be much more startling."

The will, he contends, does not operate in isolation from the physical environment. For ordinary people he recommends a toxinless diet and use of his Vivicosmic disc to remove harmful effects of fluoridation from water. So great is his fear of fluoridation that, should Los Angeles' water become fluoridated, he insists he would move his family to another area.

When he was living in the China Lake, California, area several years ago, he began to notice that he was losing his psychic power. He began to catch colds. His protégés began to suffer accidents. When he asked if the water was fluoridated, officials said no. Finally, when chemical analysis indicated fluoridation, he used his Vivicosmic disc to defluoridate his drinking water, and his powers, he says, were quickly restored. The disc, an olive stone alleged to contain healing rays, is not for sale but available for a $5 donation.

Blackschleger drinks whisky, smokes cigarettes, and eats steak.

Such violations of the normal faddist's shibboleths demonstrate that "if you have the proper amount of psychosomatic power you can eat poison and overcome it."

Nonetheless, in traditional youth doctor fashion, he urges ordinary folk to eat a variety of fruits and vegetables (*"living* food that hasn't been cooked, sprayed with insecticides, or washed in fluoridated water.")

As for the faddists, "What we have is a situation where we've got a lot of health nuts, health addicts that have all the answers to health —except they're not healthy. And I've talked to a lot of people who say drink this, use this, eat that—and they're not healthy."

Blackschleger feels that narcotics and hallucinogens are "of the devil." They are used, he says, by people starved for religious experience "to do in a hurry what it takes me five or ten years to do with a person."

He describes his technique of assistance as a "de-hypnotizing" which releases his "cousins" from their fixations, sets them on the long road toward potential divinity, and encourages them with the conviction that the path can be traveled rapidly.

The purpose of life, he asserts, is to gain experience, education, and eventual perfection. Perfection is a pleasant and enjoyable harmony of life forces—but one that includes meaningful challenge. The trouble with contemporary existence is that "the mental pressures upon people are so tremendous in some cases that a person cannot really learn a lesson or become improved as a result of passing a challenge."

His conception of perfection surpasses social relationships. "I go much farther than society. Society is merely kindergarten compared to life beyond. *All* life on this planet is but kindergarten compared to what lies beyond. And most people are merely enjoying themselves in kindergarten without preparing for first grade. Without preparing for high school. Without preparing for college."

As I talked with Blackschleger there in that dark restaurant, I began to feel what most of his cousins probably felt. Sympathy for him. Even as his words became increasingly fantastic, as he began to speak of flying saucers, his friends from other worlds, magic healing rays, men becoming gods, and so forth, he was filling in the pieces to the great puzzle. There was no false humility here (or any other kind for that matter). He, Blackschleger, had diagnosed the universe's malaise, had peeled off the masks of war, of politics, of religion, of man's self-destructive inhumanity, of his criminal insensibility and exposed the insanity of society. Of course, of *course* . . . it was all faintly ridiculous.

Why was he speaking so freely into my tape recorder when at that very moment he knew he was under investigation by the FDA? Because I had been "checked out" by his people well in advance of the interview; because I had immediately sat on his right side—not on the left; because even if he had said something stupid on tape, it would be automatically erased by his *logi* (his brand of guardian angels).

It was a stirring, half-believable fantasy.

All one's subliminal fears and hopes, he seemed to imply, were real.

There *were* answers.

As my eyes became accustomed to the dark, I noticed a woman sitting directly behind us with what could have been a tape recorder of her own on the table in front of her, who was also taking notes. She pretended not to be interested in our conversation, but it was apparent that she had no other business there. Who was she? I never found out.

My wife, who was taking Blackschleger seriously in a very concrete way, began to lead him away from the theoretical. "Can you feel the rays?" she asked him.

"Oh yes, oh yes."

"How do they feel?" she continued innocently.

"Let's say there's a man here. I hold my hands over his head about three inches away. I feel a little bit of warmth coming from his head. They feel as though they're pushing away from his head. If I use my left hand, they sort of push away. If I use my right hand, they draw to it. So I can tell whether a man is, let's say, real powerful cosmically or psychically—or real weak, or negative."

"Does the person you're doing it to have to be very receptive?" she asked.

Blackschleger explained that a person had to be at least neutral— "If they fight me, it's no deal." He said the greatest barrier to doing an effective job was the great distortion of reality wrought by religion, causing people to fail to appreciate the true mystical depths of reality. Several sterile women have implored him to render them fertile—"but they want the child in five minutes instead of waiting nine months."

A few moments later, Colleen put the healer to an actual test. "When you're doing this healing, do you have to have certain conditions? For instance, my eyes are burning now [from the smog]. Could you take that away?"

"Yes, I could, except that I'm not in a mood for it."

"Do you have to be?"

"First of all," he said somewhat wearily, "I'll draw out some of the poisons in your eye. Even though I'm not in a general healing mood right now. Because I'm discussing these things and I've got to get back somewhere else and so forth."

He thrust his right hand, fingers spread, directly in front of her face. "This'll draw the poisons out of your eye. And I'll hold them over slowly, and I'm actually drawing the undesirable, let's say, elements or rays from your eyes that are causing the problem. And then . . . I feel them coming, there, coming out . . . and there are quite a *bit* in there! In other words, apparently you're allergic to the smog. Now I feel the negative or undesirable elements leaving your eyes."

Assuming that the experiment was about to prove a bust, I tried to gentle his failure. "Colleen has very bad eyes to begin with . . ."

"Right. And now with my left hand I will put creative rays in there which will strengthen them. I can actually feel when to stop. The other eyes you'll see in about a minute . . . you'll see them start to sparkle a little more than they have been . . ."

"They *do* feel better."

"This is unbelievable, but it actually *is* happening. Look at her entire face brightening up."

Later, Colleen told me that she had felt immense relief when he began to operate with his right hand. Shortly afterward, however, as the conversation moved to other matters, her eyes became sore again. (But by the time we had left the restaurant, they felt better and stayed clear for the remainder of our stay in Los Angeles, another two days—two days during which my own eyes were painfully smog-burned.)

I began to get quite interested. "Maybe you can correct her faulty vision, too?"

"Well, this would take a little while yet . . . in order to really draw the power into her. Standing up in a bar is not the best place in the world to conduct what I call a sacred ceremony. And to me these things are sacred."

Blackschleger began to talk of his nemeses, the "zombies" who constitute the overwhelming majority. One recognizes the zombie by four characteristics: (1) he needs strict laws to tell him what's best for him (*i.e.*, "He cannot decide that it's best to stay away from narcotics. He has to have a law to keep him away from them."); (2) he finds constant fault with other people, at the same time ignoring large flaws in his own character; (3) he fails to recognize or appreciate the Holy Ghost—which Blackschleger equates with ESP. Example: President Johnson, he allows, might possess ESP, but certainly fails to use it; (4) he spends less than 10 percent of his time in the service of the cosmic, or in the service of God. ("A person has to consider the rest of humanity and he has to go beyond that and consider the fish in the ocean, the birds in the forest . . . all life. Not only all of today's life, but all future life.")

Although Blackschleger has no orthodox religious affiliation, he was born Jewish and considers himself a Christian to the extent that "Jesus was a Christian."

"I believe in Jesus as an example," he says. "I use the Bible as a reference." His favorite passage, incidentally, is the one that explains the phenomenon of a Herbert Herschel Blackschleger—John 14: 12—*Verily, verily, I say unto you, He that believeth in me, the works that I do shall he do also; and greater works than these shall he do; because I go unto my Father.*

He has great respect for yoga. "A good yogi," he says, "will take a lot of energy that enters the kundalini of a person, which is a source of power sort of near the base of the spine, and gradually bring it up to the head where it can be of use. The kundalini is near the sexual organs, and in most cases, people with a lot of capability wind up being sexual deviates or sexual enthusiasts. This is why I say there are a lot better things than sex in this world. In other words, I don't deny that sex is—"

"Can you name one?" I interrupted, genuinely curious.

"—pretty good. Well, I would say that conversing with you today, although I said more than I intended to say because of the FDA and things like that. Not that I'm afraid of them, but I don't care to be annoyed by them, if you know what I mean."

Later he confessed that sex was probably a preeminent factor in restoring youthfulness. "The efficiency of rejuvenation," he observed, "depends upon the extent of sexual activity, for which the optimum varies for each individual. The optimum could be once a year or once a day—depending on the individual."

Blackschleger maintains that, in addition to healing and rejuvenation, he can actually bring people back from the dead. An example was his brother-in-law, Herman Rief, a locksmith, who had been given last rites of the Catholic Church at the Cincinnati Jewish Hospital's intensive care ward. I tried to verify Blackschleger's story by contacting the hospital and his sister. The hospital did not answer my letter; the sister did, confirming what he had said in detail. Blackschleger tells the story as follows:

> He was ready to be put into the grave. My sister called me and said: "Herb, I don't want to lose my husband." Everybody had kissed him goodbye, and his body had been cut open so many times that he was just an experimental cadaver.
>
> He started off with blood poisoning, and they wound up cutting his colon so he could not use his normal bowel function. He ended up with uric acid poisoning . . . lead poisoning. His blood pressure when I got to the hospital was 0/70, which means that he was practically dead.
>
> I performed certain actions which included putting the creative rays into his intravenous fluid, into his body through his back, into his legs, and into his heart—and gradually his condition improved. This was so unbelievable to the doctors that, when I would ask them, or the nurse, "How is he doing?" they would say: "No change."
>
> I would say to them: "Yesterday his urine was red, today it's yellow. Isn't that an improvement?"
>
> They would say: "Well, yes, it is."
>
> I would say to them: "Yesterday his blood pressure was 0/70. Today it's normal. Isn't that an improvement?"
>
> They would say: "Well, yes, I guess so." But they couldn't believe such a thing was possible. After I went in there a few minutes and started him improving, I was kicked out of the room. They said: "Don't hurt Herman." Then they'd come in there and give him a shot of their junk, and he'd twitch and move in pain. And they said *I* was hurting him. And they would allow me in there five minutes per hour. So they made me perform in a practically impossible situation.

Now, what I did, and this is the most important thing: I said that he *shall improve.* This was a psychosomatic battle between me and the entire medical staff of the Jewish Hospital in Cincinnati. And where they would use their medical facilities and say: "He's practically dead and cannot get better," I would say: "He shall get better."

The first thing I did was clean out the ganglia of impurities in the nerves therein. And then to inject this cosmic energy into the ganglia. This spread all through his body. In addition, I put creative rays into his intravenous fluid, so that this again would bring creative forces into his body. I also held his arms and legs and placed my arms over his chest so that we could have local application of these creative rays.

And, fortunately, before they found out what was going on, I was allowed ten minutes instead of the usual five. In basically ten minutes I accomplished enough to turn the tide. Within just a few hours his condition started to improve rapidly. Then is when the psychosomatic part began. This is all supposed to be impossible.

Blackschleger refuses to sit idly by while the "zombies" of this world bring it to the brink of catastrophe. He considers himself a step or two in advance of Edgar Cayce ("The Sleeping Prophet"), who predicted that the axis of the earth will rotate in 1993. "I don't intend to let that happen," says Blackschleger, who plans to be around for "a couple of hundred years," but only "if I don't get disgusted with the people on this planet." War, as he sees it, is inevitable because Americans have "voted for war and they must have war." The next Armageddon, he says, will be the framework for his greatest demonstration, keeping the bombs from falling on Los Angeles while they obliterate other parts of the country. Since my conversation with Blackschleger, his feeling of impending doom has increased.

On September 11, 1967, he was sentenced by the Hon. Irwin J. Nebron of the Los Angeles County Municipal Court to a three-year summary probation and fined $550 for distributing his Vivicosmic disc in California. "True religious freedom," Blackschleger says, "is extinct within the State of California and virtually throughout the United States of America. For a while all will be calm, but the above decision has triggered the 'end days' during which only those of us who have been persecuted will note an improvement in conditions."

In a last desperate attempt to save the planet, the Hon. Rt. Rev. Master Herb Blackschleger, "A" student in revolutionary guerrilla warfare at USC, Thinking Agent of the Nameless One, Doctor of Sacred Theology, Doctor of Natural Sciences, Bachelor of Science in Electrical Engineering, Tau Beta Pi, Eta Kappa Nu, Prelate of the Neoplatonic Church of Religious Science, has summoned the *logi* and flying saucers to persuade the American people to elect him President of the United States in 1968.

CHAPTER FOURTEEN

Shooting the Stars

My wife's Italo-American gynecologist is normally a fountain of primitive charm, of outrageous flattery, of unreconstructed optimism. His bedside manner carries over into his office, where he conducts a ceaseless serenade to daughters, wives, and mistresses of the right people. When my pregnant wife and I walked into his office one morning, I was shocked to see him crimson with anger, pounding his mahogany desk.

"That dirty, no-good son-of-a-bitch," he fumed. "They ought to put him behind bars. When are they going to get wise to this guy? That poor girl who was just in here used to be a very talented actress. She was a star on the way up. You've heard of her. She was really going places until he got hold of her."

I asked who "he" was and precisely what he had done to the girl.

"*You* tell me who he is," he said. "You've been talking to these speed doctors. He's gotten her hooked on B-12 and methedrine. She's absolutely fragmented . . . whacked out . . . almost psychotic. She can't sleep. She cried the whole while she was in my office. I think I can pull her out of it, but it will take a lot of doing."

It would indeed take some doing. As of this writing, three months later, she was still hospitalized in the Bellevue psychiatric ward, a certified psychotic. It was easy to guess the speed doctor's identity, for he had authored similar tragedies before.

Within the past fifteen years or so, a new brand of youth doctor has appeared on the Rejuvenation scene. He specializes in relieving chronic fatigue—the number one complaint of our time. If lower-middle-class folks are content with Serutan, many upper-middle-class and Beautiful People, as Marilyn Bender calls them, are not. For the artistic and intellectual sectors of our hyperkinetic society, chronic fatigue is regarded as a personal and professional catastrophe requiring instant repair. Sleep and exercise, probably the best answer to this problem, are unfortunately disdained as bothersome intrusions upon one's precious time.

The average doctor admits that he is impotent against the mysterious "blah" feeling that topples many creative people in their prime. After eliminating the possibility of chronic infection or an endocrine malfunction, all he can do is suggest a change of physical habits or, as a last resort, a psychiatrist.

For influential people especially, this textbook fundamentalism provides no answer at all. They are not accustomed to accept the notion that problems cannot be solved quickly, no matter what scripture may hold to the contrary. Rather than settle for a dreary prognosis, they are inclined to search for a doctor who holds some kind of answer—*any* kind of answer.

The speed doctor's unofficial title derives from the magic in his hypodermic. "Speed" refers to a collection of drugs, usually given in combination, of which some are highly stimulating and others totally innocuous. They seem to sharpen the patient's sensations, perceptions, and enjoyment of life. A heavy user is called a "speed freak."

This special pharmacopoeia breaks down into varieties of hormones like ACTH, cortisone, and chorionic gonadotropin; vitamins, especially B-12; narcotics such as Demerol; amphetamines, most commonly Dexedrine and methedrine; gamma globulin; and calcium gluconate. Only Demerol, strictly speaking, is classified as addictive, although the others can be habituating.

Patients frequently describe their injections as producing sensations akin to a sexual orgasm, and the shots are referred to as "jolts," "shakes," "bucks," "flashes," or "rushes."

The end of the line comes when a patient becomes exhausted or "strung out" and goes into a "crash." At this point he may part company with his exciting, high-living speed doctor in favor of a very square doctor who can yank him out of his frenzy.

The speed doctors and their Beautiful People patients form a cosmopolitan clique. New members are picked with great care—as much for social or personal motives as for any specific clinical or financial cause. The speed doctor's "Santa Claus" façade is so important that he carries a far larger proportion of NCs (no charge patients) than do most of his orthodox brethren.

So great is the demand for his specialized service that he is at all times in total control of his patients. The Park Avenue *kvetch* or Texas boor have no place in his waiting room. His clientele consists of a flock of polyglot tip-of-the-tongue names from show business, politics, the arts, publishing, high finance, advertising, society, and fashion. If he squeezes his dukes and barons somewhat mercilessly, it is only so that he (and they) may enjoy the company of a selected few impoverished courtesans, jokers, and pages. This way the tone of the court is kept bright, salty, and, above all, fun.

At any given moment, the speed doctor's coterie would appear to be a rather jolly family. Yet the generations are very often brief. Sooner or later, patients tend to be outrun by their breakneck speed and fall victim to hard-to-define but very real physical and nervous crises. The outcome of these crises is a reluctant resolve never to set foot again in the youth doctor's office. No hard feelings, but a body can tolerate only so much acceleration.

Parting company is no easy matter for those in the doctor's inner circle. It means abandoning a way of life and starting all over again from scratch. Once accustomed to the *gemütlich Kaffeeklatsch* from 1 A.M. to 5 A.M., the pep up 6 A.M. jolt to face a board meeting or dress rehearsal, the heady involvement with the doctor's latest brainstorm (everybody works for free)—it is difficult to give them up. Besides, after a while the patient finds that he needs his speed not only to stay alert for a high-pressure twenty-hour day, but just to get by.

Often, the patient fails to appreciate the degree of his dependence on the doctor. As casual as his dispensing of drugs may seem, in fact the doctor will turn off his patients as easily as he turns them on. They are, moreover, frequently unaware of the chemistry of their jolt—so that when they request their "B-12" or "cortisone" shot from another doctor, the anticipated bang turns out to be a feeble whimper. The speed doctor alone holds the key to the patient's speed.

The jolt itself—an exhilarating, torrid body glow experienced right after the shot—is usually provided by an amphetamine or calcium gluconate, which is mixed with other substances. A well-known diet doctor told me that intravenous calcium gluconate produces the most powerful excitement of all on the autonomic nervous system. Vitamin B-12 alone, on the other hand, gives little more than a subjective placebo effect.

The immediate sensation of the speed injection is acknowledged to be extremely pleasant—especially the first time around. An ex-habitué described it this way: "First there's a hot flash that goes from the tip of your toes to your balls, then up to your head. You've never felt anything like that outside of the greatest orgasm you've ever had. And the doctor says: 'Just lie down there now. You'll be all right.' And you say: 'He's got magic,' right?"

Almost immediately depression and fatigue seem to vanish. The patient's eyes sparkle and open wide. His pallor vanishes. But within twenty-four hours, a kind of queasy desperation may over-come him. Sheepishly, he asked the doctor for more of "whatever it was you gave me." He doesn't always get it. One young Norwe-gian told me that his doctor cut him off as soon as he complained that the last jolt had been too weak.

A middle-aged Greenwich Village writer complained to his physician when the amphetamine was removed from a speed con-coction, leaving only the vitamins and the hormones. His physician discontinued his "bucks" for several weeks. The doctor resents be-ing regarded as a cheap source of thrills, at his patients' beck and call.

Many speed doctors possess a powerful charisma. Their patients boast of their wit and charm. The treatment has an almost hypnotic quality. Their injections are rumored to have wrought near-mirac-ulous reversals of hopeless conditions. Yet, somehow, their treat-ments never find their way into the medical literature, where real substantiation of results is required.

The dangers of speed injections are well-known to most patients. "Some like the feeling so much," a movie scenario writer told me, "they're like those rats whose brains are charged with electricity every time they have an orgasm. Soon it's *all* they do. They just touch that trapdoor and die there, that's all. A marvelous way to die, but die nonetheless."

Cecil B. DeMille is reported by former associates and friends to have died following extended speed treatment by a youth doctor.

One emotionally disturbed housewife found "complete relaxation and everything twelve shades brighter and clearer—not at all like marijuana" with her intramuscular cortisone injections. After eighteen months of uninterrupted euphoria, however, she stopped visiting her speed doctor. "It wasn't solving my basic problem, which was that my husband was beating me. *That* didn't change. When I realized I could spend the rest of my life not feeling *anything*, I stopped going." Shortly thereafter she divorced her husband and, a year or so later, remarried quite happily.

The speed drugs vary widely in essence and risk. Speed doctors with an overflow clientele sometimes encourage the practice of self-injection, as a kind of mutual convenience. Not only can this bring about infection and abscesses, it may also encourage the escalation from mild intramuscular shots to the far more potent intravenous injections. All the patient has to do, when the 2 cc every-other-day intramuscular shot gets too weak, is to start shooting himself in the veins. And when that, in turn, leaves him cold, he seeks out another speed doctor so that he can draw on two monthly speed prescriptions instead of one.

The withdrawal and exhaustion symptoms with, say, B-12 or gamma globulin shots are minor compared with the consequences of amphetamine habituation. Tachyphylaxis—the phenomenon of rapid immunity which decreases the impact of succeeding jolts—often obliges the patient to increase his prescribed dosage. Actual psychosis, paranoia, and memory loss then become very real dangers.

Demerol addiction, of course, is a grave concern, not only for patients, but for many doctors who succumb to the temptation of using the drug on themselves in order to transcend their personal problems and fatigue.

Although the activities of the handful of speed doctors are common knowledge in the major cities of the United States, little action has been taken against them officially. The latitude accorded all physicians in prescribing nonaddictive drugs is quite broad, and specific abuses are hard to define, much less prove.

Many patients swear that, after boarding the speed train, they never experience sickness again, not so much as a common cold. One youth doctor's cold remedy, Cortex 40 and Declomycin, is said by one of his patients to have kept his entire family cold-free for two full years.

The speed doctors, as is true of other youth doctors, also special-ize in treating degenerative conditions most doctors regard as in-curable: arthritis and rheumatism, cancer, multiple sclerosis, and even infections such as hepatitis. They claim spectacular improve-ments and cures, but rarely document their claims satisfactorily.

A former speed patient warned: "What happens is that you go in with a simple disorder—but it becomes very complex before you finish. He winds up treating you for an enormous number of differ-ent things."

Such doctors are notoriously publicity-shy, unlike the other breeds of youth doctors who need press notices to further their prac-tice. Only after pulling every string available to me was I finally able to interview the legendary Dr. Z, rejuvenator extraordinary to the social registers of several world capitals.

I refer to him anonymously here, although he did not expressly ask me to. I was allowed one—and only one—visit with him, which is one more than most writers ever get. Unfortunately, I am afraid that the pieces of the Dr. Z puzzle that I have assembled do not form a coherent representational picture—merely a fascinating ab-stract. I cannot, for instance, reconcile the reverence and affection his patients feel for him with the disparagement expressed by his physician colleagues.

The folklore surrounding Dr. Z sounds fantastic. Yet I have veri-fied story after story with his patients. He is said to have kept the en-tire company of a Broadway musical on speed for the duration of their smash out-of-town opening. He is courted by foreign ambas-sadors and has standing invitations to visit them abroad whenever he can find the time. His most celebrated friendship was with the John F. Kennedys.

Although the late President was attended by a number of physi-cians, Dr. Z was a special friend. For some time JFK had suffered from a chronic progressive adrenal cortical insufficiency, whose chief symptoms were chronic fatigue, general weakness, unnatural skin pigmentation, and hypotension.

The story goes that Dr. Z had been treating Kennedy with aque-ous adrenocortical extracts, which some modern endocrinologists would regard as old-fashioned and relatively ineffectual therapy. Introduced to the President by his spouse, who met him through a mutual photographer friend, Dr. Z quickly obtained entrée to the

White House and Hyannisport, where he was regularly welcomed. His catholicity of interests and the vital, polychromatic world of unorthodox medicine he represented made him an entertaining character if nothing else. Soon Dr. Z began to attend NASA seminars on space medicine. This quickly became a hobby.

"I just can't understand it," a hardworking physician spluttered irately to me one night as he closed up the shop. "Imagine a guy like that treating the President! Why is it that the most powerful people in the world manage to get the most horrible medical care? Look at the Pope and Adenauer—treated by cell therapy. Churchill was treated by Christine Keeler's pimp. A veteran Congressional leader, was being treated for lumbago by this back doctor—and then he died from metastases to his spinal column."

So close was the JFK-Dr. Z friendship, according to one knowledgeable source, that the President once appointed an Internal Revenue Service official to help Dr. Z straighten out his tangled income tax situation. Other reports have speculated that powerful Administration officials in Washington deliberately queered an intended surprise federal raid on Dr. Z's premises, which were thought to contain evidence of irregular pharmaceuticals. When the raiders arrived, Dr. Z's office contained nothing more suspicious than aspirin and rubbing alcohol.

Shortly before the assassination of the President, plans were drawn up for him to see a New York endocrinologist who entertained the idea of starting him on a new therapy. The relatively weak aqueous adrenocortical extracts that Dr. Z had prescribed were derided as "nebulous . . . nonsense" by the specialist. The new man also challenged Dr. Z's obsession with injections per se and speculated that their sole advantage lay in their greater placebo effect, but that otherwise they were "notoriously weaker than what we could give him by pill [in] the purified hormone form." All other things being equal, the President would see the endocrinologist sometime before Christmas, 1963. (Ironically, the arrangements to bring in the new doctor were made through the same IRS agent who had straightened out Dr. Z's accounts.)

When the sickening news broke that the President had been struck down by an assassin's bullet, the endocrinologist's first thought was to make sure that the wounded Kennedy would receive scheduled adrenocorticosteroids. Even if he had survived the gunshot wound, any delay in administration of his regular hormone injections could have brought on death. Promptly, the physician called his photographer contact's office so that instructions could be given to the Dallas hospital staff. He was informed, however, that it was too late. The President was dead. Whether in fact the hormone treatment was ever given is unknown.

I chatted one evening with a Dr. Z "regular," a patient of nine years' standing who belongs to the inner circle (those who meet in the doctor's laboratory, where, it is said, miracles of various kinds are performed nightly). The patient's Upper East Side Manhattan apartment once belonged to Huntington Hartford (described by the current owner as "everybody's patient") but since had been decorated to resemble a turned-on fishbowl. Below sensuous, washed-out oranges, reds, and blues, paddling softly in his armchair to a shuddering record player was my host, who got up every few minutes to welcome a new influx of itinerant swells who kept dropping by until I left at 5 A.M.

I asked him about the nature of Dr. Z's patients.

"I understand," he said, "that Jackie still goes. Her sister and brother-in-law, the Radziwills, they're there quite frequently, Alan Jay Lerner . . . people like Barney Balaban . . . and Adolph Zukor and Cecil B. De Mille and Harry Warner and Harry Cohen . . . Eddie Fisher . . . Maynard Ferguson . . . Johnny Mathis, Maurice Chevalier, Salvador Dali . . . have been his patients. . . .

["They are] really very active people, creatively . . . and very sexually active. They're all contemporary people, no matter how old they are. And I think that's partly because of Dr. [Z]."

I wanted to know how he rated the "high" he got from his injections, which he assumed to contain methedrine.

"Well . . ." he paused, it's very peculiar you should ask me that question. I'm probably one of the very few people in the world who *could* answer that. It's mild. But it's very very interesting. First of all, it's given to you by a doctor in his office, in a big needle in a very 'surgical' situation. And it's a doctor who commands enormous respect because his personality is so overwhelming. I mean he's got a great sense of humor. Wonderful depth."

The more I heard about him, the more incredible Dr. Z seemed. According to my friend, he uses electric eels in his medicines, dispenses wrinkle-removing creams, uses DMSO to take away sun-burn, lectures on prophylactic medicine, contracts with every pa-tient to turn him over to another doctor if not satisfied with his treatment (and sends a vial of speed with him), cures impotency, nearsightedness, bad hearing, and sloppy bridge playing, lets pa-tients blend their own formulas, sometimes injects speed into the temple or neck, claims to treat multiple sclerosis with success and banishes mental depression with speed and psychology.

My acquaintance promised to ask Dr. Z to let me interview him. Until then he had ignored my letters and phone calls. After several subsequent calls, he agreed to see me the next evening at nine. I waited for four hours to see him, which I understand is less than many of his patients have to endure. The delay is sometimes ex-plained by the minimum of one hour he is reported to spend with each of his patients.

There is an odd round-the-clock drift of people in and out of Dr. Z's waiting room. A few people kept moving past in both directions during the four-hour "delay" before our interview. A neighbor, sensing my impatience, walked over to my chair and said, "Wait for him. It'll be the greatest experience of your life."

One former patient recalls the waiting room ambiance nostalgi-cally: "You'd generally be sitting there with someone carrying a basket of eggs or fresh vegetables, several movie stars, and a clean-ing lady. There were always at least three people sleeping because they'd been waiting at least eight hours. Two or three others would be standing."

Some patients, apparently low on the totem, were uncomfortably conscious of the hierarchical arrangements that were strictly ob-served. "He had five or six little rooms," said a frequent visitor. "If you got to be in room number one, which was where [Dr. Z] mixed potions and stuff, you were in. No matter how close you got to [Dr. Z], though, you couldn't get into room number one. Because *they* were in there."

I interviewed Dr. Z in five languages. With him, each tongue as-sumed a novel character and identity. When clarity began to suffer in one, he would switch to another. There was no lack of profund-ity in his remarks, it seemed to me, merely a shortage of coherence.

He was in a back room at his desk, eating an orange, which had dripped over his shirtfront and sleeves. He was perspiring. In his late sixties, he still had completely black hair. He had studied in Europe, then collected enough money to make it to America in the 1920's. He began working for a pioneer youth doctor in the modern tradition. The job turned out to be a most fortuitous introduction to clinical rejuvenation and to rich Americans as well. After being "phased" by his employer, as Dr. Z put it, he went into practice on his own. It is difficult to imagine how this highly individualistic man could ever have been anyone's partner.

It was difficult to get him to speak of his own therapy for aging complaints, although I did manage to establish that he used what he called "immune globulin" (presumably gamma globulin) as a general prophylaxis. He said he also used organic preparations consisting of placenta, bone marrow, spleen, and lung material and had given from "50,000 to 70,000" injections.

So far, so good. Such treatments are in keeping with the biological therapy school of rejuvenation, which avoids chemotherapy except as a last resort. But he then began to speak of deep-freezing preparations to — 25° F and of electromagnetic bombardments.

His philosophy is interesting, and not terribly different from that of the other youth doctors. He would, he said, relieve me of the burden of organizing and composing my book. "I'll dictate the whole article," he assured me. "Gerontology, or should I say geriatrics . . . should make a human being function to the very last moment of his life. Life was given with the understanding that there is death. There are many privileges attached to it, and many people . . . have eaten from the tree of knowledge, but few have applied it in the right way. Aging is a mistaken concept of the way we live, the way we think, and the way we apply ourselves."

These were more than words, I realized. They were the substance of an official medical prescription for some of the most important people in the world, given by one of the most idolized youth doctors of all time. I have never met one of his patients who impugned either the man's acumen or his competence.

Another patient described his experience with Dr. Z as "not so much medicine as a way of life." As with a psychoanalyst's patients, his people keep his hours, talk his language, take their vacations when he does, and even, sometimes, fall in love with him.

"You find," said a former patient, "that you're getting up in the middle of the night and trying to get a doctor at four in the morning. You're caught in a celebrity web of favorites—like it was in high school when you tried to become teacher's pet."

Dr. Z considers his mission to be to enable his clientele to get the most out of life, to realize the full potential of the gift of life. "A gift," he observes, "is something that one gets free and it's immoral to either take advantage of it or to hide it or not to make full use of it for the benefit of other people. And that's the only point I have."

I wanted to hear more from him, particularly to elucidate a string of half-developed concepts that he had dropped into our conversation. Unfortunately, when I told him that—unlike the other people in his laboratory—I failed to detect an added third dimension and extraordinary luminescence to pictures when he passed an auto light, a laser beam, and magnets over them, he became angry with me.

"If you can't see, then don't look because you're wasting your time. You're a lousy temperamental character. Since it's very obvious to everybody else. You don't believe *yourself*. That you have to change, young man, otherwise you won't get any place. Look at the greens, the browns, we do it for you . . . but I don't give a damn, because I have news for you. We have measured it with a ten-thousand-dollar light meter that measures everything standard."

I asked if I could see him the next day. He told me to write him a letter, and I said I would.

"You see," he said, "I'm pretty articulate. I'm not sure I'll answer your letter."

And he didn't.

CHAPTER FIFTEEN

The Rejuvenating Russians

If I were to hazard a guess as to the nation and man who had most enhanced the idea of rejuvenation, I would name Russia as the nation and Elie Metchnikoff, a Russian-born Frenchman, as the man.

Admittedly, some of Russia's credit was earned by merely producing an Elie Metchnikoff—and then harassing him so unremittingly that he sought refuge in Paris where, as head of the Institut Pasteur, he won a Nobel Prize (in 1908, with the German Paul Ehrlich for work in immunity), founded the science of gerontology, defined its challenges and charted its future, and single-handedly dragged the science of rejuvenation up out of the bogs of disrepute where it had lain in the aftermath of Brown-Séquard's celebrated senile erection.

"The idea of controlling human aging," notes British gerontologist Alex Comfort, "remained the preserve of quacks and optimists until Metchnikoff and Claude Bernard tackled it a century ago."

Metchnikoff was a versatile scientist. Indeed, he was the first great generalist to address himself to aging research. He exploded many of the time-honored myths about senescence simply by using his microscope to see if what everybody "knew" to be true was in fact so. Often it was not. He also conceived the idea of establishing aging parameters to measure the rate of aging (by comparing animal size, growth periods, reproductive tax, and so forth), speculated significantly on the differences between unicellular and multicellular mortality, and offered persuasive testimony that human beings were cheated of their natural longevity by dying well before their time.

Yet, despite his contributions, Metchnikoff is the great cuckold of the science he founded and named (in 1905). Instead of being remembered as the first major intellect to examine the riddles of aging, he is known principally (but quite erroneously) as having recommended yogurt as a youth elixir.

He was born Ilya Ilyich Mechnikov on May 16, 1845, in the Ukrainian city of Ivanovka, near Kharkov, and later gallicized his name, when he emigrated to France to escape what he termed obstacles to performing serious scientific research in Romanov Russia, "coming from on high, from underneath and from the side."

Metchnikoff was both a true scientist and a genuine rejuvenationist. He was not, properly speaking, a rejuvenator, however, since he stayed in the laboratory and marketed no high-priced injections or elixirs. For him, gerontology and rejuvenation were one and the same. Whereas the overwhelming majority of contemporary gerontologists study aging as philatelists inspect postage stamps—collecting, measuring, and classifying, marveling at what they see, but drawing few useful inferences from their investigations—Metchnikoff approached his task with the overriding idea of conquering age.

Unlike the traditional youth doctor, eternally at odds with orthodox medicine, this great Russian academician was a respected member of the Establishment. In good rejuvenationist style, however, he scuffled constantly with sciolistic and bureaucratic tendencies in medicine. His own work, though, was disciplined and thorough, his experiments models of serious, controlled inquiry.

Le Père Metch, as his students called him, stayed on at the redbrick biomedical research complex on the Rue Dutot until the day he died ("in my opinion there exists no other institution where one may work so fruitfully"). He was prepared to tackle anything that threatened what he termed man's "right" to a long life. With the help of a rich Muscovite couple, V. and I. Morozov, he secured funds to grapple with the problem of syphilis. He wrote:

"Infectious diseases which come one after another in life often help to shorten human existence. . . . Among these diseases, syphilis is one of the most important. . . . It is an absolute must, if one is to prolong human life, to avoid the contagion of syphilis."

Deploring the blindered, moralistic approach to venereal disease, Metchnikoff put the problem where it belonged: in the laboratory. In *The Story of Medicine,* historian Victor Robinson, MD, describes the Institut Pasteur's inoculation of human guinea pigs with venereal disease as "one of the most mysterious and carefully-guarded [chapters] in the annals of medicine." The result of his research, aided by the great Emile Roux, was an effective prophylactic (30 percent calomel ointment) which is still the basic standby of the sexual adventurer. Hundreds of thousands of families are unaware of their great debt to Roux and Metchnikoff.

Metchnikoff saw the aging problem in a philosophical context, which he felt was intimately related to its physical manifestations. The idea of "natural death" always bothered him. Was there really such a thing? Surely, he reasoned, if death were a natural phenomenon—an assumption tacitly accepted by the Establishment until he challenged it—man would not regard its approach with panic. How, he argued, could one think of death as natural when one deficient organ could destroy an otherwise healthy body? If death were natural in the sense of being divinely ordained for a particular time, would it not happen when all the body's tissues were practically ready to fall apart from exhaustion?

He allowed that natural death might just occur, but it was probably very rare. "It is even probable," he said, "that the approach of natural death is accompanied by one of the softest sensations ever known."

To support his position, he related lawyer-gastronomist Anthelme Brillat-Savarin's account of his ninety-three-year-old aunt's passing. Thirty minutes before she died, she said: "If you ever reach my age, you will see that death becomes a need, just like sleep."

One recalls Cornaro's description of natural death at a ripe old age (he lived into his ninety-ninth year) as arriving quietly, blissfully ". . . the end caused . . . by the failure of the innate moisture which, consumed by degrees, finally becomes completely exhausted, like a lamp which gradually flickers out."

Aging, maintained Metchnikoff, was no more natural a phenomenon than death. "It is," he wrote, "doubtless an error to consider aging a physiological phenomenon. It can be considered normal because everyone ages, but only to the extent that one might consider normal the pains of childbirth that an anesthetic might relieve; on the contrary, aging is a chronic sickness for which it is much more difficult to find a remedy."

Then, did immortality exist?

He could point to at least one kind of life which did not age and die "naturally": unicellular organisms which, instead of dying of old age, simply divide into halves, the parent reincarnating as its own children by mitosis.

Generally speaking, larger animals tended to live proportionately longer than smaller animals. And yet mammals, such as man, did not live proportionately longer than various reptiles and amphibians. Why? What was it that prevented man from realizing the longevity of which he was theoretically capable?

By the process of elimination, Metchnikoff fingered the colon, or large intestine, as a major villain. The colon is a 5-foot section of the bowel which seems to have few happy and many unhappy functions. Its digestive role is trivial, limited to absorbing liquids and providing mucus for defecation. It turns out, quite often, to be a hotbed of infection, a trough for all sorts of mischievous bacteria, and is given to quirksome functional and structural abnormalities—not to mention its habit of nurturing tumors, benign and malignant. Concluded Metchnikoff: "Since the large intestine, of all the parts of the digestive tract is the richest in microbes, and since [it] is much more developed in mammifers than in any other vertebrates, it is quite correct to suppose that the length of life of the former has been notably shortened because of the chronic poisoning from their abundant intestinal flora."

Unfortunately, the hypothetical principles of autointoxication set forth by Metchnikoff quickly became a blunt instrument designed to produce financial killings in the clinic. The English surgeon Sir W. Arbuthnot Lane relieved many of his upper-class patients of their "autointoxication" problem by the simple expedient of carving off whole sections of their colons.

This indiscriminate exploitation of Metchnikoff's ideas appalled their author. In *Les Essais Optimistes*, Metchnikoff warns: "Bradyphagia [a once fashionable health fad of slow-eating] can no more be recommended as a means of combating intestinal putrefactions than the surgical elimination of the large intestine or the actual disinfection of the digestive tube."

In the United States in the early 1900's, expanding and distorting Metchnikoff's precepts, doctors concentrated heavily on all kinds of focal infections. Tonsillectomies and adenoidectomies (which many doctors are now beginning to frown upon) quickly became the rage. Surgeons tried to quell any number of aches and pains by yanking out teeth by the mouthful, appendices (with or without prior appendicitis) and gall bladders. One organ after the other was excised—all for the ostensible purpose of reestablishing "orthobiosis" or "correct living."

Perhaps Metchnikoff's greatest contribution to gerontology was his painstakingly detailed development of his theory of phagocytosis (from the Greek *phago*, I eat, and *kytos*, hollow cell) which he conceived quite suddenly on a visit to the Italian city of Messina in 1882, when he began to study specimens of starfish larvae he had plucked from the sea. He was fascinated by all kinds of embryos, for through them he could see laid out before his eyes millions of years of evolutionary development of the species.

He carefully smeared some fresh larvae onto a slide and shoved it under his microscope's stage clips. After several minutes of peering at the scampering larval cells, it suddenly occurred to him that he was watching a process that was probably similar to the organism's self-defense mechanism. Just as those baby starfish cells engulfed and digested foreign matter in their search for food, so did the body's white blood cells surround and neutralize noxious foreign intruders in defending itself against disease and infection.

Metchnikoff was to spend the next twenty-five years of his life developing and refining this landmark discovery. Overnight it diverted him from zoology to pathology, where his brilliant intellect was able to serve humanity more directly. Moreover, it furthered his work in immunity. As Metchnikoff explained the connection between immunity and his theory of phagocytosis to the Nobel Committee in Stockholm: "The ensemble of phenomena that one observes in immunity may be reduced to a series of biological acts such as phagocyte sensitivity, their active movements directed toward places threatened by microbes, and a series of physical and chemical actions which bring about the destruction and the digestion of the infectious agents."

From his observations on how white blood cells defend the body against infection, Metchnikoff moved toward a theory of the nature of the aging process. He noticed that, as a person ages, the "noble" tissues—those with specific vital functions, such as the heart, the lungs, the liver, and so forth—tend to atrophy. Replacing these useful cells is an assortment of fibrous, connective tissue formed by (he guessed) phagocyte action.

He assumed, for instance, that hair whitened as the color pigments became phagocytozed. The phagocyte, he contended, was extremely versatile, changing form and activity mysteriously and relentlessly throughout the life of the organism. He was the first to notice that the phagocytes belonged to a unique physiological system, all emanating from the mesenchymal (or middle) layer of the embryonic blastoderm, from which the adult organism develops. He was also the first to understand the vital role of phagocytes in inflammation and immunity—and to identify them as being part of the "reticuloendothelial system," or RES. At different stages of development, these same cells perform completely different functions in different parts of the body, he postulated. In the embryo, they give the body its specific shape; in the adult they defend the body; in later years they assist in the destruction—or aging—of the body.

Any rejuvenation therapy, he thought, would be required to halt the destructive, or aging, phase of phagocytosis and block the insidious incursions of fibrous connective tissue upon the vital organs. To his successors he counseled: "Since, in the organisms of the aged it is the noble, enfeebled elements which are devoured by the macrophages (a type of phagocyte) . . . it is worth thinking of a remedy capable of reinforcing the noble elements and rendering them less susceptible of being devoured."

It is only today, some sixty years after these ideas were first propounded by Metchnikoff, that their truth has begun to be appreciated by gerontologists. Virtually every major aging theoretician's notions have come back to the importance of connective tissue's role in aging. The exciting work of the biochemists Johan Bjorksten and Denham Harman, of Robert R. Kohn of Western Reserve University's Pathology Institute, of the Swiss pioneer Frederick Verzar, and of the late French biologist Alexis Carrel, can be traced directly back to the bearded old Frenchman with the thick Russian accent.

A stocky, part-time amateur wrestler with a Yul Brynner haircut has probably gone farthest in following up Metchnikoff's theoretical work. Roy L. Walford of the USC Medical School has resurrected phagocytosis in all its Metchnikovian complexity and emerged with an "autoimmune theory of aging."

Walford also sees aging as a suicidal process originating in the reticuloendothelial system. And he points to the striking positive increase of RES elements (such as spleen, lymph nodes, lymphoid tissue, gamma globulin, renal lysozymes, and so forth) at the precise break-off point between adulthood and rapidly advancing old age, *i.e.*, in the fifties.

Walford explains that the body machinery's progressive disorganization leads to a cell diversification in which cells no longer recognize themselves as kin—and begin to destroy themselves. Some believe this happens by somatic mutations; others think there may be a breakdown in normal body homeostasis, which controls the body's tolerance of foreign material. This compares roughly to the more rapid rejection mechanism of a heart or kidney transplant—except that this is a rejection of one's own cells, not a foreign donor's.

Experimental confirmation of the autoimmune theory has just begun, but Walford's preliminary results look promising. One of his first trials involved giving mice Imuran, which is normally used to suppress homograft-immune responses in transplants. The idea is that if aging is caused by autoimmunity, then autoimmune disease therapy ought to increase mice life-spans. It did. The experimental mice showed a ten-week mean life-span increase over the controls.

Elie Metchnikoff, unfortunately, is usually not credited by other modern scientists for having anticipated their experimental conclusions. One may infer from this that, had he been more carefully read earlier in the game, more progress might have been made sooner. As it is, biomedical science has only touched the surface of his rich complex of ideas on the process of phagocytosis. Further exploration should prove quite profitable.

It is ironic that Metchnikoff's recommendation of *lactobacillus bulgaricus* yogurt as an antidote for autointoxication, or poisoning of the colon by the body's alkaline bacteria and putrefying wastes, should be popularly considered the high-water mark of his career.

In fact, research at New York City hospitals has confirmed Metchnikoff's ideas on the benefits of acidophilus bacteria. Controlled studies showed that yogurt or yogurt-plus-prune-whip diets do indeed relieve many kinds of constipation and diarrhea, improve skin tone, diabetic ulcers, seborrheic dermatitis, and chronic ileus in geriatric patients, and generally improve the bowel condition.

It has not been proven whether yogurt will help a person live longer, but then Metchnikoff never said that it would. The yogurt makers, however, have greatly profited from this common misconception. The tart milk food is now served all over the world in twenty-five flavors, and in 1967 alone the French consumed over 2,000,000,000 potsful. In the United States, where the fad is just beginning to catch on, yogurt manufacturers grossed an estimated $20,000,000 in 1967.

Aware that he would probably be branded a quack and faddist if he, the great gerontologist, failed to live to well beyond the normal life-span, Metchnikoff, in a wry mood after recuperating from a heart attack, wrote in his diary: "I hope that those who think that, according to my principles, I ought to live to be at least one hundred, will forgive my premature death in view of attenuating circumstances hereinafter indicated: intense and precocious activities, fretful character, nervous temperament, and tardy start on a sensible regime."

He was seventy-one when he died, and his critics proved to be drearily predictable.

If Metchnikoff was the Prodigal Son of Russian rejuvenation, Bogomolets was the stay-at-home-and-fatten-the-calf-for-the-family Elder Son in the story. The parallel breaks down toward the end somewhat, since Metchnikoff never returned to Russia to seek forgiveness or a blessing. In a sense, however, his widow Olga Nikolaevna did it by proxy when she returned the Nobel Prize winner's effects and papers to the Soviet Union, where they are still proudly displayed.

Aleksandr A. Bogomolets, a pupil of Metchnikoff's, stayed home when the going was rough. He was not averse to taking an occasional *cure* abroad when the Moscow vapors got the better of him. But through the Stalinist purges and World War II, Bogomolets stuck it out in the Soviet Union.

Bogomolets developed an antireticular cytotoxic serum (ACS), which was designed to stimulate the body's natural immunity in the reticuloendothelial system against agents of disease and aging. He probably owed most of the theoretical basis for his work to Metchnikoff, but he was parsimonious in passing on any credit to his mentor. For his labors, he was awarded Stalin and Lenin prizes, membership in the important medical societies, high university posts, and editorship of powerful scientific journals. Abroad, ACS struck out as far as orthodox medicine was concerned. It was either ballyhooed as a panacea or rejuvenating elixir by optimists or denounced as a quack nostrum by conservative medical circles.

Gilles Lambert recently depicted Bogomolets in *Niehans ou la Vieillesse Vaincue* as Stalin's deathbedside physician who injected ACS in a desperate gamble to restore the despot's teenage tenacity and life force. "The result [*i.e.,* effectiveness of the serum]," he writes, "was unconvincing since patient and doctor died just a few months apart." (The truth is that, unless Bogomolets crept out of his grave to do it, he couldn't have treated Stalin in his agony. Bogomolets died seven years before Stalin.

"With the demise of Bogomolets' No. 1 guinea-pig, Stalin," Lambert asserts, "the vogue for ACS passed." The author obviously has never glanced at the shelves of his neighborhood *pharmacie*. He's sure to find ACS there. Mainly used today as an adjunct to conventional therapy for both geriatric and nongeriatric conditions, it is sold all over the Continent and in the Soviet Union, as well.

After years of animal and human trials, Bogomolets announced the development of his serum on June 23, 1941, the day that Hitler's Wehrmacht began to overrun western Russia. It was produced by injecting human connective tissue, such as bone marrow, lymph, spleen, and liver from young accident victims, into the bloodstream of animals, mainly horses in the beginning—and rabbits later. It was thought that by extracting the antibodies formed in the horse and injecting them in small amounts into humans, a healthy stimulation of the recipient's immunological system would result. It probably did just that, and as a general systemic shock therapy, the results obtained were not bad. But against specific conditions, it proved a quixotic panacea. It would cure ailments it wasn't supposed to affect, and do nothing for those it was said to cure best. One doctor could make ACS do therapeutic handsprings, so to speak; another, trying it under similar circumstances for the same complaint, would get nowhere with it.

Its most widespread use was at the front to speed wound healing and knit bone fractures. It was also used for mental illnesses, pneumonia, senility, frostbite, eczema, minor heart ailments, asthma, ulcers, cataracts, and so forth. New applications appeared in almost every edition of the Ukrainian Academy of Sciences publication *Medichniy Zhurnal,* edited by Bogomolets, and some two thousand scientific papers have, in general, confirmed Bogomolets' claims for ACS. It produced what its West German manufacturer (Schwarzhaupt, Cologne) apologetically called a "perplexingly diversified field of application."

Remedies for which a "perplexingly diversified field of application" is alleged by the author usually wind up being acidly termed by the profession "quack nostrum" or "witch doctor's brew." This is just what happened to ACS.

One reason for Bogomolets' broad claims may have been political. During the war the Soviet Union began to feel a painful pinch, scientifically, from having isolated itself from the rest of the world. Stalin pressured his medical cadres to come up with Soviet "discoveries"—or else.

ACS even seemed helpful against the bits and pieces of cancerous tissue remaining in the patient's organism after X rays or surgery had destroyed the more obvious tumors, performing a post operative prophylactic function.

Bogomolets never advertised ACS as a "rejuvenation serum" per se. But he firmly believed that stimulating the RES—which ACS purportedly achieved—would invigorate the body's defenses against various agents of senescence.

"A man is as old as his arteries," the French say. Bogomolets changed this to: "A man is as old as his connective tissue."

In emphasizing the role of the mesenchyme (Bogomolets used the term interchangeably with connective tissue and RES)—as the body's ubiquitous cellular defense mechanism was variously referred to—Bogomolets in effect was picking up Elie Metchnikoff's theory of phagocytosis where the old master had left it. In fact, when the callow Bogomolets (fresh out of Odessa's Novorossiysk University Medical School) first tramped into Metchnikoff's office at the Institut Pasteur in Paris, he must have looked to the old man like a long-lost son who could continue his work. The youth immediately threw himself into study of the mesenchyme riddle—but emerged with opinions as to its role in senescence that were diametrically opposed to his mentor's.

Metchnikoff had fretted about connective tissue's inexorable invasion of the body's "noble tissues," gumming them up with colloids. Bogomolets, on the contrary, figured the antibody-manufacturing elements of connective tissue were the body's indispensable guarantee of health—and youthfulness.

Bogomolets probably failed to perceive that Metchnikoff's broad theory of phagocytosis included exactly what he was talking about. But, upon his return from abroad, he rhetorically labored his differences with his mentor: "Metchnikoff committed a serious error. The 'aroused phagocytes' he speaks of are the result and not the cause of death of old cells. The phagocytes devour the dying, aging, lifeless cells, fulfilling—in this case—the function of scavengers."

His own precepts for keeping young were based on the principle that: "The ability to lengthen life is, first of all, the ability not to shorten it." To this end he recommended avoidance of "fear and boredom" as injurious to the sympathetic nervous system. The old adage "Milk is children's wine, and wine is old people's milk" he subscribed to, as long as it wasn't exaggerated. He believed nicotine detrimental and shared Metchnikoff's anxiety about autointoxication of the colon. On the positive plane, he recommended hard work, intensive breathing (to get rid of poisons), a low meat and protein, higher fat and carbohydrate diet, regular exercise and massage, cleanliness, seven to eight hours' sleep daily (with one hour after the main meal), and a "reasonable" sex life.

He met German-born Helmut Eugene Benjamin Gellert ("Gayelord") Hauser in Paris. After discussing the faddist's "miracle foods," such as blackstrap molasses, brewer's yeast, wheat germ, and so on, the Russian found them severely wanting. "What is especially miraculous," he observed, "is the aplomb of this prophet and the credulity of his 'pupils.' "

Hauser was kinder to Bogomolets. Lumping him along with a list of other rejuvenationists, each of whom emphasized a particular area of senescent sensitivity, Hauser noted: "I believe that the answer lies not just in the glands, the colon, the arteries, the connective tissues, the blood, or in any one part of the body, but in the *whole* body. . . . In short, I believe you are as young as your diet."

During the Great Patriotic War, as the Russians called the Second World War, Bogomolets began using horses in his serum's preparation. From twenty horses he obtained enough serum for two million injections. This was possible because he found that "in large doses it weakens, but in weak doses, on the contrary, it reinforces the vital activity of the physiological system."

Eventually rabbits became the preferred donor animals. They are prepared by repeated injections of an emulsion containing nine parts spleen and one part sternal bone marrow from a human accident victim, ideally no more than six or seven hours after death. ACS in liquid form keeps for about three months, the lyophilized ampules for about three years. Initial injections are minute (0.02 cc for starters). Provided the skin shows no undue inflammation, they are increased in subsequent applications.

If the serum proved to be no surefire panacea, it at least appeared to be virtually harmless in prescribed dosages.

Since he died shortly after the war, Bogomolets never had the time to test ACS for degenerative aging disorders. Taking up where he left off, however, Viennese-American rejuvenationist Max Wolf's Biological Research Institute created a similar serum, using goats. Wolf says he has obtained results similar to Bogomolets', although he feels that ACS's most effective application is in arteriosclerosis. "It destroys the necrobiotic artery tissues," explains Wolf, "and allows them to regenerate themselves. It has a catabolic action. You can't *build up* anything in the body (although sometimes you can substitute), you can only *destroy*. But if you destroy the proper things, then you are in effect building up."

Aleksandr Bogomolets never really did what he set out to do, that is, fill the shoes of Elie Metchnikoff. His ACS was a pale attempt to fulfill clinically the great promise of his mentor's brilliant theoretical groundwork. The Soviet's place in rejuvenation history is not without honor. But the Russian who came closest to discovering what aging is all about, and whose prescience is only now being confirmed by laboratory research in many countries, is Elie Metchnikoff, the father of modern gerontology.

As the Russians would say, it is not for nothing that two of the motherland's most prominent medical scientists were rejuvenationists. The idea of vigorous, rich, long life is as Russian as the *piroshki* or onion-top domes.

If scientists elsewhere take a dim view of the fantastic longevity claims made by the inhabitants of the Soviet Caucasus, for a Russian to do so would be regarded as heresy.

It is the rare citizen who questions the "scientific fact" that Georgians and Azerbaidzhanis frequently live to a leathery, garlicky one hundred and fifty or so, at which age they are said to grind their *shashlik* with razor-sharp gums, noisily swill their daily two liters of *tsinandali* wine, outrun each of their twenty or thirty children, and unless they're at death's door, delight in cuckolding their nephews and grandsons.

A recent item in the Soviet trade union newspaper *Trud* illustrates how hoary age has become a mystique in the USSR:

A rickety old Dagestani—Aleksandr Andreyevich Koshlotov by name—exploited his many years to freeload in every restaurant in the village of Makhachkalinsky, to ride buses and trolleys gratis, and to cadge apparel from softhearted state store managers. Sometimes, even without begging for it, he'd find a passerby pressing an odd kopek or ruble into his gnarled fist.

"Why shouldn't they have obliged the old man?" wrote *Trud,* "After all, he was one hundred and eighteen years old!"

And, of course, as he strolled down the streets everyone asked the secret to his many years. "But," fussed the paper, "a secret there was not. This venerable oldster finally turned out to be the commonest kind of swindler. . . . In his tattered passport, over the birthdate 1897, he had erased the 9 and put down a 4—automatically becoming older by fifty years!"

The purpose of this fakery was to get a new apartment for himself, seniority being the operative clause and his gerontion years the key to the hearts of his neighbors. He even passed his wife off as his granddaughter.

Koshlotov's scheme was eventually exposed, but the anecdote exemplifies the kind of credulity Western gerontologists are always accusing their Soviet counterparts of when it comes to believing stories of one-hundred-plus ages in the Caucasus.

The chief compiler of age statistics in the sensitive areas of Georgia, Dagestan, Armenia, and Azerbaidzhan is G. Z. Pitskelauri. Half believer, half scientist, Pitskelauri resembles a baggy-pants burlesque comic with his paperweight spectacles and laconic, dead-pan style. All he needs is a floor-length cravat to complete his cos-tume.

A Georgian by birth, Pitskelauri has, if we are to believe him, shaken the hand of a one-hundred-and-fifty-year-old Transcaucasian named Igor Koroiyev.

"Koroiyev died in 1957," says Pitskelauri. "He assured me that he was born in 1801 in the Djavsk district. I'm con-vinced he was at *least* one hundred and fifty. I was able to confirm this by looking at his military papers. He was a cook to General Ermolov, Governor of Transcaucasia under Aleksandr I. He ac-companied the general into France and Italy, and remembered this distant past astonishingly well."

It may well be that folks in Armenia, Azerbaidzhan, Abkhazia, Georgia, and Dagestan actually do live on into three-figure ages. Perhaps we find it hard to believe simply because *we* don't live that long. Still, even the Russians are reexamining their statistics on the post-one-hundreds. According to a recent census, there are twenty-one thousand Soviet citizens one hundred or older. The Georgians alone, for example, claim fifty-one centenarians per one hundred thousand residents. Expressing wonder at these figures, I asked Pitskelauri how certain he was of their accuracy.

"Absolutely certain," he said. "We went around twice to make sure. The first time we found twenty-six thousand. The second time we managed to cut it by five thousand."

Pitskelauri could not be haggled down. Twenty-one thousand—rock-bottom last price. Take it or leave it. Declining to describe the survey methods, he said only that local authorities collabo-rated with his outfit, the Soviet Gerontological Center, in their compilations.

Several authors have visited the Caucasus recently with the in-tention of digging up some publishable secrets of rejuvenation and longevity. Gilbert Gensac a few years ago squeezed out barely fifty pages in a little book entitled *Nous Vivrons 150 Ans* from his first-hand Russian sojourn. He, like others, discovered that to chat with an old man is not necessarily to find out what makes him old.

Without niggling on the actual annual count, Pitskelauri's old mountain people have at least attained respectable age, and his findings are without doubt interesting. At first, he credited "favorable social conditions" as the major factor responsible for Caucasian longevity.

Smelling propaganda, I asked him what this meant.

"Ah," he said, "it's the social structure of the Union of Soviet Socialist Republics . . . socialist pensions, socialist medical care . . . all the benefits of the revolution."

"Is that all?" I asked.

"Well," he added, "there's also socialist air . . ."

". . . and socialist genes, socialist exercise, socialist mountains?"

"Perhaps," said Pitskelauri, deadpan.

That out of the way, his profile of this unique population revealed that they are, on the whole, far from decrepit, over half of the over-eighty group well enough to work (mostly on their private garden plots), and 99.99 percent of them married.

Curiously, he found, among his long-lived fellow Georgians, that women can endure the demise of a spouse more easily than men. Loss of a wife is, almost invariably, the kiss of death for a Georgian husband.

Over 90 percent of the women were married before twenty-five with most of them bearing children almost immediately (if not beforehand), and some having pregnancies into their sixties. Broods of eighteen to twenty children were not unusual. According to Pitskelauri, Georgia's temperate climate, high altitudes (from 1,500 to 4,500 feet), "rich ultraviolet rays," * oxygen sparsity, exercise, and work activity help explain the increased longevity of its natives.

The average old person's diet consisted of vegetables and fruit, strong seasonings, small quantities of natural (homemade) wines and small amounts of other liquors, but no tobacco.

"Cases of cohabitation," he said, "were marked at the age of one hundred years and over." Even if the statistic is exaggerated, one cannot doubt that the idea of making the most out of life is part of the Soviet peoples' heritage. It has been officially incorporated into past five-year plans and the present seven-year plan. As science nears new breakthroughs in the understanding of senescence, the Russians are ready and waiting to make the most of them.

* Many Western gerontologists, however, find the sun's ultraviolet rays a major factor in the aging of skin and other body tissues.

When Soviet gerontologists declare that they are "seriously studying aging," they are not being academic. With that singleness of purpose of the *prastiye lyudyi* (straightforward people), as Baedeker called them, the Russians are making a strong bid to grab the rejuvenation jackpot. Despite its deceptively peaceful nature, this contest may have vast implications for the space race—as well as for the political power balance in centuries to come.

Although this may sound extravagant, the possibility is a very real one. The ultimate domination of space may well be usurped by the state that first solves the aging riddle. A trip to neighboring stars will require a minimum of thirty years. In all likelihood, within twenty years we shall be contemplating the possibility of space flights lasting up to one hundred years. The advantages of conducting such flights with a single generation of astronauts would be crucial—given the limitations of payload, and so forth.

Currently there is no provision for an aging-retardation program in the U. S. space effort. And the space effort itself seems to be the first area to suffer in every budget squeeze. A few Western gerontologists, such as Johan Bjorksten, have played Jeremiah, warning that our inaction may give the Russians an insurmountable lead in age-extension research. He contends that only a wholesale reorientation of our space and gerontology programs will permit us to catch up.

Bjorksten thinks that "those concerned with the conquest of space, the air medical groups and NASA, are so absorbed in getting the first man to the moon that they are eschewing work on anything having a longer range."

As remote as these fears may seem now, it is unquestionably true that the Russians are taking rejuvenation research far more seriously than the United States. Pitskelauri, for one, has declared that longevity increases are "one of the most significant state tasks." But, even more revealing, the man Western gerontologists suspect of being the *glavny konstructor* (chief architect) of the Soviet life-prolongation program* is a slender, thoughtful young Muscovite theoretician named Lev Vladimirovich Komarov.

---

* To be distinguished from their general gerontology effort, which is headed by Professor N. N. Garev of the Institute of Gerontology and Experimental Pathology in Kiev.

"This problem," Komarov recently told a scientific symposium, "should be solved with even more resolution than that devoted to the solving of the A-bomb problem a while back, or the current problem of conquering the cosmos."

Western research administrators are inclined to dismiss Komarov's priorities as all wrong. They think that in trying to solve the problem of aging before they have been able to define it, the Russians have gotten way ahead of themselves. They also feel that any present all-out attempt to control senescence is bound to be a futile, million-to-one shot.

Komarov is an earnest, affable philosopher and scion of a distinguished scientific family who looks as though he'd be more at home writing sonnets than working in a laboratory. He speaks a halting English, but the sense of his argument about the importance of the rejuvenation race has made a deep impression on many of his international colleagues—with the single exception of the Americans.

"Komarov," declared Baltimore Gerontological Research Center Chief Nathan W. Shock recently, "asked me who is working with his approach in the United States. I couldn't think of a single, solitary soul outside of [Denham] Harman." (Johan Bjorksten, a biochemist working on a grant from the Upjohn Co., is another.)

Though crediting Komarov with having "a pretty good idea," Shock thinks his optimism is unjustified. "I suspect," said Shock, "that the most practical people are those who are trying to reduce the incidence of coronary artery disease through the dietary fat alteration."

Shock and Komarov couldn't be farther apart. The Russian acknowledges that his ideas are presently in the minority. But, he says, even if coronary artery disease *were* eliminated in an all-out campaign, it would, at most, lengthen the life-span by five or six years. If, on the other hand, the admittedly more complex riddle of senescence itself were understood and the "main links" in the aging process eliminated, longevity could be *doubled,* or even *trebled* beyond the present eighty- to one-hundred-year life-span. Privately, the Russians are talking in terms of prolonging human life up to six hundred or seven hundred years.

What it all boils down to, says Komarov, is the decision to go in one of two directions. Either one invests heavily in trying to solve the *causes* of aging—or one continues merely to explore the *symptoms* of aging.

Based on my interview with Komarov in Vienna, and a reading of his papers, the Soviet position may be summarized thus:

(1) There is no reason to believe that we are genetically and inevitably programmed to age and die as we do. Therefore, we may scientifically aim to postpone the onset of senescence by prolonging the mature (*i.e.,* after twenty-five or thirty) period of life, not the last years.

(2) There is no alternative to discovering an effective method of rejuvenation and life-prolongation if we are to win the battle against senescence.

(3) This can be achieved only by a crash program that emphasizes overwhelmingly biochemistry and biophysics.

(4) Programs (such as the United States') which deal with "the removal of factors leading to premature aging, including various sociological improvements, disease control, work and living conditions" will yield only a small fraction of the benefits of a rejuvenation program per se.

(5) With the aging process itself understood and means of liquidating, "link by link," factors in the destructive nature of senescence, we conceivably may achieve virtual immortality.

On the concrete, laboratory level, Komarov's approach is exquisitely simple. He is testing dietary supplements and trace elements on model cell cultures to ascertain which substances prolong cell life and which shorten it.

He believes that the arms race has outrageously diverted funds from a hard-core aging-retardation program into wasteful and destructive military expenditures. The cost, he says, is not merely monetary, but far greater in human life than has previously been calculated.

"It is necessary to emphasize," he says, "that every billion dollars used for war and not allocated to realizing the means of artificially prolonging human life deprives all people everywhere of several scores of years (on the average) . . . including those empowered with the decision of spending it on Death or Life.

"Every year's delay," he adds, "means that some of us will lose decades . . . others perhaps even hundreds of years."

It is tempting to scoff at Komarov's optimistic forecasts as science fiction. Yet we might recall how the Pentagon tut-tutted Soviet space scientist Anatoly A. Blagonravov's casual statement in Washington during the fall of 1957 that Russia would soon launch a space satellite. Within a few days, on October 4, Sputnik I began to circle the globe at 18,000 miles per hour. It was a classic eye-opener on the high cost of smugness. We haven't caught up yet.

Alex Comfort, who toured Soviet aging research institutions in 1967, came away enthusiastic. "What is exciting," he says, "is that they now have got a very nice Institute [in Kiev] and some very high-grade general scientists specializing in gerontology, a competent section in endocrinology, molecular biology, and so on . . . and there is nothing peculiar or eccentric about it. It's straightforward bread-and-butter research."

The Soviet interest in rejuvenation has traditionally been fierce. The paramount task of American gerontology till now has been trying to bribe scientists of Nobel Prize quality to enter the field. On the other hand it has always been tough to lure the best Soviet medical brains *away* from gerontology. The list of great Russian rejuvenationists includes such stellar intellects as Metchnikoff, Botkin, Pavlov, Filatov, Milman, Nagorny, Frankel, Strazhesko and Bogomolets.

According to Professor D. F. Chebotarev, of the Kiev Gerontological Institute, the first conference devoted to senescence was held in Kiev in 1938, and the first major collection of gerontological research papers was published in the Soviet Union in 1939.

The Soviet preoccupation with the subject is further attested to by the fact that the Soviet Academy of Medical Sciences directly administers over one hundred gerontological research and medical institutions. It also organizes frequent seminars and symposia and keeps a close tab on research overseas.

It is yet to be seen whether Komarov's ideas on basic aging-study priority will prevail in the Soviet Union. If they do, if they throw the weight of gerontological effort into biochemistry and biophysics, the American scatter-shot approach will, more and more, look like a Topsy, who reflected, "I 'spect I growed. Don't think nobody never made me."

CHAPTER SIXTEEN

The Respectables

If a physiologist were to study the problem of ageing from scratch, he would not even begin to try to modify the time course of senescence by the administration of vitamins or elixirs compounded from the juices of glands. He would first of all try to piece together a full empirical description of the phenomenon of ageing as it is reflected in structural changes of tissues and cells. . . .

SIR PETER B. MEDAWAR
Nobel Prize Winner

In the high-pressure, flimflam world of rejuvenation there is a caste of Brahmins who keep aloof from the other rejuvenators. They are deeply offended by any identity confusion and constantly emphasize their distinguishing characteristics. These are the Respectables. They make no house calls, own no chichi clinics or spas, market no packaged youthefiers, earn modest wages, and would consider it unthinkable to treat a human patient for any ailment whatsoever.

Their only patients are rats and mice, although some of them treat fruit flies or microscopic, wheel-like pond rotifers. At least one is working with several sets of matched Beagles.

They include biochemists, biophysicists, and physiologists, and they may be regarded as the Great White Hope of furrowed-brow, no-nonsense gerontology. Without them, rejuvenation would be the exclusive domain of the Niehanses, the Aslans, the Popovs— the practitioners. With them, rejuvenation has a better-than-even chance of evolving from a rather recondite art into a two-plus-two-equals-four science.

The laboratory rejuvenationists are off to a very late start and have a lot of catching up to do—quickly. Just before World War II, when the slightest wink from the federal government at medical research was considered an immoral proposition, the National Institutes of Health was established with a budget of less than $2,000,000. Today, NIH has approximately $1,500,000,000 to play with and supports 40 percent of the biomedical research in the country. Of this money the brand-new $7,500,000 Gerontological Research Center in Baltimore will be spending some $5,000,000 in 1968, of which $3,200,000 will be devoted to research and $1,800,000 to training. To many gerontologists, terrified by the magnitude of the aging problem in this country, the small piece of the pie for aging research is a national disgrace. Even the most basic questions about aging (What is it? When does it start?) are still unknown. Why are we so abysmally ignorant?

For one thing, the young are more concerned with their own bewildering problems than they are with their elders' vacant, gray despair. Dr. Ernest Henderson, President of the American Geriatrics Society, sees it this way: "Young executives wait impatiently for old executives to turn 65. . . . People don't want to keep Aunt Minny alive to 110—they want to have her in a home away from their home. And young people never feel that they are going to be old."

Charles Barrows, Jr., chief of the Section on Nutritional Biochemistry at the Center, thumbnailed the history of the government's involvement in aging this way: "Administratively, no one cared an awful lot about aging till seven or eight years ago. Then, suddenly, it became a shock to someone. O my God, look at all these old people! Our country has changed from a two- or three-family house, where grandma and grandpa lived with their daughter and son-in-law and their kids. Because of this, grandma and grandpa are now left alone. Where do they go? They go to the government . . . which is now faced with an economic, medical, and social problem of too damned many old people with no one taking care of them."

At the same time, the politicians awakened to the frustrating, gnawing reality that next to nothing was known about the aging process itself. In a crash response, the Gerontological Society (founded in 1945) was commissioned a few years ago to collect all available data on the subject and pass it on down to the clinical level—to nurses, physicians, homes for the aged, and so forth.

While the far greater share of aging funds are spent on stop-gap geriatric relief, small sums have begun to trickle into research— such as that done at the Baltimore Center.

Research money is money well spent. The ultimate answers to the great problems posed by senescence will undoubtedly come out of the laboratory. Any rejuvenation therapy that fails to jibe with our basic biochemistry can be considered at best a glorified placebo or temporary palliative. (Nonetheless, the assumption of some gerontologists that nothing can or should be done against aging's miseries until we know precisely what it's all about is unpardonable ivory-towerism. While our knowledge of migraine headaches is rudimentary, common analgesics, such as aspirin, can alleviate mild attacks—even though we don't know *how* they work.)

The clumsiness of the federal government's first attempts to come to grips with the aging problem is still in evidence, despite efforts by a few administrators to eliminate the trivial, go-nowhere descriptive studies in order to pursue the best guesses of the keenest minds in science.

While admitting that it is not always easy to discern a significant from a useless project, Gunther Eichhorn, the intense, thoughtful chief of the Section on Molecular Biology in Baltimore, thinks the program could stand improvement.

"There is," he says, "a fair amount of unsophisticated research going on. If you can make any kind of measurement, you can make that measurement a function of age and you have a 'gerontological study.'"

Barrows, a robust, jolly, articulate professorial sort is more sanguine about the program than Eichhorn. "The days of pubic hair-counting are over," he declares, implying that the aging research show is on the road at last.

A few years ago, after being turned down for the umpteenth time for an aging grant, one of NIH's most persistent critics, the biochemist Johan Bjorksten, published a partial list of projects which *had* been accepted that year. The list included such devious paths to the Fountain of Youth as: Adult Learning of Differently Reared Bright-Dull Rats, Electromyographic Studies of Pathological Mouse Muscle, Epidemiology of Urinary Tract Infections, Factors Influencing Adult Social Behavior, Temporal Aspects of Hearing Loss, The Effect of Age on Arthritis in Poultry.

"Would these projects," asked Bjorksten rhetorically, "even if one hundred percent successful, bring us appreciably closer to control of the progressive deterioration which takes place in aging?"

Robert R. Kohn, of Western Reserve University's Institute of Pathology, who has neatly synthesized what he considers the most salient advances in aging research into a philosophical pattern, has tried to persuade his colleagues to stop behaving like poor, lost babes in the wood.

"It is," avers Kohn, "no longer sufficient to list a series of possibilities and claim that aging remains a mystery. Those of us who have spent a number of years studying aging processes are obliged to have some strong views about which aspects of the problem appear significant and worthy of future work, and which findings or notions are trivial."

Kohn argues further that much valuable time and money may be wasted in trying to discover a general process of aging that would hold for *all* animals.

"A mechanism proposed for the aging of man does not have to explain aging of insects, rotifers, and cells in culture; but probably should be capable of explaining aging in rats."

What do the Respectables consider their studies have revealed about why we grow old—and what can be done about it?

One rather solidly documented principle appears to be that overeating shortens mammal life—and near-starvation can dramatically lengthen it.

Would this hold true for humans as well?

"I don't see why not," says Barrows confidently. "The concept that dietary restriction must be carried out *early* in life is real. We can do it on rotifers. We can do it on rats. We can do it on mice. Presumably it has been done on *Drosophila* [fruit flies]."

The important word is "early." To achieve extended life in rats, the starvation diet must be started immediately after weaning. Even though Cornaro, the grand old man of sixteenth-century Venice, claimed to have rejuvenated himself and lived to ninety-nine after embarking on an ascetic's diet as late as his seventh decade, gerontologists say it just won't work that way with adult animals.

Kohn's feelings about rotifers notwithstanding, Barrows thinks he can infer important aging principles from his rotifer experiments. For one thing, he believes that aging is genetically programmed. In other words, age is by and large determined by the chromosomes inherited from one's parents.

This does not rule out therapy for the aging process. It merely means that, if this concept is valid, science probably can do less to extend the life-span than it could if aging were, for instance, the result of time's natural hazards and assaults. The idea of an aging "program" is generally accepted at the Baltimore Center.

The most convincing indication of a genetic aging program is the monotonous predictability of the major physiological events. Gestation, teething, crawling, loss of baby teeth and appearance of permanent teeth, puberty, and the menopause all occur within strikingly narrow statistical limits.

Interestingly enough, however, even some of the Baltimore studies have raised serious questions about the validity of the program concept. Rats that have been rejuvenated by starving show disturbing variations in enzyme production patterns from those that would be seen in chronologically younger rats. If there is a program, logically it should develop like a home movie film. The frames might pass by at a faster or a slower speed, but their sequence should be the same. That is, the normal "read-out" of the genetic program should not differ greatly from animal to animal. In light of this challenge, Barrows is going to reexamine those studies. It might be, he thinks, that there's nothing invalid in the program principle—just that other conditions may have been superimposed upon a basic program of enzyme changes.

Like most gerontologists, Barrows is not a theoretician. He is, on the contrary, a self-styled "hard-nosed spoiler" of aging theories.

"For a guy who wants to be loved like I do," he confides, "this is tough."

Others, more bold (or perhaps more foolish), have taken great running belly-flops into the bay of theory. It is when one hears out the authors on their theories that one realizes just how intensely individualistic science is—especially so young a science. Gerontology cannot be dealt with anonymously. It is a popular journalistic device to pretend that the scientific world is a big happy family, praying and voting with a single voice. But it is unfair and misleading to write "Doctors say," "Science says," for the simple reason that there is so little consensus.

Categorization of aging theory is bound to be whimsical at best. I will use Nathan Shock's convenient tripartite division, but others would serve as well. Some, for example, would have merely severed "program" from "nonprogram" theories. I have purposely left out some rather old-fashioned concepts, which survive only by the diligence of their creators, and added some not usually included with the others.

The German physicist Max Planck once declared, "The only way for a new theory to become accepted is for the adherents of the old theories to die." To which Johan Bjorksten appends the wistful comment "This process is slow, and in the meantime many of us die, too."

To confuse matters thoroughly, there exists a sect of nontheorists who persist in proposing aging theories. The perfect example is Dr. Hans Selye of Montreal University. Selye has published articles on his theories in scientific journals ("Calciphylaxis: Key to Aging?"; "Stress Theory of Aging"). Calciphylaxis he defines as a biological response through which the organism can selectively send large amounts of calcium salts to certain organs and cause their complete petrification. Still, Selye insists he doesn't believe in an aging theory any more than he does in a "growing-up theory."

"I am afraid," he says, "we must forever relinquish this task to the philosophers. We have long abandoned the search for a panacea against 'disease' and today no serious scientist is likely to spend his time looking for the universal remedy that could prevent all maladies. Why is it then that when applied to the aging of living matter, the hopelessness of this approach is not equally recognized?"

Of such nontheorists, the French wit Bernard de Fontenelle once observed: "To despise theory is to have the excessively vain pretension to do without knowing what one does, and to speak without knowing what one says."

Shock's division of theories gives us three categories:

1. The exhaustion or accumulation theories, which assume that we grow older because our bodies gradually lose certain necessary substances or acquire certain harmful substances.

2. The error theories, which postulate that atypical, or mutant, molecules of nucleic acids (such as DNA or RNA), the ultimate carriers of hereditary physical characteristics and controllers of enzyme patterns, are formed as the body grows older, thus producing mistakes in the formation of protein which, in turn, cause organic deterioration.

3. The eversion theories, which explain aging in terms of changes in various molecules *after* they have been formed.

Within all three groups there are both proponents and opponents of the important idea of aging's genetically born scheme. The subcategories are endless, and I shall touch on only those that continue to excite discussion.

Modern accumulation theories probably originated with the work of the late, enigmatic French biologist Alexis Carrel. Carrel found that only young serum was able to keep his famous chicken heart alive and beating in a dish for thirty-two years. When old serum was added to chicken heart tissue cultures, the organs promptly expired. Similarly, in his scarification work, he noted that wounds tend to heal more slowly in older people than in younger.

The old expression about a failing enterprise needing "young blood" to regenerate it goes back to seventeenth-century experiments, in which at least two old mongrels were apparently rejuvenated by transfusions from young pups. Today, the Manhattan plastic surgeon and dermatologist Norman Orentreich believes that he can rejuvenate human patients—not by adding young blood, but by removing what he calls aging-accelerating factors from an adult's bloodstream.

To achieve this, he is following up leads provided by Carrel. Orentreich, however, is using strict scientific controls, which were largely absent from Carrel's speculative ventures. In view of the skin doctor's fierce interest in Carrel, Rockefeller University allowed Orentreich to have a peek at the late Frenchman's unpublished papers (they were embargoed from publication for twenty-five years following Carrel's death in 1943, according to his will), which at this writing are still kept under lock and key at the Georgetown University Medical School.

"Carrel," says Orentreich, "created such animosity and antagonism in American medicine that, unfortunately, everything that he has done is looked at with suspicion."

Orentreich has picked up several threads of Carrel's work, of which the most fascinating is the plasmapheresis experiments (from the Greek *aphairesis*—withdrawal) in which large quantities of blood are removed from an animal (Carrel tried it on dogs), washed clean of the plasma, with its supposed toxins, and replaced in the organism. After brief respites, the plasmapheresis is repeated.

For the past two years, Orentreich has been working with two groups (of four each) of paired Beagles. As he performs plasmapheresis, the technique involves withdrawing whole blood via a vacuum pump, then centrifuging it under refrigeration and returning only the red blood cells in a physiological solution (minus the plasma).

One dog in each group is a control. The second dog is "moderately" plasmapheresed, that is, 15 percent of the blood volume is removed each week. The third is "intensively" (30 percent) plasmapheresed. The fourth is merely bled regularly and then reinfused with its own blood—to act as a control for the stress of the bleeding operation and presence of the anticoagulant.

I was permitted by Dr. Orentreich to witness his first human plasmapheresis, on October 29, 1966, in the offices of the Orentreich Medical Group at 909 Fifth Avenue, New York. The patient was an edgy man in his early forties who had been suffering from psoriasis for twenty-five years. It had been suggested to him that plasmapheresis might clear it up.

"I don't want to live to be a hundred and ten," he told me, "I just want to get rid of my psoriasis. I've tried everything. The best results I've had were with hypnosis—but I stopped it because of my doctor's advice."

He was attended by three doctors and a nurse. It was obvious that the doctors knew *what* they wanted to do, but were unsure precisely *how* they would proceed. It was agreed that no board would be needed to keep the arm to be tapped for blood stiff, and that the blood would be centrifuged for fifteen minutes at 2,000 rpm (instead of eight minutes at 2,500 rpm).

A small vacuum pump drew two pints of the patient's blood through plastic tubes into a polyethylene sack which was rocked back and forth to slosh the blood around. Thirty minutes after the tubes were severed and the blood taken away, a doctor returned with two bags of equal volume—one with plasma, the other with the red blood cells.

"They separated very nicely," he told the patient.

Unfortunately, what with the talk of possible "heart strain" and repeated warnings to avoid all activity for a while, the patient, who had begun to shiver (apparently from cold and nerves) decided not to go through with his anti-psoriasis rejuvenation therapy. Since then, I am told, other patients have volunteered and are being regularly plasmapheresed. While plasmapheresis is not a new process, this is the first time since Carrel that it has been used intensively to achieve rejuvenation.

Several leading gerontologists, such as Bernard Strehler and Alex Comfort, believe that plasmapheresis is well worth trying. "I suggested this a long time ago," says Comfort. "I think a lot of Carrel's work was nonsense, but some of it might be interesting to see again."

The Czech biologist Zdenek Hruza, who has specialized in protein-aging research, sees many merits in Orentreich's plasmapheresis work.

"I think it can work," he says. "So far we have only showed that collagen, a fibrous protein, ages. But it may be demonstrated that a similar thing occurs with so-called 'soluble' proteins, such as blood proteins. Now, if you take away this old protein, you practically cause the animal to stimulate production of new protein."

Many aging experts are bothered by the prospect, ten or twenty years hence, of great advances in rejuvenation that would produce a world crowded with long-lived, robust "vegetables." Their fear is based on the fact that brain and nerve cells inexorably diminish with age—so much so that an old man dies with about half the brain cells he was born with.

Orentreich disagrees.

"Whatever technique you use that would permit you to live three or four hundred years [which he believes quite possible] would prevent the brain cells from deteriorating."

Would plasmapheresis check this brain cell deterioration?

"I don't know . . . I would simply say that . . . toxic substances, damaging substances, prevent [brain cell] reproducibility and also enhance their rate of destruction."

Another mysterious aspect of "accumulation" in the aging organism, never satisfactorily explained, is the increase in lipofuscin, or so-called aging pigment, in certain cells. So far, scientists know very little about lipofuscin, except that it doesn't appear in the cells of children and tends to collect in adults' cells. But whether it truly possesses a degenerative *function*—one that might interfere with metabolism, or protein formation, or any other vital activity—has yet to be determined. Within a year or two, however, research in Baltimore under Dr. William Reichel is expected to provide some answers.

The accumulation theories are a counterpart of the exhaustion theories. A few encompass both concepts. Perhaps the most (clinically) popular exhaustion theory is that of diminishing endocrine secretions. Yet, this can probably be regarded as a surface explanation of certain phenomena, rather than as a lowest-common-denominator cause of the aging process itself.

Hormones, which are secreted by the endocrine glands, are chemical regulators of the body's physiological processes. They help maintain homeostasis, the body's internal balance, through a complicated interplay upon one another, through the central nervous system, and in direct action upon cells and tissues.

In the old days of rough-rider rejuvenation, sexual decline and aging were regarded as one and the same. The rejuvenators of the nineteenth and twentieth centuries used testicular extracts, shreds of gonadal debris, implants, every sort of sexual whatnot, to "cure" senility and impotence. What actually was achieved (when it worked) was probably a slight positive hormonal effect.

The endocrines do develop chronologically and they may even

show signs of aging. The thymus gland, for example, ceases to function during adolescence. Progesterone almost vanishes from the system during middle age. Estrogens and androgens are found at about one-third of their former strength in old age. Excess growth hormone in old age seems partly responsible for osteoarthritis, and ordinary arthritis can be exacerbated by loss of corticoid levels. Gonadal steroids are strongly implicated in the general loss of water in the tissues that marks aging. Various respiratory infections in old people may stem from the disappearance of hormones that enhance immune reactions, coupled with the retention of other hormones which provide hospitality for infectious agents.

Through the process of elimination (by removing various glands in experiments), it is nonetheless apparent that no hormone, alone or in combination, can be identified as responsible for accelerating the aging syndrome.

Dr. Thomas H. McGavack, Professor Emeritus of Clinical Medicine at New York Medical College and an authoritative endocrinologist, is understandably reluctant to tie aging changes inextricably to endocrinal behavior.

"While it is doubtful that we can consider senescence and death as directly due to aging changes in the endocrine glands," he told a Gerontological Society meeting a few years ago, "such alterations may nevertheless play a very definitive supporting role."

Replacement therapy will surely play an increasing role in treating the male and female climacterics. It is with the female menopause that hormones have scored their greatest clinical impact so far. The idea of staying "Feminine Forever" (to use Dr. Robert A. Wilson's best-selling book title) mirrors the quality of excitement that goat-gland male rejuvenation stirred up back in the twenties and thirties. It also smacks of goat-gland huckstering. *"Feminine Forever,"* reads one ad, tells "how to avoid menopause completely in your life, and stay a romantic, desirable, vibrant woman as long as you live." Dr. Joseph W. Goldzieher of the Southwest Foundation for Research and Education in San Antonio goes so far as to describe the menopause as "one of nature's mistakes." (Mistake though it may seem to be to the aging woman and her harassed doctor, it characterizes all of the higher primates. When most female animals are through reproducing they are either

killed or die naturally. When her ovaries die. the rest of her pre-
pares to follow suit.)

Treatment during the menopause is based on a rather simple
rationale, explains Dr. Herbert Kupperman: "If you lack thyroid
hormone, we give you thyroid. If you lack adrenal hormone, we
give you adrenal. Or if your thyroid is overactive, we control it to
a certain extent. The same applies to so-called sex glands."

"We can," Kupperman adds, "prevent some of the retarding
effects of aging. We can improve the cardiovascular system. We
can improve the texture of the skin. We can prevent some of the
increased hair growth on the face. . . . If you want to call this rejuvenation, then this is rejuvenation."

With doses of ovarian hormone, the postmenopausal woman
cannot procreate, but they do seem to help her avoid the hot
flushes, depression, and neuroses attendant upon normal cessation
of ovarian function.

Alex Comfort objects to "just bunging the stuff in. One wants,"
he says, "to find out what the decline [in endocrine production]
is a measure of. It wouldn't stop aging if you *filled* one with hormones. As a matter of fact, I'm certain of it."

Dr. Georgeanna Seegar Jones of the Johns Hopkins Women's
Clinic is just as certain as Comfort. One of her studies showed no
difference in the life expectancy of ovariectomized women with or
without estrogen replacement therapy. Interestingly, though,
differences in the cause of death were very much in evidence.
Those taking hormone treatments had a greater tendency to die of
carcinoma (cancer), while untreated women had a higher incidence of cardiovascular disease. The implication is that women
may be choosing the manner—if not the date—of their death.

The error theories, in Shock's estimation, provide "the most
attractive formulation to explain most of the facts of aging which
are known at the present time, although it is far from proved."

Unfortunately, not all theoreticians agree on what constitutes
an error and what doesn't. In its narrowest sense, error has to do
with the formation of slightly atypical molecules of messenger
RNA, which then cause errors in the formation of protein molecules. Ultimately, these faulty proteins create organic havoc and,
in later life, sharply intensify their lethal effect. Or so one theory
goes.

Some error theorists contend that progressive changes in the organism's genetic code leave the older person with a faded or greatly distorted copy of the originally clear structural blueprint. Could anything reverse this tendency toward genetic chaos?

Dr. John H. Heller, Executive Director of the New England Institute for Medical Research at Ridgefield, Connecticut, has suggested an ingenious reversal strategy based upon DNA's transplantability from one cell to another and the fact that the recipient cell faithfully copies all of the traits of the donor throughout successive generations. To date, however, this has been accomplished only in laboratory tissue cultures of mammalian liver and human bone marrow.

"Let us," suggests Heller, "take a young man or woman at the time when his nucleic acids [DNA and RNA] are being faithfully replicated, and take X amount of cells—white blood cells, if you will. Let us extract the nucleic acids, put them in a cryostat [deep freeze], bring them down to liquid helium temperatures, and store them away in a bank for twenty years or forty years—for whatever length of time until degenerative changes appear in this individual.

"By this time, it is hoped we will know the techniques of injecting them properly. The individual then would get a reinjection of a faithful new record to help counteract the blurred and scratched master disc. It would in effect be using youth to conserve youth, to stave off the onset of senescence."

When Dr. Heller was asked if his idea was practical, he replied: "I don't know. If it can happen in a test tube, I think we'd be fools not to try it *in vivo*."

The biochemists who have experimented with the life code tend to reject this sort of thinking on several grounds. They maintain that the DNA molecule must be a very stable thing, otherwise the whole chain would be too easily lost. If the DNA (and thus the RNA) "worsened" with age, then offspring from older mothers and older fathers should show more genetic aberrations than they do (by comparison with offspring from younger parents). Further, the dissenters argue that DNA in its pure form seems to carry an aging program right from the start. This is why there is a world of difference between the life-span of the mayfly (*Ephemera*), which lives a few hours, and John Doe, with a potential life-span of a hundred years. Certainly this gap is accounted for by fundamental variations in each animal's DNA makeup. This does not, however, preclude the possibility that random errors in RNA synthesis might couple with the DNA's original aging program to shorten life further.

Until quite recently, radiation (which produces great changes in DNA and thus in cellular protein) was thought to shorten life by accelerating the aging process. Reports from the Atomic Bomb Casualty Commission (ABCC), however, have refuted this concept. It is quite true that radiation shortens life, but not by hurrying aging itself.

Nathan Shock and the eminent cellular biologist Paul Weiss of Rockefeller University are advocates of a new twist to aging theory.

"I keep thinking," says Shock, "that the key to this aging problem may not be these isolated, detailed mechanisms. The real age problem may arise when we start trying to functionally coordinate the activities of a lot of different specifics."

Shock contends that the largest age changes in any species of life are in what he calls "total animal performance." The more complicated the organism gets, the more of an age-change one is apt to witness. With separated mitochondria (minute, semisolid bodies in cell cytoplasm), for instance, one cannot tell if it came from a young or an old cell. The act of coordinating uncountable variegated activities and functions may just be the kind of stress that produces aging, Shock thinks.

Weiss seems to be saying much the same thing. He maintains that aging is an "integral facet of the continuous progress of development of an organism." Whereas most gerontologists date the onset of aging from fertilization of the ovum, or from birth, or from a point of "growth cessation" (usually somewhere in the teens), Weiss says that growth in its widest sense goes on steadily throughout the life of the organism and never stops. Cell death begins with the embryo. So do all the other elemental attributes of the aging syndrome.

"What really troubles the organism," says Weiss, "is rather the increasing disharmony of *mutual relations* among the various component activities, a loss of integration. . . . If . . . we compare the system of interdependent component processes to an elastic network, more and more meshes will thus be strained beyond the stress limit and snap. More and more of the alternate bypasses formerly available to vicariate and compensate for lost interaction pathways will thereby be put out of commission."

Weiss deals harshly with concepts of "aging agents," or "aging factors" or "metabolic slags" (*i.e.*, wastes). These notions, he says, only misguide research the same way Ponce de Leon deceived the naïve into believing in a Fountain of Youth.

Can anything be done to stem aging, if one accepts Weiss' theory?

Yes—but not much. One can, he says, "stem impending disintegration within limits by appropriate compensatory and substitutive counter measures," that is, by keeping "the latter faculties in training by practice throughout life." What Weiss seems to be saying is simply that one ought to keep trim—mentally and physically.

While the rejuvenation-minded cannot glean much hope from this deterministic view, it must be regarded as a quite serious conjecture by one of biology's most knowledgeable and versatile intellects.

Far more encouraging are the eversion theories of aging (*i.e.*, molecular changes *after* formation), where one finds most of the fun and fireworks of aging theory. Advocated by distinguished, serious men of science, the eversion hypothesis holds forth the prospect of drastic extensions of the human life-span.

A particularly vital figure here is a research "outsider" who has doggedly labored a simple concept which, if correct, could turn out to be the single most valuable concept in medical history. His name is Johan Bjorksten.

For years, gerontologists have been lulled by the cliché (which began its long career as an astute observation by the brilliant British zoologist Peter Brian Medawar) that no autopsy ever showed a person to have died from unadulterated old age. This later developed into one notion that aging does not kill people, and another (by inference from the first) that science would be better occupied if it busied itself in studying diseases such as cancer, heart disease, infections, and so forth, instead of aging.

Bjorksten's notion is a brutal rejection of such neo-Medawarian or, rather, pseudo-Medawarian, thinking. He maintains that, appearances to the contrary, what most old people *really* die of is, in fact, aging. His arguments are quite persuasive.

When he began to set forth his theory in the 1940's, he was frequently derided as a simplistic, reckless theorist, a do-no-research-but-talk-it-up expounder of high-flown dreams, an opportunist and sensationalist. But as one biochemical finding after another has confirmed his predictions, his name has slowly begun to command respect within academic gerontology's hallowed walls—walls which once bore his initials only in insulting graffiti.

This, at least, is my impression. I might be wrong. It might just be that everybody is scared stiff of him.

Bjorksten breaks *all* the rules. When his pleas for financial help are rejected by the government, he has the temerity to *publish* the correspondence (making venerable NIH officials look like prize morons). He is not choosy about his publications,* and does not hesitate to print his brainstorms in popular or semipopular magazines.

West Coast science writer Bob Prehoda, a Bjorksten fan, warned me that anything said at NIH against Bjorksten was simply the result of prejudice. I was therefore surprised to find that the Gerontological Research Center chiefs spoke about him with deference, if not with mother love.

"I have no ax to grind with this man at all," said one, who asked that his comments on Bjorksten remain off the record.

"I just wish he'd *do* some experiments rather than talk about them. Has he done any?" asked another, in the harshest tone I heard. When I informed him that Bjorksten had been given a $250,000 grant from the Upjohn Company to do the practical work he'd previously been too poor to do, the gerontologist's attitude immediately changed.

"Good. Good for him. I always battled loud and long to get him the money," he protested. "My impression is that he's an honest

---

* Medical ethics are complicated. With few exceptions, the major gerontologists cooperated with the author wholeheartedly. A handful, however, were afraid that their interviews with a lay journalist would be frowned upon by their colleagues or collectives. NICHD researcher Harry Eldon, for instance, asked me if *The Youth Doctors* would be "technical or non-technical." When I said non-technical, he refused to be interviewed.

believer. . . . But his requests were always large and involved the purchase of a lot of heavy, expensive equipment."

The idea that the "peer review groups" (university scientists) who control grants at NIH might have turned down Bjorksten on grounds of expense was unacceptable to Dr. Leroy E. Duncan, Jr., who administers NIH's aging program.

"I don't know," said Duncan, "whether they were high or not. In general, the study sections don't turn down a grant because they think too much money is asked for it. If they think the research is good, but the budget is extravagant, then they recommend approval of research at a reduced budget."

Would the increasing acceptance of Bjorksten's ideas on aging influence the study groups more favorably in the future?

"I think," said Duncan cagily, "it's generally agreed that there is increased cross-linking of collagen as animals grow older. But that fact wouldn't necessarily lead to his request being approved."

Bjorksten is a loner, which is an oddity in the closely knit field of gerontology. His current academic ties are apparently nil, except for membership in several professional societies. Fellow members of the Gerontological Society (which he pointedly omits mentioning in his curriculum vitae) complain that he rarely attends meetings, and, when he does, is usually silent. His qualifications include a BS (1927) and PhD (1931) in protein chemistry from Helsingfors University. In the 1930's he was sponsored by the International Education Board of the Rockefeller Foundation for work at the University of Minnesota. A brilliant chemist, he holds patents for a metal foaming process, a method of continuously drawing vitreous silica fibers, and a unique formula for metal-coating glass and silica.

It is reasonable to assume that his well-paid consulting jobs to the military and industry have aroused envy among gerontologists of the "poorer-but-purer-science" stripe. He's worked, variously, for Pepsodent, Ditto, the Felton Chemical Company, and the Quaker Chemical Products Corporation; he has also created his own research consulting firm, which has won large government and commercial contracts. His consulting profits have, until recently, financed the nonprofit Bjorksten Research Foundation.

As for being in any manner "ashamed" of his working hand in

glove with pharmaceutical firms, quite the contrary—Bjorksten maintains that "the American drug industry is the principal spearhead of world pharmaceutical research." He adduces to his argument the fact that, of the six hundred and four new chemical remedies produced in America between 1941 and 1964, the drug companies produced three hundred and twenty-nine and NIH (his apparent nemesis) produced but one.

Bjorksten does not subscribe to the inevitability of aging, or the idea of hard-and-fast genetic programming. He points to Mc-Cay's and Lansing's rat and rotifer experiments to show that so-called normal life-spans can be greatly increased with the simplest of techniques (starvation and temperature changes). Conceivably, he thinks, man could live eight hundred years with the proper rejuvenation therapy.

What is keeping us from this glorious golden age? The operative term is molecular cross-linkage. This essentially is a fancy, modern view of what M. G. Marinescu and Leopild Ruzička in the last century described as colloid aging, that is, the deterioration of nonliving parts of the body such as the elastic fibers of the arterial walls, cartilage, and so forth. The idea is that such tissues go down in time in much the same way that glue, paper, or certain plastics do. Interestingly, Bjorksten's ideas on human aging emanate directly from his work as an industrial chemist.

"When we look at the changes most conspicuous in aging tissue —loss of elasticity, loss of bound water, of solubility, reduction of swelling—then some of us, the polymer chemists, the paint chemists, the textile-finishing chemists, those cosmetologists who have worked with hair, will all say this certainly can be caused only by cross-linkage."

The remark is arresting. I have noticed that aging theorists almost without exception wear their theories like old school ties. The radiologist thinks that aging is caused by X rays. It was a short step from Metchnikoff's discovery of phagocytosis to his conclusion that phagocytosis caused aging. *La théorie, c'est l'homme.* A polymer chemist thinks that aging is caused by free radicals, which he has studied closely over the years. Free radicals are atoms or atom groups carrying an unpaired electron and no charge, and are often involved in various living tissue reactions as brief, highly active intermediates.

It has been established beyond doubt that colloid molecules in connective tissue do, in fact, acquire cross-links with age, making that tissue tougher, more rigid, less springy. Cross-linkage explains why prime filet mignon is so tender, and why another cut of steak is fit only for meatballs.

Bjorksten gives the following illustration of cross-linking's action upon the body: "The effect is like what would happen in a large factory with thousands of workers if someone slipped a pair of handcuffs on one hand of each of two workers, to tie them together. This obviously would reduce their ability to do their work, and if the process were allowed to spread through the factory, even at a slow rate, it would ultimately paralyze the entire operation unless means were found to remove the handcuffs faster than they were being applied."

This, he contends, is what goes on throughout the whole body. Not only in connective tissue (which is not formed of cells), but in cellular tissue as well. The "workers" are large molecules, performing useful functions. They may be protein, or its chemical precursor, nucleic acids. The "handcuffs" are cross-links which immobilize and inactivate the molecules by causing them to clump together. Cross-linking agents (Bjorksten calls them "cross-linkers") are polyvalent metals, aldehydes, dibasic acids, quinones, eneamines and free radicals of any kind. He believes the average person has anywhere from ten to one hundred quintillion cross-linkers in his body.

Many cross-linkages are broken up by natural enzymes almost as quickly as they are formed. It's the ones that are stout enough chemically to resist enzyme action that make a person grow older, less resilient.

Age pigment, which other scientists still consider a mystery, is no mystery to Bjorksten. It is cross-linked material (highly deleterious, he says, to the brain, heart, kidney, and nerve cells). In an older person up to 10 percent of some cells' volume can be occupied by this brown pigment. He also claims to have found this pigment in the hearts of stillborn babies.

What results from cross-linking is a "frozen metabolic pool," as Bjorksten calls it, which destroys tissue and cells by clogging them, smothering them, putting them out of commission. Whence the aging syndrome.

Bjorksten has covered all bets by propounding the theory of cross-linkage in both connective tissue and the body's cells. But for some scientists, like Robert R. Kohn, making a case for intra-cellular cross-linkage is a waste of time. Cell loss, by cross-linkage or any other mechanism, is not enough to explain aging, he argues. The body has an enormous reserve of cells in vital organs. Cell turnover is rapid and efficient in getting rid of faulty cells. Even if we were to lose a third of our cells, the only thing that would happen would be that we would shrink somewhat, he says. Period. No, says Kohn, *"alterations in fibrous proteins [such as collagen or elastin or reticulin] of connective tissue can explain almost all of the serious mammalian aging."*

Collagen's importance, he says, is preeminent. It provides a flexible, sturdy framework for vessels and muscles. It bears stresses, controls elasticity, encages mobile organs such as the lungs and arteries. It is the vital barrier between the cells and the blood vessels.

"In simple terms," says Kohn, "aggregation of collagen would result in tissues becoming more rocklike with age, approaching a state which is obviously incompatible with life."

To Bjorksten, however, the key word is not *collagen*—but *cross-linking*, wherever it occurs, in collagen, in the cell, wherever. It is, he proclaims, "the primary event in aging generally."

The end result of this cross-linking process is "a continuing loss of resistance to all forms of damage," he says.

This is where Bjorksten's great idea begins. Viewed superficially, it is an utterly commonplace observation. In another sense, it is a most penetrating insight into general geriatric pathology and the whole business of gerontology. The idea itself may be stated thus:

At least 90 percent of all deaths are due to aging, because 90 percent of them would not have happened if the victims had been as healthy as they were at age fifteen—when they easily fought off their afflictions. An infection or bruise that a fifteen-year-old boy shakes off can be fatal to a ninety-year-old man.

"When a very old person dies from, say, pneumonia," declares Bjorksten, "we set that down as the cause of death and too easily lose sight of the fact that the underlying loss of resistance due to age was very much more at fault."

As that astute old English bishop Thomas Sherlock once noted:

"Most men take least notice of what is plain, as if that were of no use; but puzzle their thoughts, and lose themselves in those vast depths and abysses which no human understanding can fathom."

When Bjorksten formally presented his idea to an assemblage of his colleagues in gerontology some time ago, not a single voice was raised to oppose him. He pointed to longevity tables over the past few decades and demonstrated that all medicine had done was to reduce mortality in the early years, but not a jot had been accomplished in extending the far end of the life-span. Plainly, his thinking makes sense.

What fails to make sense is the fact that a contemptible one half of one percent of the total NIH $1,000,000,000 budget should go for aging study. If all the major diseases put together were cured tomorrow, the most that could be gained would be "about fifteen years of increasingly precarious existence," says Bjorksten. Conquer aging, on the other hand, and the extension of life could be phenomenal. The anti-Bjorksten people have not satisfactorily answered this formidable argument for a far more serious campaign against aging.

If cross-linking *is* the human race's bête noire, what can be done about it?

Since May 9, 1966, Bjorksten personally has been engaged in a hush-hush series of practical experiments for the Upjohn Company. The work revolves around his old dream of finding otherwise innocuous enzymes that will reverse cross-linkages.

His first step presumably will be to break down cross-linked protein from old animals with known enzymes. This would leave a deposit of the cross-linkages that are toughest to turn back. This deposit would be used as the sole food for a mixed culture of soil insects with a wide variety of enzymes in them. Eventually, only those insects with gerolytic (*i.e.*, capable of digesting cross-linked material) enzymes would survive, he theorizes. Even if those enzymes themselves should prove harmful to the human organism, he believes that a strain might be developed that could perform the medical miracle of all time: to impede or even reverse the aging process itself!

Even now, there are substances that do turn "old" (insoluble) collagen back into "young" (soluble) collagen. Two University of

Southern California professors, Lucien Bavetta and Marcel Nimni have experimented successfully with a modified amino acid called penicillamine.

Penicillamine, derived from penicillin, is commonly used to treat Wilson's disease, a congenital condition where abnormal amounts of copper accumulate in the liver, brain, kidney, and eye. The drug not only helps the system eliminate copper, but causes a loss of skin tensile strength. Was it, Bavetta and Nimni asked themselves, in effect reversing collagen cross-linkage?

"No question about that," says Bavetta. "We've simply injected it or fed it [to animals] and studied the type of collagen formed. Whenever we use penicillamine, there is a decrease in the dimers [heavily cross-linked, or "old," collagen]."

"It might," speculates Bavetta, "influence the kind of skin you have. There is another possibility that this will reduce artery hardening."

Bavetta revealed that some human experiments in collagen rejuvenation were under way, but that they were secret.

Other sources of connective tissue rejuvenation are collagenases (collagen-dissolving enzymes), elastases, lathyrogens (agents causing nervous, paralytic symptoms), and enzymes which naturally dissolve old collagen in the uterus following pregnancy.

Denham Harman, an MD and brilliant biochemist at the University of Nebraska, for the past fourteen years has been working on a type of accumulation or eversion theory (take your pick) which he calls the "Free Radical Reaction Aging Theory."

Free radicals and cross-linkages are closely related phenomena. Both are difficult to reverse. Examples of free radicals include smog, rancid butter, sour milk, dried paint. Essentially, free radicals are high-energy sites desperately looking for something to react with. ("Like a convention delegate when he manages to get away from his wife," as a specialist once defined the term.)

The advent of biochemical techniques has meant that, at last, scientists can begin to explore the process of senescence on its most fundamental, molecular basis. The importance of this approach was recently underscored by Harman, who observed: "If you're looking for one underlying [aging] factor on the molecular level, you'll probably either look at one free radical or one cross-linking form."

In some respects, Harman is farther along in advancing his rejuvenation experimentation than Bjorksten is with his. To Harman, a serious, modest Midwesterner with an encyclopedic grasp of biochemistry, the secret to longevity lies in mastering free radical reactions within the organism. While the body naturally protects itself by raising levels of antioxidants (which scavenge for free radicals) in critical areas, such as the eye lens, it doesn't do this sufficiently elsewhere. "If mother nature had a perfect system for minimizing the free radical reactions," notes Harman, "and did nothing more, nothing less—then we might become immortal."

A certain number of free radical reactions are bound to take place no matter what, however, since our body's aqueous environment needs oxygen catalysts for metabolic oxidative reactions.

Harman has tested the use of dietary antioxidants in rat and mice studies, to see whether he could extend the natural animal life-span. Although antioxidants occur naturally in vitamins (A, C, E), he used synthetic antioxidants in a series of experiments covering several years. The results caused the gerontological world to sit up and take notice.

In one set of mice experiments, Harman was able to extend the half-survival time (age at which half of the mice in any single group are dead) of animals fed an antioxidant called BHT (butylated hydroxytoluene) by 50.3 percent over the control group. In other terms, at the end of 14.9 months one half of the controls were dead. But half of the antioxidant-fed group were still alive at 22.4 months. Other positive results were obtained using 2-mercaptoethylamine hydrochloride and cysteine hydrochloride.

Harman believes that his antioxidants are preventing the harmful side effects that result from free radical equations. Among these, he suggests, are oxidation of connective tissue, removing hydrogen atoms from nucleic acids, piling up of age pigment, and irritation of vessel walls leading to arteriolocapillary fibrosis.

An interesting sidelight of Harman's experiments is a finding that tumors increase in animals with higher fat (*including* polyunsaturates) diets. Fats and polyunsaturation per se are tinder for free radical reactions. Harman believes that the possibility of lowering serum cholesterol levels by eating only polyunsaturated fats (such as safflower oil) may indeed lower the coronary rate—but *increase the cancer rate.*

As rejuvenationists, both Bjorksten and Harman are sitting

ducks for criticism within the scientific community. Barrows, for one, is skeptical about finding an enzyme that could reverse only the harmful cross-linkages in the body. "You've got to be awfully specific," he says. "You can start chopping up things you don't want to chop up, too. Enzymes are not necessarily as specific as lots of people would like to think. This becomes a problem. It's like treatment of cancer with fluorouracil. It doesn't distinguish between normal cells and cancer cells."

A weakness of the free radical theory is the difficulty scientists have of positively identifying free radicals with present technology. "We're not ready yet to identify a free radical," admits Harman. "You can find ten or twenty different types of free radicals in cigarette smoke, and probably some of these may cause cancer, but these are not identifiable."

According to Harman, there may be events occurring in nucleic acids which could alter the genetic code in cells just enough to impair function without hindering reproductive capacity. Such events, he believes, are more likely to be the more complex free radical reactions rather than cross-linkage. Any comprehensive aging theory, thinks Harman, would have to explain just such cellular phenomena. Some gerontologists reject Bjorksten's notion of intracellular cross-linkage, but find intracellular free radicals quite plausible.

What is truly fascinating is not the differences between Harman and Bjorksten, but how close they are, and how they traveled from disparate origins to strikingly similar biochemical conclusions about the nature of aging. There are other scientists round the world, such as Rumania's Simon Oeriu, who, from a third perspective, has arrived at almost the same destination. Oeriu's fol-cysteine, according to Harman, provides a rejuvenating effect most probably by reducing free radical attack on various tissues and organs.

All three men are optimistic about the prospects for considerable extensions of human longevity.

There are in academe, however, far more cynics, know-nothings, and critics than there are doers.

"I don't understand it," says Denham Harman. "People are losing sight of the ultimate goal. [Gerontology] isn't just a purely academic pursuit. The basic purpose of all this business is: How do we get to live longer better? If we can't live longer, let's live better. I think we can do both, though."

Unfortunately, the orthodox establishment is greatly to blame for our having lost sight of the ultimate goal. Even attempts at intermediate rejuvenation goals meet with shallow, ritual mockery by those who know nothing about the men and treatments they so casually vilify.

James D. Watson, who with Francis Crick was awarded a Nobel Prize for discovering the DNA structure in 1953, noted in *The Atlantic* serialization of their story that his partner "did not worry about these skeptics. Many were cantankerous fools who unfailingly backed the wrong horses. One could not be a successful scientist without realizing that, in contrast to the popular conception supported by newspapers and mothers of scientists, a goodly number of scientists are not only narrow-minded and dull, but also just stupid."

Scoffing at bold endeavors is relatively easy. It attracts the crowd, who fallaciously consider their numbers as proof of intelligence and right. Creativity is an intrinsically undemocratic and lonely affair. It makes fierce demands upon the would-be innovator's courage and stamina.

This is why the youth doctors, almost to a man, are such fascinating human beings. If nothing else, they possess rare character and ingenuity. Many have, as well, a transcending, almost mystical, empathy for their patients that might well serve as model for general practice.

They are a picaresque crew. Rejuvenation's heroes and fools, missionaries and merchants, saviors and opportunists, its Erector Set and Respectables, even its cranks and kooks, have all contributed to one worthwhile purpose. They have kept alive a dream that long ago was pronounced dead by "authority." The dream is that man *can* live longer better.

Subtly, almost unconsciously, we are witnessing a momentous convergence of man's oldest wish and the promise of science: mother nature serving human nature to fulfill the destiny of both. The spectacle is deeply ironic in at least one respect. For even in their most wanton hokum, the Brinkleys and the Voronoffs would never have dared to offer what respectables today speak of rather glibly: the possibility of man's living as long as Methuselah—and a damned sight better.

Bibliography

ALEXANDER, PETER, and CONNELL, D. I., "Differences Between Radiation-induced Lifespan Shortening in Mice and Normal Aging as Revealed by Serial Killing." *Symposium on Cellular Basis and Aetiology of Late Somatic Effects of Ionizing Radiation* (March 27–30, 1962), London, Academic Press.

Ancient and Medieval Science, René Taton, ed. New York, Basic Books, 1957.

"Aspects of the Biology of Ageing," H. W. Woolhouse, ed. *Symposia of the Society for Experimental Biology,* No. 21. New York, Academic Press, 1967.

BAITSELL, GEORGE ALFRED, *Manual of Biology,* 6th ed. New York, Macmillan Company, 1941.

BEAUCHENE, ROY E., Ph.D; ROEDER, LOIS M., B.A.; and BARROWS, CHARLES H., JR., Sc.D, "The Effect of Age and of Ethionine Feeding on the Ribonucleic Acid and Protein Synthesis of Rats." *Journal of Gerontology,* Vol. 22, No. 3 (July, 1967).

BELL, BENJAMIN, M.D.; ROSE, CHARLES L., A.M.; and DAMON, ALBERT, M.D., Ph.D, "The Veterans Administration Longitudinal Study of Healthy Aging." *The Gerontologist* (December, 1966).

BEST, ALBERT A., M.D., and HELLMAN, LEON I., Ph.D, "Psychological and Emotional Effect of Cosmetic Surgery." *Western Medicine* (July, 1960).

BIRREN, JAMES E.; BUTLER, ROBERT N.; GREENHOUSE, SAMUEL W.; SOKOLOFF, LOUIS; and YARROW, MARIAN R., *Human Aging: A Biological and Behavioral Study.* Public Health Service Publication, No. 986. Washington, D.C., U.S. Government Printing Office.

BJORKSTEN, DR. JOHAN, "Aging, Primary Mechanism." *Gerontologia,* Vol. 8 (1963).

———, "Could We Live Longer?" *New Scientist* (September 13, 1962).

———, "Deterrence of Aging Must Be Longevity's Reward." Address before the Chicago Technical Societies Council, November 23, 1965.

———, "Thoughts in My Garden." *The Chemist* (August, 1963).

BJORKSTEN, DR. JOHAN; ANDREWS, FRED A.; and PRAHL, HELMUT F.,

"Anhydrous Hydrogen Fluoride as a Tool in Studying Cross-linkages in Proteinaceous Substances Accumulating with Age." *Finska Kemists,* Medd. 71, No. 3 (1962).

BLACKSCHLEGER, HERBERT, *Hide: A Challenge to the Devotees of Freud, Pasteur, Darwin and Marx!* Boston, Forum Publishing Company, 1959.

BORTZ, EDWARD L., M.D., *Creative Aging.* New York, Macmillan Company, 1963.

BOURLIÈRE, PROFESSOR FRANÇOIS, "The Future of Research in the Biology of Ageing." *Excerpta Medica,* Section XX, "Gerontology and Geriatrics" (July, 1964).

———, *Le Vieillissement de Fonctions Psychologiques et Psychophysiologiques.* Colloques Internationaux du Centre National de la Recherche Scientifique, 1961.

———, "Longévité et Milieu: Le Role des Facteurs Écologiques dans le Processus de Sénescence." *La Revue du Practicien* (March 11, 1966).

———, "Principes et Méthodes de Mésure de l'Age Biologique chez l'Homme." *Bulletin de la Société d'Anthropologie de Paris,* 11th Series (1963).

BOURLIÈRE, PROFESSOR FRANÇOIS; CENDRON, H.; and CLÉMENT, F., "Le Vieillissement Individuel dans une Population Rurale Française Étude de la Commune de Plozévet, Finistère." *Les Cahieres du Centre de Recherches Anthropologiques,* Vol. 10, 11th Series (1966).

BROCAS, J., and VERZÁR, F., "Measurement of Isometric Tension During Thermic Contraction as Criterion of the Biological Age of Collagen Fibres." *Gerontologia,* Vol. 5 (1961).

BUTLER, J. A. V., *The Life of the Cell.* New York, Basic Books, 1964.

CARLYLE, THOMAS, *English and Other Critical Essays.* Everyman's Library. Letchworth, England, Temple Press for J. M. Dent & Sons, 1915.

CARNE, CEDRIC, "The Man Who Seeks the Secret of Eternal Youth." *Sunday Express* (November 15, 1964).

CARRERAS, DR. ANTONIO SOLDEVILLA, *Kasuistik über die Behandlung der Multiplen Sklerose mit Wobe-Mugos.* Privately published, undated.

CARSON, GERALD, *The Roguish World of Doctor Brinkley.* New York, Holt, Rinehart and Winston, 1960.

COHEN, DAVID, "Magnetic Fields Around the Torso: Production by Electrical Activity of the Human Heart." *Science* (May 5, 1967).

COMFORT, ALEX, *The Process of Ageing.* New York, Signet Science Library Books, 1961.

CORNARO, LUIGI, *How to Live Long.* The Health Culture Company, 1916.

CRAMP, ARTHUR J., M.D., *Nostrums and Quackery and Pseudo-medicine,* Vol. 3. Chicago, American Medical Association, 1936.

"Criteria for Estrogen Replacement Offered." *Medical Tribune* (May 15, 1967).

DUNCAN, LEROY E., JR., M.D., "Research in Aging and the National Institute of Child Health and Human Development." Talk before the American Geriatrics Society, June 16, 1967.

DU NOÜY, LECOMTE, *Human Destiny.* New York, David McKay Co., 1947.

ELLER, JOSEPH J., M.D., and WOLFF, SHIRLEY, "Skin Peeling and Scarification." *Journal of the American Medical Association* (March 8, 1941).

ETTINGER, ROBERT C. W., *The Prospect of Immortality.* New York, Macfadden Book, published by arrangement with Doubleday, 1964.

FANESTIL, DARREL D., M.D., and BARROWS, CHARLES H., JR., Sc.D, "Aging in the Rotifer." *Journal of Gerontology* (October, 1965).

Federal Food, Drug, and Cosmetic Act as Amended. U.S. Department of Health, Education and Welfare, Food and Drug Administration, 1966.

"Feminine Forever," *Time* (April 3, 1967).

FISCHER, KURT JOACHIM, *Niehans: Arzt des Papstes.* Munich, Andermann, 1956.

FREDERICKS, CARLTON, Ph.D, *Nutrition Your Key to Good Health.* California, London Press, 1964.

GENSAC, GILBERT, *Nous Vivrons 150 Ans.* Paris, Éditions Mondiales, 1960.

GIESE, HANS, "Cellulartherapie homosexueller Mannër." *Der Nervenarzt* (March, 1959).

———, *L'Homosexualité de l'Homme.* Paris, Payot, 1959.

GOETZE-CLAREN, WOLFGANG, M.D., *Cellular and Genetic Therapy: A Fundamental Explanation of Its Origin, Development and Practice.* Privately published, 1966.

GRUMAN, PROFESSOR GERALD J., *A History of Ideas About the Prolongation of Life.* Transactions of the American Philosophical Society (December, 1966).

HAMMOND, E. CUYLER, Sc.D, "Some Thoughts on the Biological Aspects of Aging." *Research in Gerontology: Biological and Medical, Reports and Guidelines from the White House Conference on Aging* (August, 1961).

Handbook of Aging and the Individual Psychological and Biological Aspects, James E. Birren, ed. Chicago, University of Chicago Press, 1959.

HARMAN, DENHAM, M.D., "Free Radical Theory of Aging: Effect of Free Radical Inhibitors on the Life Span of Male LAF$_1$ Mice." Talk before the 19th Annual Meeting of the Gerontological Society in New York, November 3, 1966.

HARPOLE, JAMES, *Leaves from a Surgeon's Case-book*. The New Home Library Edition. Philadelphia, Frederick A. Stokes Co., 1942.

HASERICK, JOHN R., M.D., "Skin Problems of the Aged." *Geriatrics* (October, 1963).

HAUSER, GAYELORD, *Treasury of Secrets*. A Fawcett Crest Book, reprinted by arrangement with Farrar, Straus & Giroux, Copyright 1951, '52, '55, '61, '63.

HENRY, DR. RENÉ B., *La Thérapeutique Cellulaire: Ou Thérapeutique de Niehans*, Editions du Centre Médical d'Études et de Recherches chez l'Auteur. Paris, 54 rue Beaubourg, 1961.

HOEPKE, PROFESSOR DR. HERMANN, *For the 80th Birthday of Professor Dr. Paul Niehans*. Berne, Ott Verlag Thun, 1962.

INGLIS, BRIAN, "Recharging Health and Vitality: Progress Report from Two European Doctors on the Controversial Uses of Cellular Therapy." *Vogue* (January 15, 1968).

International Society for Research of Cellular Therapy. Proceedings of the Third International Congress for Cellular Therapy. Berne and Stuttgart, Verlag Hans Huber, 1962.

JACOB, STANLEY W., M.D., F.A.C.S., and FRANCONE, CLARICE ASHWORTH, *Structure and Function in Man*. Philadelphia, W. B. Saunders Co., 1965.

JACOBSEN, A. WILMOT, M.D., "De Senectute: A Pediatrician Takes a Long Look." *Journal of the American Geriatrics Society*, Vol. 14, No. 5 (1966).

JACOBSON, M.D., and RESSLER, CHARLES, M.D., "Rapid Therapy of Infectious Hepatitis." *New York State Journal of Medicine* (1956).

JARVIS, D. C., M.D., *Arthritis and Folk Medicine*. Fawcett Publications, reprinted by arrangement with Holt, Rinehart and Winston, Copyright 1960.

KNOX, JOHN M., M.D., "Etiological Factors and Premature Aging." *Journal of the American Medical Association* (February 24, 1962).

KOMAROV, L. V., *A Theory of the Aging of Organisms and the Paths of its Development (Teoriya Stareniya Organismov i Puti yeyo Rasrabotki)*. Izdatelstvo Nauka, 1966.

——, "The Problem of Radically Increasing Life Prolongation (*Problema Radikalnogo Uvelicheniya Prodolzhitelnosti Zhizni*)." *Problemi Dolgoletiya*, Press of the Academy of Sciences of the USSR (1963).

——, "Some Potential Areas for Research on Means of Drastically

Increasing the Human Life Span." *Acta Gerontologica et Geritrica Belgica*, Vol. 4, No. 2 (1966).

LAMBERT, GILLES, *Niehans ou la Vieillesse Vaincue*. Paris, Librairie Arthème Fayard, 1958.

LARIVIÈRE, DR. ANDRÉ, *Les Fontaines de Jouvence*. Paris, Editions Bernard Grasset, 1955.

LÉPINE, PIERRE, *Elie Metchnikoff et l'Immunologie*. Paris, Pierre Seghers, Editeur, 1966.

Literaturverzeichnis der Zellulartherapie. Berne and Stuttgart, Verlag Hans Huber, 1962.

LORD, RUSSELL, *The Wallaces of Iowa*. Boston, Houghton-Mifflin Co., 1947.

LORINCZ, A. L., "Physiology of the Aging Skin." *Illinois Medical Journal*, 117:59 (February, 1960).

LUBOWE, IRWIN I., M.D., F.A.C.A., *New Hope for Your Skin*. Pocket Books, by arrangement with E. P. Dutton and Co., Copyright 1963.

MACDONALD, DWIGHT, *Henry Wallace: The Man and the Myth*. New York, Vanguard Press, 1947.

MAXIMOW, ALEXANDER A., and BLOOM, WILLIAM, *A Textbook of Histology*, 6th ed. Philadelphia, W. B. Saunders Co., 1930.

McGRADY, PAT, SR., *The Savage Cell: A Report on Cancer and Cancer Research*. New York, Basic Books, 1964.

Medichnii Zhurnal (Medical Journal), edited by A. A. Bogomolets and published by the Ukrainian Academy of Sciences. Numerous articles on antireticular cytotoxic serum or Bogomolets Serum, by authors such as P. D. MARCHUK, R. E. KAVETSKY, N. E. KAVETSKY, N. B. MEDVEDEVA, G. A. SPASSOKOKUTSKY, T. I. NOVIKOVA-DANTZIGER, E. A. TATARINOV, M. B. PARTASHNIKOV, A. A. BOGOMOLETS, A. L. MIKHNEV, E. M. ZALKIND, E. A. CHERNOBROVKINA, B. A. YEGOROV, F. A. GLUZMAN, and O. O. BOGOMOLETS.

MEREDITH, BRONWEN, "The Latest Facts on Prolonging Youth." *Harper's Bazaar* (October, 1966).

METCHNIKOFF, ELIE, *Essais Optimistes*. Paris, A. Maloine, 1907.

MICHELFELDER, WILLIAM, *It's Cheaper to Die*. Connecticut, Monarch Books, 1960.

MILLER, CHARLES A., "Remarks at Washington State Conference on Health, Fraud and Quackery," Seattle, Washington, May 7, 1966.

MOSS, LOUIS, M.D., *Acupuncture and You*. New York, Citadel Press, 1964.

MULLER, FÉDIA, *Vevey and the Trois Couronnes Hôtel*, trans. by Challinor James. Privately published, 1958.

New and Nonofficial Remedies, American Medical Association, ed. Chicago, American Medical Association, 1929.

"New Beauty Spa in Mexico." *Vogue* (1961).

NIEHANS, PAUL, M.D., "Cancer Prophylaxis." Lecture at the Papal Academy of Rome, April 22, 1966. Privately published.

———, *Cellular Therapy from the Viewpoint of Doctor and Patient.* Berne, Verlag Ott Thun, 1964.

———, *From the Cell to Therapy.* Berne and Stuttgart, Verlag Hans Huber, 1964.

———, *La Senéscence et Le Rajeunissement.* Vevey, Switzerland, Société de l'Imprimerie et Lithographie Klausfelder, 1937.

———, *La Thérapeutique Cellulaire.* Paris, Payot, 1958.

———, *Thérapie Cellulaire: Exposé à la Société d'Histoire Naturelle à Soleure.* Berne, Verlag Ott Thun, 1955.

———, *Traitement Biologique des Maladies Organiques par Injection de Cellules Vivantes.* Berne, Verlag A. Schmid & Co., 1949.

———, *Vingt Ans de Transplantation de Glandes Endocrines: Regards en Arrière et Voies Nouvelles.* Berne, Verlag Hans Huber, 1948.

———, *Von der Zelle zur Zellulartherapie.* Berne and Stuttgart, Verlag Hans Huber, 1962.

NIV, MOLLY, M.D.; LEVY, WALTER, M.D.; and GREENSTEIN, NATHAN M., M.D., "Yogurt in the Treatment of Infant Diarrhea." *Clinical Pediatrics* (July, 1963).

NYOITI, SAKURAZAWA, *You Are All Sanpaku.* English version by William Dufty. New York, University Books, 1965.

OLMER, JEAN, "Désordres Sanguins Mortels Après 'Thérapie Cellulaire Fraiche.'" *Bulletin de l'Académie Nationale de Médecine,* Vol. 143, Nos. 30 and 31 (1959).

"One Hundred Year Life Expectancy Predicted for 2000 A.D." *Today's Health* (January, 1968).

ORENTREICH, NORMAN, M.D., "Pathogenesis of Alopecia." *Journal of the Society of Cosmetic Chemists* (November, 1960).

PANGMAN, W. JOHN II, M.D., and WALLACE, ROBERT M., M.D., "The Use of Plastic Prosthesis in Breast Plastic and Other Soft Tissue Surgery." Paper read before the Sixth Congress of the Pan-Pacific Surgical Association, Honolulu, Hawaii, October 7–18, 1954.

PANGMAN, W. JOHN II, M.D., F.I.C.S., D.A.B., "Breast Trauma: Surgical and Psychic." *The Journal of the International College of Surgeons* (November, 1965).

Papers. Seventh International Congress of Gerontology. Vienna, 1966.

PAROT, DR. S., "Recherches sur la Biometrie du Vieillissement Humain." *Bulletin de la Société d'Anthropologie,* Vol. 2, 11th series (1961).

PAULING, LINUS, *General Chemistry*, 2d ed. San Francisco, W. H. Freeman and Co., 1954.

PHILLIPS, M. C., *Skin Deep: The Truth About Beauty Aids—Safe and Harmful*. New York, Vanguard Press, 1934.

PIERANTONI, H., "Les Soins de Beauté aux U.S.A." *Nouvelles Esthétiques* (November, 1966).

PIERSON, JEAN, "Hair Myths." *Vogue* (January 15, 1968).

PITSKELAURI, G. Z., "Some Factors of Longevity in Soviet Georgia." Proceedings of the Seventh International Congress of Gerontology, Vienna, Austria, June 26–July 2, 1966.

PREHODA, ROBERT W., *Designing the Future: The Role of Technological Forecasting*. Philadelphia, Chilton Press, 1967.

————, *Extended Youth*. New York, G. P. Putnam's Sons, scheduled for publication, September, 1968.

Rapports du Premier Congrès Français de Thérapeutique Cellulaire. Editions du Centre Médical d'Etudes et de Recherches, 1958.

RAUSCHKOLB, RUTH ROBISHAW, M.D., "Some Signs and Symptoms and Their Meaning to a Dermatologist." *Journal of the American Medical Women's Association* (April, 1967).

REICHEL, WILLIAM, M.D., "The Biology of Aging." *Journal of the American Geriatrics Society* (May, 1966).

REITER, TIBERIUS, M.D., "Testosterone Therapy." *British Journal of Geriatric Practice,* Vol. 4, No. 2 (1967).

Revue Médicale du Centre de Thérapeutique Cellulaire de Liège. Belgium, Imprimerie Wagelmans-Visé, 1966.

ROBINSON, VICTOR, M.D., *The Story of Medicine*. New Home Library Edition, Copyright 1931 by Albert & Charles Boni, Copyright 1943 by Froben Press.

SCHMID, PROFESSOR DR. F., and STEIN, DR. J., *Cell Research and Cellular Therapy*. Berne, Verlag Ott Thun, 1967.

SEDIVY, DR. (Primarius des Bezirkskrankenhauses Pribran/CSSR), *Erfahrungsberichte über die Behandlung der Multiplen Sklerose mit Wobe-Mugos*. Privately published, 1963.

SELYE, HANS, M.D., Ph.D, "Calciphylaxis: Key to Aging?" *Consultant* (January, 1965).

SELYE, HANS, M.D., and PRIORESCHI, P., "Stress Theory of Aging." *Aging*, published by the American Association for the Advancement of Science, 1960.

SHAIR, H. M., "Treatment of the Skin of the Aged." *Illinois Medical Journal,* 117:67 (February, 1960).

Siccacell Abstracts. Zurich, Pharmakon Ltd., undated.

SIGERIST, HENRY E., M.D., *The Great Doctors: A Biographical History of Medicine*, trans. by Eden and Cedar Paul. New York, Doubleday & Co.

SOBEL, HARRY, Ph.D, "When Does Human Aging Start?" *The Gerontologist*, Vol. 6, No. 1 (March, 1966).

STANLEY, WENDELL M., and VALENS, EVANS G., *Viruses and the Nature of Life*. New York, E. P. Dutton and Co., 1961.

Stedman's Medical Dictionary, 20th ed., completely revised. Baltimore, Williams & Wilkins Company, 1961.

The Study of Aging. Orentreich Foundation for the Advancement of Science. New York, undated.

TIBBITTS, CLARK, and DONAHUE, WILMA, *Aging in Today's Society*. Englewood Cliffs, New Jersey, Prentice-Hall, 1960.

VLADIMIROV, V., "Affairs of the Oldster *(Aferi 'Dolgozhitelya')*." *Trud* (November 30, 1962).

VON SALZA, ANDREW, ·*Return to Youth: An Interesting Explanation of Rejuvenation Through Live Cell Therapy, with Numerous Case Histories*. Privately published, undated.

VORONOFF, SERGE, *La Greffe Testiculaire du Singe à l'Homme*. Paris, Doin, 1930.

———, *La Durée de la Greffe des Glandes Endocrines*. Paris, Doin, 1948.

WALLACE, HENRY A. "Letters of Henry A. Wallace." Courtesy of the Henry A. Wallace Family and Dr. Max Wolf.

"Warburg behauptet seine Krebstheorie." *Der Spiegel* (July 18, 1966).

WEISS, PAUL, "Aging: A Corollary of Development." *Perspectives in Experimental Gerontology*, Nathan W. Shock, ed. Springfield, Illinois, Charles C. Thomas, 1966.

WOLF, MAX, M.D., *Diseases of Advancing Age*. Privately published, 1967.

WORDEN, HELEN, "I Took the Niehans Treatment." *Vogue* (January 15, 1966).

INDEX

Index

Novocain, 84. *See also* Procaine therapy
Novorossiysk University Medical School, Odessa, 290
Nucleic acids, 307, 313, 324. *See also* DNA; RNA
Nudism, 19
Nutrition, 175. *See also* Diets

O'Brien, Dolly, 64
Ochsner, Edward, 139, 147, 148, 150-52, 154, 162
Oeriu, Simon, 324
Oils, as nostrums, 199
Okinaka, Arthur, 27
Old age. *See* Longevity
Olmer, Jean, 105
Ooms, McDougall, Williams & Hersh, 235
Orang-utangs. *See* Monkey gland transplants
Oregon, University of, Medical School, 30
Orentreich, Norman, 173, 208-11, 307-10
Organ specificity, 102
Organ transplants, 88
Organotherapy, 69
Orgasm, in Taoist rejuvenation theory, 34
Orvietan, 31
Osservatore Romano, Il, 84-85
Osteoarthritis. *See* Arthritis
Ovarian cells, in cell therapy, 89, 92
Ovarian implants, 43
Overeating, 28

PABA. *See* Para-aminobenzoic acid
Paints, as nostrums, 199
Palma, Anthony, 223, 224, 225, 229, 231, 247, 249
Palma, Charles, 226
Pancreas, 95
Pangman, W. John, 207, 231-32
Paolucci, Professor, 84
Papyrus
 Eber, 88
 Therapeutic, 177
Para-aminobenzoic acid (PABA), 188
Paracelsus, 36-37, 40, 89
Paraffin masks, 217

Paralysis agitans, 49
Parathyroid cells, in cell therapy, 89
Parathyroid glands, 67, 68
Parets, Hal, 256
Parhon, Constantine I., 186, 188, 189
Paris Medical School, 179. *See also* Faculté de Médecine
Parker, Jean, 224, 230
Parkinson's Disease, 182, 191
Parr, Thomas ("Old"), 26
Pasqualina, Sister, 79, 83, 84
Pasternak, Boris, 251
Patent Office, United States, 235
Pavia, Royal University of, 51 n.
Pavlovich, Professor, 169
Peaches, as "hsien," 33
Pearl salt, as nostrum, 31
Peck, Samuel, 198
Penicillamine, 322
Pepsodent, 317
Pereira, Javier, 27, 28
Perfumes. *See* Aromatics
Pesticides, 137
Peter II, King, 165
Petrolatum, as nostrum, 199
Phagocytosis, 285-88, 290, 291, 318
Pharmacology, 35-36
Phenol peel, 221-50. *See also* Face peel
Phillips, M. C., 198
Philosophers' stone, 30-31
Philosophes, 37-38
Phoenix theme, in longevity, 29
Pholis Grunellus, 95
Phyballooomm, 32
Pickett, Dorothy, 229
Picouret, André, 104-5
Pitskelauri, G. Z., 293-95
Pituitary cells, in cell therapy, 89, 92, 94, 103-4, 105
Pituitary tissular graft, 76-77
Placebo effect, 41, 45, 76, 94, 119, 251-67, 272
Placenta, in speed therapy, 278
Placenta cells, in cell therapy, 82, 99, 105, 121
Placenta extracts, 166, 169-70, 198, 202
Planck, Max, 306
Plasmapheresis, 208, 209, 308-10
Plastic surgery, 193-97, 203-8, 213-19
Poisoning, results of, 106-7

Pollens, as nostrums, 199
Pollutants, 23
Polyclinic Hospital, New York, 196
Polycythemia, 65-66
Polyps, removal of, 256-57
Ponce de León, Juan, 14, 30
Pontifical Academy of Sciences, 86
Pope Nicholas IV, 31
Pope Pius XII, 57, 63, 64, 79-85, 92, 103, 114, 130, 275
Popov, Ivan, 76, 163, 165-80, 217, 302
Post Office, United States, 222, 243, 244
Potassium metadisulphite, 183
Potency tonics, 19
Power of suggestion, 251. *See also* Placebo effect
Prehoda, Robert, 316
Presse Médicale, 177
Priestley, Joseph, 37
Printemps, Yvonne, 64
Procaine therapy, 22, 132, 143, 145, 158, 161, 181-92
Proceedings of the National Academy of Sciences, 101
Progesterone, 311
Projekt Jot, 168
Prostate treatment, 47
Niehans, 63
Psoriasis
treatment with cell therapy, 118-19
treatment by plasmapheresis, 308-9
Psyche, role of, 253
Psychic complaints, 182
Psychic healing, 251-67. *See also* Placebo effect
Psychotherapy, in homosexuality, 93
Puberty, 47
Punishment, in homosexuality, 93
Pyne, Joe, 256

Quackery, 18, 19, 30, 38, 43-44, 53, 84, 257, 288
Quaker Chemical Products Corporation, 317
Quintana, Leonardo, 65
Quintessence, 35

Radziwill, Lee, 200, 276
Raft, George, 224

Ramsey, William R., 234
Rancho la Puerta, 17
Ransberger, Karl, 142, 146, 147, 152, 154, 157
Ravina, A., 176, 177
Reactivation, 47
Reconstructive surgery, 197
Reflexotherapy, 179
Regeneration, 172
as euphemism, 18
Regeneresen, 132
Reichel, William, 310
Reiter, Tiberius, 20
Rejuvenates. *See* individual names
Rejuvenation
claims and theories, 25-41
defined, 69
Rejuvenation farm, 172
Rejuvenation Institute Fund, 40
Rejuvenation machine, 21
Rejuvenator, definition of, 15
Renal lysozymes, as RES elements, 287
Repigmentation of hair, 181, 184-85
Replacement therapy, in treating climacteric, 311-12
RES. *See* Reticuloendothelial system
Research on gerontology
in Russia, 281-99
in United States, 301-25
Resorcin (resorcinol), 217, 228
Retardation, mental, 145
Reticuloendothelial system (RES), 286, 287, 289, 290
Reversing senescence, 18
Revitalization, 69
as euphemism, 18
Revlon, 200-3
Rhein-Chemie Factory, Heidelberg, 92
Rheumatism, 100, 182
and speed therapy, 274
Rhinoplasty, 204, 205, 208, 214
Riddle, Robert, 227
Rief, Herman, 265
Riegel, Klaus F., 253
RNA, 60, 102, 110, 139, 190, 307, 312, 313, 314
Robertson, George W., 229
Robinson, Ann, 17
Robinson, Frank and Libbie, 135
Robinson, Victor, 283

Rockefeller University (Rockefeller Institute), 101, 308, 314
Rogers, Ginger, 224
Rosenberg, Maurice, 242
Roses, 180, 198
Rothschild, Philippe de, 200
Roux, Emile, 283
Royal jelly, 81, 166, 170, 199
Rumanian Academy of Medicine, 185, 189
Russians
  longevity of, 293-95
  rejuvenation research, 281-99
Ruzička, Leopold, 318

Sajckar, Balkans, 74
Saks Fifth Avenue, 200
Sala, Emma N., 246
Salerno Medical School, 86
Salicylic acid, 233
Salk, Jonas, 190
Salts, as nostrums, 199
San Quentin Prison, 49
Sarcoma, bone, 85
Saturday Evening Post, 202, 217
Schmid, Fritz, 90, 91, 98, 127
Schultz autohypnosis, 156
Schwarzhaupt company, 290
Sclerosis, 100, 121. See also Amyotrophic lateral sclerosis; Multiple sclerosis
Scorpaena scrofa, 95
Scott, Robert Falcon, 30
Sea voyages, 69
Searle, Alan, 64, 116-22
Seaweed, as nostrum, 199
Seborrheic dermatitis, and yogurt therapy, 288
Selachian Scyllium canicula, 95
Selassie, Haile, 61
Selye, Hans, 306
Selznick, Jennifer Jones, 200
Sénéscence et le Rajeunissement, La (Niehans), 69
Serbia, King of, 75
Sertoli cells, 78, 92
Seth, 26 n.
Sevek, 166-67
Sex, in Taoist rejuvenation theory, 34
Sex-stimulating devices, 19
Sexual rejuvenation, 19, 20, 48, 118,

127. See also "Erector Set"; Impotence
Shampoos, 166, 171, 173
Shangri-la legend, in longevity, 28
Shark liver extract, 143, 154
Sheep cells, as "cancer resistant" in cell therapy, 96
Sheppard, Judge Harold, 242
Sherlock, Thomas, 320
Shock, Nathan W., 297, 306, 307, 312, 314
Siccacells, 82, 91, 92, 94, 99, 100, 121, 130, 131, 133, 153
Silicone implants, 204, 206-8
Silk, in testicular implants, 57
Simard, Albert C. J., 190-91
Sin, Roger Bacon on, 35
Sinatra, Frank, 208
Skin, 116, 118, 119
  aging, 30, 199, 212-13
  improvement of, 100, 133, 193-250, 288
  smoothing, 16
Skin Deep (Phillips), 198
Slater, Philip, 243
Sleep, 197, 270. See also Autohypnosis; Insomnia
Sleeping Beauty theme, in longevity, 29
Slenderella, 202
Smith, Ralph Lee, 184
Smith, Robert, 226, 247
Smoking, 26, 27. See also Tobacco
Société de Biologie, Paris, 39, 40
Sonnenfels, 61, 79, 83
Southern California, University of, 235, 287, 321-22
Southwest Foundation for Research and Education, 311
Soviet Academy of Medical Sciences, 299
Soviet Gerontological Center, 294
Soya protein, 141
Space race, and implications for rejuvenation, 296-97
Speed therapy, 269-79
Spermatozoa, 47
Spleen
  as RES element, 287
  in speed therapy, 278